A-Level

Mathematics

for AQA Core 1

CGP

The Complete Course for AQA C1

Contents

About this book

In this book you'll find...

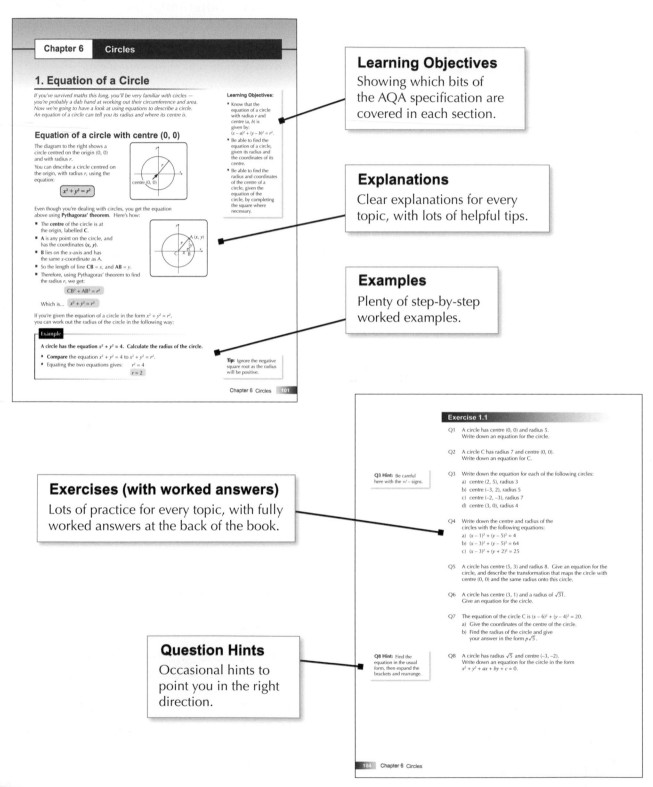

Learning Objectives
Showing which bits of the AQA specification are covered in each section.

Explanations
Clear explanations for every topic, with lots of helpful tips.

Examples
Plenty of step-by-step worked examples.

Exercises (with worked answers)
Lots of practice for every topic, with fully worked answers at the back of the book.

Question Hints
Occasional hints to point you in the right direction.

Review Exercise — Chapter 6

Q1 Give the radius and the coordinates of the centre of the circles with the following equations:
 a) $x^2 + y^2 = 9$
 b) $(x - 2)^2 + (y + 4)^2 = 4$
 c) $x(x + 6) = y(8 - y)$

Q2 Give the equation for the circles with the following properties:
 a) centre (3, 2), radius 6
 b) centre (–4, –8), radius 8
 c) centre (0, –3), radius $\sqrt{14}$

Q3 A circle has the equation $x^2 + y^2 - 4x + 6y - 68 = 0$.
 Find the coordinates of the centre of the circle and its radius.

Q4 A circle is shown below with equation $(x - 2)^2 + (y - 1)^2 = 100$ and centre C.
 A, B and D are all points on the circle.

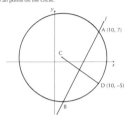

 CD bisects AB. Find the equation of the line *l*, which passes through A and B, in the
 form $ax + by + c = 0$.

Q5 The circle C has equation $x^2 + y^2 - 12x + 2y + 11 = 0$.
 The point A (1, –2) lies on the circle.
 Find the equation of the tangent at A.

Review Exercises

Mixed questions covering the whole chapter, with fully worked answers.

Exam-Style Questions — Chapter 6

1 C is a circle with the equation: $x^2 + y^2 - 2x - 10y + 21 = 0$.

 a) Find the centre and radius of C. *(4 marks)*

 The line joining P(3, 6) and Q(q, 4) is a diameter of C.

 b) Show that $q = -1$. *(3 marks)*

 c) Find the equation of the tangent to C at Q, giving your answer in the form
 $ax + by + c = 0$, where a, b and c are integers. *(4 marks)*

2 A circle C is shown here. M is the centre of C, and J lies on C.

 a) Write down the equation of C in the form $(x - a)^2 + (y - b)^2 = r^2$. *(3 marks)*

 The line JH is a tangent to circle C at point J.

 b) Show that angle $JMH = \tan^{-1} 2$. *(4 marks)*

3 The diagram shows a circle C, with centre P. M is the midpoint of AB, a chord.

 a) Show that $p = 5$. *(4 marks)*

 b) Find the equation of circle C. *(3 marks)*

Exam-Style Questions

Questions in the same style as the ones you'll get in the exam, with worked solutions and mark schemes.

Formula Sheet

Contains the C1 formulas you'll be given in the exam.

Glossary

All the definitions you need to know for the exam, plus other useful words.

Practice Exam Papers (on CD-ROM)

Two printable exam papers, with fully worked answers and mark schemes.

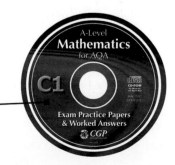

A-Level
Mathematics
for AQA
C1
Exam Practice Papers
& Worked Answers
CGP

Published by CGP

Editors:
Ceara Hayden, Helena Hayes, Paul Jordin, Sharon Keeley-Holden, Simon Little, Caley Simpson,
Charlotte Whiteley, Jonathan Wray, Dawn Wright.

Contributors:
Josephine Gibbons, Allan Graham, Phil Harvey, Barbara Mascetti, Alan Mason, Andy Park, Andy Pierson,
Rosemary Rogers, Janet West.

ISBN: 978 1 84762 802 2

With thanks to Helen Greaves and Glenn Rogers for the proofreading.

Printed by Elanders Ltd, Newcastle upon Tyne.
Clipart from Corel®

1. Algebraic Expressions

This first chapter will cover some of the basic algebra skills that you'll need again and again throughout the course — so you'll need to make sure you're completely comfortable with everything here. The good news is you should have seen a lot of it before.

Expanding brackets

Single brackets

When you've got just **one set of brackets** multiplied by a single number or letter — multiply each term in the brackets by the number or letter outside the brackets.

$$a(b + c + d) = ab + ac + ad$$

Double brackets

For **two sets** of brackets multiplied together (where there are **two terms** in each) — multiply **each term** in one set of brackets by **each term** in the other. You should **always** get **four terms** from multiplying out double brackets (though sometimes two of the terms will **combine**).

$$(a + b)(c + d) = ac + ad + bc + bd$$

Squared brackets

Squared brackets are just a **special case** of double brackets where both brackets are the **same**. Write them out as two sets of brackets until you're comfortable with it.

$$(a + b)^2 = (a + b)(a + b)$$
$$= a^2 + ab + ba + b^2 = a^2 + 2ab + b^2$$

A common **mistake** is to write $(a + b)^2 = a^2 + b^2$ — you must remember that $(a + b)^2$ is **actually** $(a + b)(a + b)$ to avoid this trap.

Learning Objectives:

- Be able to use and expand brackets.
- Be able to identify common factors and take them outside the brackets.
- Be able to simplify complicated expressions including algebraic fractions.

Tip: Remember **FOIL**: First Outside Inside Last as a rule for multiplying out double brackets. It's just an easy way to remember it.

Long brackets

Long brackets are brackets with **many terms**. Just like with double brackets, you need to multiply every term in the first set of brackets by every term in the second — you'll just need to do it with more terms.

Write out the expression again with each term from the first set of brackets separately multiplied by the second set of brackets. Always use this middle step so that you can't get confused by all the terms.

$$(x + y + z)(a + b + c + d)$$
$$= x(a + b + c + d) + y(a + b + c + d) + z(a + b + c + d)$$

Then multiply out each of these single brackets, **one at a time**.

Many brackets

When you've got **many sets** of brackets multiplied together — multiply them out **two at a time** treating each set of two as double brackets or long brackets.

Multiply out the first **two** sets of brackets...

$$(a + b)(c + d)(e + f)$$
$$= (ac + ad + bc + bd)(e + f)$$

Tip: Once you've multiplied out the first pair, the resulting terms may cancel or simplify — making the second step easier.

...then multiply out the remaining **two sets**.

$$= ac(e + f) + ad(e + f) + bc(e + f) + bd(e + f)$$

Now multiply out each of these single brackets, **one at a time**.

Examples

Single Brackets Expand $3xy(x^2 + 2x - 8)$.

Multiply each term inside the brackets by the bit outside — separately.

$$(3xy \times x^2) + (3xy \times 2x) + (3xy \times (-8))$$
$$= (3x^3y) + (6x^2y) + (-24xy)$$
$$= 3x^3y + 6x^2y - 24xy$$

Multiply the numbers first, then put the letters together.

Tip: Putting brackets round each bit makes it easier to read.

| Squared Brackets | **Expand $(2y^2 + 3x)^2$.** |

Either write it as two sets of
brackets and multiply it out...

$$(2y^2 + 3x)(2y^2 + 3x)$$

$$= 2y^2 \cdot 2y^2 + 2y^2 \cdot 3x + 3x \cdot 2y^2 + 3x \cdot 3x$$

$$= 4y^4 + 6xy^2 + 6xy^2 + 9x^2$$

$$= \boxed{4y^4 + 12xy^2 + 9x^2}$$

...or do it in one go.

$$(2y^2)^2 + 2(2y^2)(3x) + (3x)^2$$

$$\quad a^2 \qquad 2ab \qquad b^2$$

$$= \boxed{4y^4 + 12xy^2 + 9x^2}$$

Tip: The dots used here just mean 'multiplied by' — just like the × sign.

| Long Brackets | **Expand $(2x^2 + 3x - 6)(4x^3 + 6x^2 + 3)$.** |

Multiply each term in the first set of brackets by the whole second set of brackets:

$$= 2x^2(4x^3 + 6x^2 + 3) + 3x(4x^3 + 6x^2 + 3) + (-6)(4x^3 + 6x^2 + 3)$$

Now multiply out each of these sets of brackets and simplify it all:

$$= (8x^5 + 12x^4 + 6x^2) + (12x^4 + 18x^3 + 9x) + (-24x^3 - 36x^2 - 18)$$

$$= \boxed{8x^5 + 24x^4 - 6x^3 - 30x^2 + 9x - 18}$$

| Many Brackets | **Expand $(2x + 5)(x + 2)(x - 3)$.** |

Start by expanding the first two sets of brackets.

$$(2x + 5)(x + 2)(x - 3)$$

$$= (2x^2 + 4x + 5x + 10)(x - 3)$$

$$= (2x^2 + 9x + 10)(x - 3)$$

Now expand the long bracket.

$$= 2x^2(x - 3) + 9x(x - 3) + 10(x - 3)$$

Expand the single brackets and simplify.

$$= (2x^3 - 6x^2) + (9x^2 - 27x) + (10x - 30)$$

$$= \boxed{2x^3 + 3x^2 - 17x - 30}$$

Q1 Expand the brackets in these expressions:
   a) $5(x + 4)$
   b) $a(4 - 2b)$
   c) $-2(x^2 + y)$
   d) $pq(r - q)$
   e) $6mn(m + 1)$
   f) $7z^2(2 + z)$
   g) $3xy(3 - x^2 - xy)$
   h) $-4ht(t^2 - 2ht - 3h^3)$
   i) $7xy(x^2 + z^2)$
   j) $4(x + 2) + 3(x - 5)$
   k) $p(3p^2 - 2q) + (q + 4p^3)$

Q2 Expand and simplify:
   a) $(x + 5)(x - 3)$
   b) $(2z + 3)(3z - 2)$
   c) $(u + 8)^2$
   d) $(ab + cd)(ac + bd)$
   e) $(10 + f)(2f^2 - 3g)$
   f) $(7 + q)(7 - q)$
   g) $(2 - 3w)^2$
   h) $(4rs^2 + 3)^2$
   i) $(5k^2l - 2kn)^2$

Q3 Expand and simplify the following expressions:
   a) $(l + 5)(l^2 + 2l + 3)$
   b) $(2 + q)(3 - q + 4q^2)$
   c) $(m + 1)(m + 2)(m - 4)$
   d) $(r + s)^3$
   e) $(4 + x + y)(1 - x - y)$
   f) $(2c^2 - cd + d)(2d - c - 5c^2)$

Factorising

Common factors

The **factors** of a term are all the bits that **multiply together** to make it up — if something is a factor of a term, the term will be **divisible** by it.

Tip: The definition of a **term** is a collection of numbers and letters all multiplied together.

For example consider the term $12xy^2$ — it has many factors including:
- All the **factors of 12** — 1, 2, 3, 4, 6 and 12.
- The variable x.
- The variable y (and also y^2).
- Any combinations of these multiplied together e.g. $3xy$, $12y^2$, $6x$ etc.

Example 1

Find all the factors of $6x$.

A good way to do this is to break it up as much as you can:
$$6x = 1 \times 2 \times 3 \times x$$
None of these have any other factors so we can't break it down further.
Now list all possible combinations of 1, 2, 3 and x:

1,   2,   3,   6, x, $2x$, $3x$, $6x$

1 is always a factor.

The term itself is also a factor.

A factor which is in every term of an expression is a called a **common factor**. They can be 'taken out' and put outside brackets to simplify the expression. When you've taken out **all** possible factors, the expression is **factorised**.

Example 2

Factorise $2x^3z + 4x^2yz + 14x^2y^2z$ completely.

Look for any factors that are in each term.

$$2x^3z + 4x^2yz + 14x^2y^2z$$

<u>Numbers:</u> There's a common factor of 2 here because 2 divides into 2, 4 and 14.

<u>Variables:</u> There's at least an x^2 in each term...

...and there's a z in each term.

So there's a common factor of $2x^2z$ in this expression.

This can be seen more easily if you write each term as $2x^2z \times$ 'something':

$$2x^3z + 4x^2yz + 14x^2y^2z = 2x^2z \cdot x + 2x^2z \cdot 2y + 2x^2z \cdot 7y^2$$

Write the common factor outside a set of brackets...

$$= 2x^2z(x + 2y + 7y^2)$$

...and put what's left of each term inside the brackets.

The three terms in the brackets have no common factors — so this expression is completely factorised.

You can check that you did it right by multiplying it out again and checking you get the original expression:

$$2x^2z(x + 2y + 7y^2) = 2x^3z + 4x^2yz + 14x^2y^2z$$

> **Tip:** The key here is the phrase '**at least**'. There is an x^3 in one term but only an x^2 in the other two, so each term has at least an x^2 in it.

> **Tip:** After factorising, you should always check that your answer multiplies out to give the original expression. (You can do this in your head — if you trust it.)

It's not just numbers and variables that you need to look for — you can sometimes take out **whole sets of brackets** as factors of an expression.

Example 3

Express $(y + a)^2(x - a)^3 + (x - a)^2$ as a product of factors.

This can be written:

$$(y + a)^2(x - a)(x - a)^2 + (x - a)^2$$

$(x - a)^2$ is a common factor — so write the common factor outside a set of brackets and put what's left of each term inside the brackets:

$$(x - a)^2((y + a)^2(x - a) + 1)$$

This term will give $(x - a)^2$.

This term will multiply to give $(y + a)^2(x - a)^3$.

The two terms in the brackets share no common factors so the expression is factorised.

> **Tip:** 'Expressing as a product of factors' just means writing it as numbers, variables or sets of brackets multiplied together. The things you multiply together are the **factors** of the expression.

Difference of two squares

If you expand brackets of the form $(a - b)(a + b)$ the 'ab' terms cancel and you're left with one square minus another:

$$(a - b)(a + b) = a^2 + ab - ba - b^2 = a^2 + ab - ab - b^2 = a^2 - b^2$$

This result is called the **difference of two squares**:

$$a^2 - b^2 = (a - b)(a + b)$$

You need to watch out for it when factorising — if you spot that an expression is just 'something squared' minus 'something else squared', you can use this result to rewrite the expression as a pair of brackets, i.e. to factorise it.

Tip: For more on factorising quadratics see pages 16-19.

Example 4

Factorise $x^2 - 36y^2$.

36 is a square number so $36y^2$ can be written as a square:

$$x^2 - 36y^2 = x^2 - 6^2y^2$$
$$= x^2 - (6y)^2$$
$$= (x - 6y)(x + 6y)$$

This is a difference of two squares.

Exercise 1.2

Q1 Factorise the following expressions completely:

a) $9k + 15l$

b) $u^2 - uv$

c) $10w + 15$

d) $2x^2y - 12xy^2$

e) $f^2g^2 - fg$

f) $3u^2v^2 + 5u^4v^4 + 12u^2v$

g) $p^3 + 3pq^3 + 2p$

h) $abcde - bcdef - cdefg$

i) $11xy^2 - 11x^2y - 11x^2y^2$

j) $mnp^2 + 7m^2np^3$

Q2 Hint: Remember to look for a difference of two squares.

Q2 Write the following expressions as products of factors:

a) $x^2 - y^2$

b) $9a^2 - 4b^2$

c) $25x^2 - 49z^2$

d) $a^2c - 16b^2c$

Q3 Express the following as the product of factors.

a) $(4 - z)^2(2 - z) + p(2 - z)$

b) $(r - d)^3 + 5(r - d)^2$

c) $(b + c)^5(a + b) - (b + c)^5$

d) $l^2m(a - 2x) + rp^2(2x - a)$

Q3d) Hint: Remember that $(b - a) = -(a - b)$

Q4 Simplify each expression, leaving your answer in its factorised form.

a) $(p + q)^2 + 2q(p + q)$

b) $2(2x - y)^2 - 6x(2x - y)$

c) $(r + 6s)^2 - (r + 6s)(r - s)$

d) $(l + w + h)^2 - l(l + w + h)$

Q5 Hint: Look for common factors first — if you can't see any, try to multiply out the brackets and see if it simplifies that way.

Q5 Simplify these expressions by expanding brackets, factorising or both.

a) $(m + 5)(m^2 - 5m + 25)$

b) $(p - 2q)(p^2 + 2pq + 4q^2)$

c) $(u - v)(u + v) - (u + v)^2$

d) $(c + d)^3 - c(c + d)^2 - d(c + d)^2$

Algebraic fractions

You should have seen all these methods before when working with numerical fractions — but you need to learn them for **algebraic fractions** too.

The first rule is that if you're **adding fractions** together and they all have the same **denominator** — you can just add the **numerators**.

$$\frac{a}{x} + \frac{b}{x} + \frac{c}{x} \equiv \frac{a + b + c}{x}$$

Tip: This equals sign with 3 lines ≡ means it's true for all values of a, b, c or x — this is called an **identity**.

x is called a **common denominator**. If the fractions you want to add don't have a common denominator you can 'find' one — **rewrite** the fractions so that the denominators are the same by multiplying **top** and **bottom** by the same thing.

Example 1

a) **Simplify** $\frac{1}{2x} - \frac{1}{3x} + \frac{1}{5x}$.

You need to rewrite these so that all the denominators are equal. What you want is something that all these denominators divide into.

30 is the lowest number that 2, 3 and 5 all go into and each denominator contains an x. So make the common denominator $30x$.

Multiply the top and bottom lines of each fraction by whatever makes the bottom line $30x$.

$$\frac{1}{2x} - \frac{1}{3x} + \frac{1}{5x} = \frac{1}{2x} \cdot \frac{15}{15} - \frac{1}{3x} \cdot \frac{10}{10} + \frac{1}{5x} \cdot \frac{6}{6}$$

$$= \frac{15}{30x} - \frac{10}{30x} + \frac{6}{30x}$$

$$= \frac{15 - 10 + 6}{30x}$$

$$= \boxed{\frac{11}{30x}}$$

Always check that these cancel down to give what you started with.

b) **Simplify** $\frac{3}{x + 2} + \frac{5}{x - 3}$.

Again, the first step is to rewrite the fractions so that they have a common denominator.

You need an expression that both $(x + 2)$ and $(x - 3)$ divide into — you can get one by multiplying the denominators together to give a common denominator of $(x + 2)(x - 3)$.

Make the denominator of each fraction into the common denominator.

$$\frac{3(x - 3)}{(x + 2)(x - 3)} + \frac{5(x + 2)}{(x + 2)(x - 3)}$$

Multiply the top and bottom lines of each fraction by whatever makes the bottom line the same as the common denominator.

Combine into one fraction

$$= \frac{3(x-3) + 5(x+2)}{(x+2)(x-3)}$$

All the bottom lines are the same — so you can just add the top lines.

$$= \frac{3x - 9 + 5x + 10}{(x+2)(x-3)}$$

All you need to do now is tidy up the top.

$$= \frac{8x + 1}{(x+2)(x-3)}$$

c) **Simplify $\dfrac{3}{2x^2} + \dfrac{6}{5x}$.**

Finding a common denominator here is a bit more tricky. You could still multiply the two denominators together to get $10x^3$ — but this wouldn't give the simplest one.

You've got $2x^2 = 2 \times x \times x$ and $5x = 5 \times x$ and you need to find a term which both of them divide into. You must include each different factor at least once in your term — but some more than once.

The different factors are 2, 5 and x so you need at least one of each — there are two x's in the first denominator so you'll need an x^2, but you don't need another for the x in the second denominator since this is accounted for by multiplying by the x^2.

So the common denominator is $2 \times 5 \times x \times x = 10x^2$.

$$\frac{3}{2x^2} + \frac{6}{5x} = \frac{3 \times 5}{2x^2 \times 5} + \frac{6 \times 2x}{5x \times 2x}$$

Rewrite fractions with a common denominator.

$$= \frac{15}{10x^2} + \frac{12x}{10x^2}$$

$$= \frac{15 + 12x}{10x^2}$$

Add the numerators.

$$= \frac{3(5 + 4x)}{10x^2}$$

Factorise the numerator.

Tip: Finding any old common denominator is easy — just multiply all the denominators together. But if you're careful and don't include any bits twice, you'll have a lot less simplifying to do at the end.

Algebraic fractions can sometimes be simplified by cancelling **terms** that appear in both the top and bottom lines.

You can do this in **two ways**. Use whichever you prefer — but make sure you understand the ideas behind both.

Example 2

Simplify $\dfrac{ax + ay}{az}$.

You can either...

① Factorise — then cancel.

Factorise the top line.

$$\frac{ax + ay}{az} = \frac{a(x + y)}{az} = \frac{\cancel{a}(x + y)}{\cancel{a}z} = \frac{x + y}{z}$$

Cancel the 'a'.

...Or

② Split into two fractions — then cancel.

$$\frac{ax + ay}{az} = \frac{ax}{az} + \frac{ay}{az}$$

This is just the rule from p.7 for adding fractions — but backwards.

$$= \frac{\cancel{a}x}{\cancel{a}z} + \frac{\cancel{a}y}{\cancel{a}z} = \frac{x}{z} + \frac{y}{z} = \frac{x + y}{z}$$

Exercise 1.3

Q1 Express each of these as a single fraction.

a) $\dfrac{x}{3} + \dfrac{x}{4}$　　　　b) $\dfrac{2}{t} + \dfrac{13}{t^2}$　　　　c) $\dfrac{1}{2p} - \dfrac{1}{5q}$

d) $\dfrac{ab}{c} + \dfrac{bc}{a} + \dfrac{ca}{b}$　　e) $\dfrac{2}{mn} - \dfrac{3m}{n} + \dfrac{n^2}{m}$　　f) $\dfrac{2}{ab^3} - \dfrac{9}{a^3b}$

Q2 Express the following as single fractions in their simplest form.

a) $\dfrac{5}{y - 1} + \dfrac{3}{y - 2}$　　b) $\dfrac{7}{r - 5} - \dfrac{4}{r + 3}$　　c) $\dfrac{8}{p} - \dfrac{1}{p - 3}$

d) $\dfrac{w}{2(w - 2)} + \dfrac{3w}{w - 7}$　e) $\dfrac{z + 1}{z + 2} - \dfrac{z + 3}{z + 4}$　f) $\dfrac{1}{q + 1} + \dfrac{3}{q - 2}$

Q3 Simplify these expressions.

a) $\dfrac{2x + 10}{6}$　　　　　　b) $\dfrac{6a - 12b - 15c}{3}$

c) $\dfrac{np^2 - 2n^2p}{np}$　　　　d) $\dfrac{4st + 6s^2t + 9s^3t}{2t}$

e) $\dfrac{10yz^3 - 40y^3z^3 + 60y^2z^3}{10z^2}$　f) $\dfrac{12cd - 6c^2d + 3c^3d^2}{12c^2de}$

2. Surds

- Be able to simplify expressions containing surds.
- Be able to rationalise denominators.

This section will cover how to simplify expressions containing square roots. There are laws for simplifying these expressions — make sure you learn them, as you'll use them throughout AS and A2 Maths.

The laws of surds

Put $\sqrt{2}$ into a calculator and you'll get 1.414213562...
But square 1.414213562 and you get 1.999999999.

Tip: A rational number is a number that can be expressed as $\frac{p}{q}$ where p and q are integers and $q \neq 0$. An irrational number is just one which is not rational.

No matter how many decimal places you use, you'll never get exactly 2. This is because $\sqrt{2}$ is an **irrational number** — its decimal expansion **continues forever**.

The only way to express a number like this **exactly** is to leave it as a root. Numbers like $\sqrt{2}$ that can only be written exactly using roots are called **surds**. The number $\sqrt{3}$ is a surd because it can't be written exactly without a root — $\sqrt{9}$ is **not** a surd because it can be simplified to 3.

There are three rules you'll need to know to be able to use surds properly:

$$\sqrt{ab} = \sqrt{a}\sqrt{b}$$
$$\sqrt{\frac{a}{b}} = \frac{\sqrt{a}}{\sqrt{b}}$$
$$a = (\sqrt{a})^2 = \sqrt{a}\sqrt{a}$$

Simplifying surds usually just means making the number in the $\sqrt{}$ sign smaller or getting rid of a fraction inside the $\sqrt{}$ sign.

Examples

a) **Simplify $\sqrt{12}$.**

$\boxed{\sqrt{ab} = \sqrt{a}\sqrt{b}}$

$\sqrt{12} = \sqrt{4 \times 3} = \sqrt{4} \times \sqrt{3} = \boxed{2\sqrt{3}}$

b) **Simplify $\sqrt{32}$.**

$\boxed{\sqrt{ab} = \sqrt{a}\sqrt{b}}$

$\sqrt{32} = \sqrt{16 \times 2} = \sqrt{16} \times \sqrt{2} = \boxed{4\sqrt{2}}$

Tip: Make sure you simplify the surds fully — for part b), an easy mistake is to write $\sqrt{32} = \sqrt{4 \times 8} = 2\sqrt{8}$. However, this isn't the simplest form (it actually simplifies to $4\sqrt{2}$) — make sure you use the biggest square possible when you factorise (i.e. 16 not 4).

c) **Simplify $\sqrt{\frac{3}{16}}$.**

$\boxed{\sqrt{\frac{a}{b}} = \frac{\sqrt{a}}{\sqrt{b}}}$

$\sqrt{\frac{3}{16}} = \frac{\sqrt{3}}{\sqrt{16}} = \boxed{\frac{\sqrt{3}}{4}}$

d) Find $(2\sqrt{5} + 3\sqrt{6})^2$.

You'll need to multiply out squared brackets here. Remember:

$$(a + b)^2 = (a + b)(a + b) = a^2 + 2ab + b^2$$

$$(2\sqrt{5} + 3\sqrt{6})^2 = (2\sqrt{5} + 3\sqrt{6})(2\sqrt{5} + 3\sqrt{6})$$

$$= (2\sqrt{5})^2 + (2 \times (2\sqrt{5}) \times (3\sqrt{6})) + (3\sqrt{6})^2$$

$$= (2^2 \times \sqrt{5}^2) + (2 \times 2 \times 3 \times \sqrt{5} \times \sqrt{6}) + (3^2 \times \sqrt{6}^2)$$

$= 4 \times 5 = 20$

$$= 20 + 12\sqrt{30} + 54$$

$= 9 \times 6 = 54$

$$= 74 + 12\sqrt{30}$$

$= 12\sqrt{5}\sqrt{6} = 12\sqrt{30}$

Tip: Multiply surds very carefully — it's easy to make a silly mistake.

e) Express $\sqrt{63} - \sqrt{28}$ in the form $k\sqrt{x}$ where k and x are integers.

Try to write both numbers as 'a square number' $\times x$. Here x is 7.

$$\sqrt{63} - \sqrt{28} = \sqrt{9 \times 7} - \sqrt{4 \times 7}$$

$$= \sqrt{9}\sqrt{7} - \sqrt{4}\sqrt{7}$$

$$= 3\sqrt{7} - 2\sqrt{7}$$

$$= \sqrt{7}$$

The square root of a square number simplifies.

Tip: An integer is just a positive or negative whole number, including 0.

Tip: So in this case, k is just 1.

Exercise 2.1

Q1 Simplify the following surds:
   a) $\sqrt{8}$ b) $\sqrt{24}$ c) $\sqrt{50}$ d) $\sqrt{63}$
   e) $\sqrt{72}$ f) $\sqrt{\frac{5}{4}}$ g) $\sqrt{\frac{7}{100}}$ h) $\sqrt{\frac{11}{9}}$

Q2 Evaluate the following.
   Give your answer as either a whole number or a surd.
   a) $2\sqrt{3} \times 4\sqrt{3}$ b) $\sqrt{5} \times 3\sqrt{5}$
   c) $(\sqrt{7})^2$ d) $2\sqrt{2} \times 3\sqrt{5}$
   e) $(2\sqrt{11})^2$ f) $5\sqrt{8} \times 2\sqrt{2}$
   g) $4\sqrt{3} \times 2\sqrt{27}$ h) $2\sqrt{6} \times 5\sqrt{24}$
   i) $\frac{\sqrt{10}}{6} \times \frac{12}{\sqrt{5}}$ j) $\frac{\sqrt{12}}{3} \times \frac{2}{\sqrt{27}}$

Q3 Express the following in the form $k\sqrt{x}$, where k and x are integers and x is as small as possible.
   a) $\sqrt{20} + \sqrt{5}$ b) $\sqrt{32} - \sqrt{8}$
   c) $\sqrt{27} + 4\sqrt{3}$ d) $2\sqrt{8} - 3\sqrt{2}$
   e) $3\sqrt{10} + \sqrt{250}$ f) $4\sqrt{27} + 2\sqrt{48} + 5\sqrt{108}$

Q3 Hint: To add two or more surds, you'll need to make sure the $\sqrt{x}$ bit is the same in each term.

Q4 Expand the following expressions.
Give your answers in the simplest form.

a) $(1 + \sqrt{2})(2 + \sqrt{2})$ b) $(3 + 4\sqrt{3})(2 - \sqrt{3})$

c) $(\sqrt{11} + 2)(\sqrt{11} - 2)$ d) $(9 - 2\sqrt{5})(9 + 2\sqrt{5})$

e) $(\sqrt{3} + 2)^2$ f) $(3\sqrt{5} - 4)^2$

Q5 Triangle ABC is right-angled with angle ABC = 90°.
Side AC has length $5\sqrt{2}$ cm and side AB has length $\sqrt{2}$ cm.
Find the length of side BC in the form $k\sqrt{3}$ cm,
where k is an integer.

Q5 Hint: You'll need to use Pythagoras here.

Rationalising the denominator

Surds are pretty complicated — they're probably the last thing you want at the bottom of a fraction. You can remove surds from the denominators of fractions by **rationalising the denominator**.

To rationalise the denominator you multiply **top and bottom** of the fraction by an **expression** that will get rid of surds in the denominator.

Tip: Multiplying a fraction by the same thing on the top and bottom won't change its value.

> **Examples**
>
> a) **Show that $\dfrac{9}{\sqrt{3}} = 3\sqrt{3}$.**
>
> To get rid of the surd multiply top and bottom by $\sqrt{3}$.
>
> $$\frac{9}{\sqrt{3}} = \frac{9 \times \sqrt{3}}{\sqrt{3} \times \sqrt{3}} = \frac{9\sqrt{3}}{3} = \boxed{3\sqrt{3}}$$
>
> Cancelling 3 from top and bottom.
>
> b) **Rationalise the denominator of $\dfrac{1}{1 + \sqrt{2}}$.**
>
> If a fraction is of the form $\dfrac{1}{a + \sqrt{b}}$, multiply top and bottom by $a - \sqrt{b}$ — the denominator with the opposite sign in front of the surd.
>
> $$\frac{1}{1 + \sqrt{2}} \times \frac{1 - \sqrt{2}}{1 - \sqrt{2}} = \frac{1 - \sqrt{2}}{(1 + \sqrt{2})(1 - \sqrt{2})}$$
>
> $$= \frac{1 - \sqrt{2}}{1^2 + \sqrt{2} - \sqrt{2} - \sqrt{2}^2}$$
>
> $$= \frac{1 - \sqrt{2}}{1 - 2}$$
>
> The surds cancel each other out.
>
> $$= \frac{1 - \sqrt{2}}{-1}$$
>
> $$= \boxed{-1 + \sqrt{2}}$$

Tip: This method works because of the difference of two squares rule:
$(a + b)(a - b) = a^2 - b^2$

If there is a square root in the brackets, it goes away when you square it.

c) Rationalise the denominator of $\dfrac{7 + \sqrt{5}}{3 + \sqrt{5}}$.

$$\frac{7 + \sqrt{5}}{3 + \sqrt{5}} \times \frac{3 - \sqrt{5}}{3 - \sqrt{5}} = \frac{(7 + \sqrt{5})(3 - \sqrt{5})}{(3 + \sqrt{5})(3 - \sqrt{5})}$$

$$= \frac{(7 \times 3) - 7\sqrt{5} + 3\sqrt{5} - (\sqrt{5})^2}{3^2 + 3\sqrt{5} - 3\sqrt{5} - (\sqrt{5})^2}$$

Multiply top and bottom by $3 - \sqrt{5}$.

$$= \frac{21 - 4\sqrt{5} - 5}{9 - 5}$$

The surds cancel each other out.

$$= \frac{16 - 4\sqrt{5}}{4}$$

Now cancel 4 from each term.

$$= 4 - \sqrt{5}$$

Exercise 2.2

Q1 Simplify the following, giving your answers in the form $p\sqrt{q}$, where p and q are integers:

a) $\dfrac{6}{\sqrt{3}}$

b) $\dfrac{21}{\sqrt{7}}$

c) $\dfrac{30}{\sqrt{5}}$

d) $\sqrt{45} + \dfrac{15}{\sqrt{5}}$

e) $\dfrac{\sqrt{54}}{3} - \dfrac{12}{\sqrt{6}}$

f) $\dfrac{\sqrt{300}}{5} + \dfrac{30}{\sqrt{12}}$

Q2 Express the following in the form $a + b\sqrt{k}$, where a, b and k are integers:

a) $\dfrac{4}{1 + \sqrt{3}}$

b) $\dfrac{11}{4 - \sqrt{5}}$

c) $\dfrac{8}{\sqrt{7} + 3}$

d) $\dfrac{8}{-1 + \sqrt{5}}$

e) $\dfrac{1}{\sqrt{26} - 5}$

f) $\dfrac{18}{\sqrt{10} - 4}$

Q3 Express the following in the form $p + q\sqrt{r}$, where r is an integer, and p and q are integers or fractions:

a) $\dfrac{\sqrt{2} + 1}{\sqrt{2} - 1}$

b) $\dfrac{\sqrt{5} + 3}{\sqrt{5} - 2}$

c) $\dfrac{3 - \sqrt{3}}{4 + \sqrt{3}}$

d) $\dfrac{3\sqrt{5} - 1}{2\sqrt{5} - 3}$

e) $\dfrac{\sqrt{2} + \sqrt{3}}{3\sqrt{2} - \sqrt{3}}$

f) $\dfrac{2\sqrt{7} - \sqrt{5}}{\sqrt{7} + 2\sqrt{5}}$

Q4 Solve the equation $8 = (\sqrt{5} - 1)x$ giving your answer in the form $a + b\sqrt{5}$ where a and b are integers.

Q5 Solve the equation $5 + \sqrt{7} = (3 - \sqrt{7})y$ giving your answer in the form $p + q\sqrt{7}$ where p and q are integers.

Q6 A rectangle has an area of $(2 + \sqrt{2})$ cm² and a width of $(3\sqrt{2} - 4)$ cm. Find the length of the rectangle. Give your answer in the form $a + b\sqrt{2}$ where a and b are integers.

Review Exercise — Chapter 1

Q1 Which of these are identities (i.e. true for all variable values)?

Q1 Hint: Remember, an identity is just an equation where the left hand side is identical to the right hand side, no matter what values you choose.

A $(x + b)(y - b) = xy + b(y - x) - b^2$

B $(2y + x^2) = 10$

C $a^2 - b^2 = (a - b)(a + b)$

D $a^3 + b^3 = (a + b)(a^2 - ab + b^2)$

Q2 Remove the brackets and simplify the following expressions:

a) $(a + b)(a - b)$

b) $(a + b)(a + b)$

c) $35xy + 25y(5y + 7x) - 100y^2$

d) $(x + 3y + 2)(3x + y + 7)$

Q3 Take out the common factors from the following expressions:

a) $2x^2y + axy + 2xy^2$

b) $a^2x + a^2b^2x^2$

c) $16y + 8yx + 56x$

d) $x(x - 2) + 3(2 - x)$

Q4 Simplify the following expressions by putting them over a common denominator:

a) $\dfrac{2x}{3} + \dfrac{y}{12} + \dfrac{x}{5}$

b) $\dfrac{5}{xy^2} - \dfrac{2}{x^2y}$

c) $\dfrac{1}{x} + \dfrac{x}{x + y} + \dfrac{y}{x - y}$

Q5 Simplify these expressions:

a) $\dfrac{2a}{b} - \dfrac{a}{2b}$

b) $\dfrac{2p}{p + q} + \dfrac{2q}{p - q}$

Q6 Hint: 'Exact answers' means leave your answers as surds (and don't forget that there'll be 2 solutions to each equation).

Q6 Find exact answers to these equations:

a) $x^2 - 5 = 0$

b) $(x + 2)^2 - 3 = 0$

Q7 Simplify:

a) $\sqrt{28}$

b) $\sqrt{\dfrac{5}{36}}$

c) $\sqrt{18}$

d) $\sqrt{\dfrac{9}{16}}$

Q8 Show that:

a) $\dfrac{8}{\sqrt{2}} = 4\sqrt{2}$

b) $\dfrac{\sqrt{2}}{2} = \dfrac{1}{\sqrt{2}}$

Q9 Find $(6\sqrt{3} + 2\sqrt{7})^2$.

Q10 Rationalise the denominator of $\dfrac{2}{3 + \sqrt{7}}$.

1   Simplify

a) $(5\sqrt{3})^2$

(1 mark)

b) $(5 + \sqrt{6})(2 - \sqrt{6})$

(2 marks)

2   Express $\dfrac{5 + \sqrt{5}}{3 - \sqrt{5}}$ in the form $a + b\sqrt{5}$, where a and b are integers.

(4 marks)

3   Write $\sqrt{18} - 2\sqrt{8} + \dfrac{4}{\sqrt{2}}$ in the form $n\sqrt{2}$, where n is an integer.

(4 marks)

4   Show that $\dfrac{4\sqrt{32}}{\sqrt{2}} - 2\sqrt{3} + \dfrac{4\sqrt{5}}{\sqrt{20}} + \sqrt{12}$ is an integer.

(4 marks)

5   Simplify $\dfrac{4}{3x^2} - \dfrac{2}{7x}$.

(2 marks)

6   a)   Express $4x(3x + 4)^2 + (3x + 4)$ as a product of factors.

(2 marks)

b)   Show that $4x(3x + 4)^2$ can be written as $36x^3 + 96x^2 + 64x$.

(2 marks)

7   Factorise completely

$$2x^4 - 32x^2.$$

(3 marks)

1. Quadratic Equations

In this section, you'll learn three methods that are used for solving quadratic equations — factorising, completing the square and the quadratic formula. These methods will also help you to sketch graphs of quadratic functions later in the chapter.

Factorising a quadratic

Quadratic equations are equations of the general form:

$$ax^2 + bx + c = 0$$

where a, b and c are constants (i.e. numbers) and $a \neq 0$.

Factorising a quadratic means putting it into two brackets called **factors** — the **solutions** to the equation can be easily worked out from these factors. These solutions are the **roots** of the equation.

There are **two cases** that you need to know:

Factorising when $a = 1$

Fortunately, there's a step-by-step method you can follow when factorising this sort of quadratic:

Tip: Expressions such as $ax^2 + bx + c$, with terms in different powers of x, are also known as polynomials. They can include higher powers of x, e.g. x^3, x^4 etc.

Tip: All quadratics can be rearranged into this standard form.

> To factorise a quadratic with $a = 1$:
>
> - Rearrange into the standard $ax^2 + bx + c$ form.
>
> - Write down the two **brackets**:
> $$(x \quad)(x \quad)$$
>
> - Find two numbers that **multiply** to give 'c' and **add / subtract** to give 'b' (ignoring signs).
>
> - Put the numbers in the brackets and choose their **signs**.

This will all make more sense once you've seen a worked example...

Example 1

Solve $x^2 - 8 = 2x$ by factorising.

(1) Rearrange into standard $ax^2 + bx + c = 0$ form.

Subtract $2x$ from both sides to give...

$$x^2 - 2x - 8 = 0$$

So $a = 1$, $b = -2$, $c = -8$.

(2) Write down the two brackets with x's in:

$$x^2 - 2x - 8 = (x \quad)(x \quad)$$

Since $a = 1$, you know that there will be an x in each bracket, which will multiply together to give x^2.

(3) Find the numbers.

Find two numbers that **multiply** together to make c but which also **add or subtract** to give b (you can ignore any minus signs for now).

1 and 8 multiply to give 8 — and add / subtract to give 9 and 7.

2 and 4 multiply to give 8 — and add / subtract to give 6 and 2.

These are the values for c and b you're after — so this is the right combination: 2 and 4.

(4) Find the signs.

So far you've got: $x^2 - 2x - 8 = (x \quad 4)(x \quad 2)$

Now all you have to do is put in the plus or minus signs.

It must be $+2$ and -4 because $2 \times (-4) = -8$ and $2 + (-4) = 2 - 4 = -2$

$$x^2 - 2x - 8 = (x + 2)(x - 4)$$

If c is negative, then the signs must be opposite.

Tip: If two things multiplied together give a negative answer, they must have opposite signs.

Now that you've factorised using the step by step method — you can use the factors to solve the equation.

$$(x + 2)(x - 4) = 0$$

The factors (brackets) multiply to give 0, so one of them **must** be 0.

$$\Rightarrow x + 2 = 0 \text{ or } x - 4 = 0$$

$$\Rightarrow x = -2 \text{ or } x = 4$$

Tip: If two things multiply together to give 0, one of them must be equal to 0.

Don't forget this last step. The factors aren't the answer.

Example 2

Solve $x^2 + 4x - 21 = 0$ by factorising.

- It's already in the standard form, so start by writing down the brackets:
$$x^2 + 4x - 21 = (x \qquad)(x \qquad)$$

- 1 and 21 multiply to give 21 — and add / subtract to give 22 and 20.
3 and 7 multiply to give $\boxed{21}$ — and add / subtract to give 10 and $\boxed{4.}$

These are the values you need so 3 and 7 are the right numbers:
$$x^2 + 4x - 21 = (x \quad 3)(x \quad 7)$$

- c is negative so we must need opposite signs.
The signs must be -3 and $+7$ because $7 - 3 = 4$ and $7 \times (-3) = -21$

So... $\qquad x^2 + 4x - 21 = (x - 3)(x + 7)$

And solving the equation to find x...
$$(x - 3)(x + 7) = 0$$
$$\Rightarrow x = 3 \text{ or } x = -7$$

Factorising when $a \neq 1$

The basic method's the same as before — but it can be a bit more awkward.

> **To factorise a quadratic with $a \neq 1$:**
>
> - Rearrange into the standard $ax^2 + bx + c$ form.
>
> - Write down the two brackets, but instead of just having x in each, you need two things that will multiply to give ax^2:
> $$(nx \qquad)(mx \qquad)$$
> where n and m are two numbers that multiply to give a.
>
> - Find two numbers that multiply to give 'c' but which will give you bx when you multiply them by nx and mx, and then add / subtract them.
>
> - Put the numbers in the brackets and choose their **signs**.

Tip: In practice, this third step is a case of working through all possible cases until you get it right.

Again, a worked example will help.

Factorise $3x^2 + 4x - 15$.

(1) This quadratic's already in the standard form so you don't need to rearrange it.

(2) As before, write down two brackets — but instead of just having x in each, you need two things that will multiply to give $3x^2$. It's got to be $3x$ and x here.
$$3x^2 + 4x - 15 = (3x \qquad)(x \qquad)$$

③ Work out the numbers.

You need to find two numbers that multiply together to make 15 — but which will give you $4x$ when you multiply them by x and $3x$, and then add / subtract them.

$(3x \quad 1)(x \quad 15) \Rightarrow x$ and $45x$
which then add or subtract to give $46x$ and $44x$.

$(3x \quad 15)(x \quad 1) \Rightarrow 15x$ and $3x$
which then add or subtract to give $18x$ and $12x$.

$(3x \quad 3)(x \quad 5) \Rightarrow 3x$ and $15x$
which then add or subtract to give $18x$ and $12x$.

$(3x \quad 5)(x \quad 3) \Rightarrow 5x$ and $9x$
which then add or subtract to give $14x$ and $4x.$

This is the value you're after — so this is the right combination.

Tip: It's a good idea to write out the brackets for each possible number combination — it makes it easier to see if you've got the right numbers.

④ Add the signs.

You know the brackets must be like these...

$(3x \quad 5)(x \quad 3) = 3x^2 + 4x - 15$

'c' is negative — that means the signs in the brackets are opposite. The numbers must be -5 and $+3$ since $9x - 5x = 4x$ and $-5 \times 3 = -15$.

So...

$$(3x - 5)(x + 3) = 3x^2 + 4x - 15$$

If you'd been asked to solve the equation $3x^2 + 4x - 15 = 0$, you'd then just solve $(3x - 5)(x + 3) = 0$ to get the solutions $x = \frac{5}{3}$ and $x = -3$.

Tip: You've only got two choices for the signs of the numbers, -5 and 3 or 5 and -3. If you're unsure which it is, just multiply each case out to see which is right.

Exercise 1.1

Q1 Factorise the following expressions.

a) $x^2 - 6x + 5$

b) $x^2 - 3x - 18$

c) $x^2 + 22x + 121$

d) $x^2 - 12x$

e) $y^2 - 13y + 42$

f) $x^2 + 51x + 144$

g) $x^2 - 121$

h) $x^2 + 2\sqrt{3}x + 3$

Q1 Hint: If b or c is zero, use the factorising methods from Chapter 1.

Q2 Solve the following equations.

a) $x^2 - 2x - 8 = 0$

b) $2x^2 + 2x - 40 = 0$

c) $p^2 + 21p + 38 = 0$

d) $x^2 - 15x + 54 = 0$

e) $x^2 + 18x = -65$

f) $x^2 - x = 42$

g) $x^2 + 1100x + 100\,000 = 0$

h) $3x^2 - 3x - 6 = 0$

Q2 Hint: Look out for questions where the equation can be simplified before factorising — for example by dividing through by a number.

Q3 Factorise the following expressions.
a) $4x^2 - 4x - 3$ b) $2x^2 + 23x + 11$
c) $7x^2 - 19x - 6$ d) $-x^2 - 5x + 36$
e) $2x^2 - 2$ f) $6x^2 + 11x + 4$

Q4 Solve the following equations.
a) $-5x^2 - 22x + 15 = 0$ b) $32x^2 + 60x + 13 = 0$
c) $5a^2 + 12a = 9$ d) $8x^2 + 22x + 15 = 0$

Q5 Solve $(x - 1)(x - 2) = 37 - x$.

Q6 $f(x) = -x^2 + 7x + 30$. Find the x coordinates of the point or points at which the graph of f(x) meets the x-axis.

Q6 Hint: The graph of f(x) meets the x-axis when f(x) = 0.

Q7 Factorise $x^2 + 6xy + 8y^2$.

The quadratic formula

You should now be comfortable with solving quadratics by factorising. But there are two important points to bear in mind:

- The expression **won't** always factorise.
- Sometimes factorising is so messy that it's **easier** to just use other methods.

So if the question doesn't tell you to factorise, **don't assume** it will factorise.

Example

Solve $6x^2 + 87x - 144 = 0$.

This will actually factorise, but there are 2 possible bracket forms to try:

$$(6x \quad)(x \quad) \quad \text{or} \quad (3x \quad)(2x \quad)$$

And for each of these, there are 8 possible ways of making 144 to try.

If you tried to factorise this example, you'd be going all day.

Luckily, there's a formula which will work out the **solutions** of a quadratic equation, even when you can't factorise — it's known as **the quadratic formula**.

If $ax^2 + bx + c = 0$ then:
$$x = \frac{-b \pm \sqrt{b^2 - 4ac}}{2a}$$

The quadratic formula will solve **any** quadratic equation — no matter what.

Example 1

Solve the quadratic equation $3x^2 - 4x = 8$, leaving your answer in surd form.

The mention of surds in the answer suggests that the quadratic will be too hard to factorise, so we'll use the quadratic formula instead.

- Get the equation in the standard $ax^2 + bx + c = 0$ form.

$$3x^2 - 4x = 8$$

So... $\quad 3x^2 - 4x - 8 = 0$

Tip: If the question asks you to give your answer in surd form or as a decimal, that's a big hint to use the quadratic formula instead of trying to factorise.

- Write down the coefficients a, b and c — making sure you don't forget minus signs.

$$3x^2 - 4x - 8 = 0$$

$a = 3$

$b = -4 \qquad c = -8$

Tip: If any of the **coefficients** (i.e. if a, b or c) in your quadratic equation are **negative**, be especially careful.

- Very carefully, plug these numbers into the formula. It's best to write down each stage as you do it.

$$x = \frac{-b \pm \sqrt{b^2 - 4ac}}{2a}$$

$$x = \frac{-(-4) \pm \sqrt{(-4)^2 - 4 \times 3 \times (-8)}}{2 \times 3}$$

$$x = \frac{4 \pm \sqrt{16 + 96}}{6}$$

These minus signs multiply together to get a plus.

Tip: There are a couple of minus signs in the formula which can catch you out if you're not paying attention.

Simplify your answer as much as possible, using the rules of surds.

$$x = \frac{4 \pm \sqrt{112}}{6}$$

$$x = \frac{4 \pm \sqrt{16}\sqrt{7}}{6}$$

$$x = \frac{2 \pm 2\sqrt{7}}{3}$$

The $\pm$ sign means that you actually have two different expressions for x, which you get by replacing the $\pm$ with + and −. Doing this gives you the two solutions to the quadratic equation.

$$x = \frac{2 + 2\sqrt{7}}{3} \quad \text{or} \quad x = \frac{2 - 2\sqrt{7}}{3}$$

Example 2

Solve the quadratic equation $2x^2 = 4x + 3$, leaving your answer in the form $p \pm q\sqrt{r}$ where p, q and r are whole numbers or fractions.

Rearranging $2x^2 = 4x + 3$ you get $2x^2 - 4x - 3 = 0$ and so $a = 2$, $b = -4$ and $c = -3$

So plugging these values into the quadratic formula, you get:

$$x = \frac{-b \pm \sqrt{b^2 - 4ac}}{2a}$$

$$x = \frac{-(-4) \pm \sqrt{(-4)^2 - 4 \times 2 \times (-3)}}{2 \times 2}$$

$$x = \frac{4 \pm \sqrt{16 + 24}}{4} = \frac{4 \pm \sqrt{40}}{4} = \frac{4 \pm 2\sqrt{10}}{4} = \frac{2 \pm \sqrt{10}}{2}$$

$$= \frac{2}{2} \pm \frac{1}{2}\sqrt{10} = \boxed{1 \pm \frac{1}{2}\sqrt{10}}$$

Exercise 1.2

Q1   Solve the following equations using the quadratic formula, giving your answers in surd form where necessary.

a) $x^2 - 4x = -2$ b) $x^2 - 2x - 44 = 0$

c) $x^2 - 14x + 42 = 0$ d) $4x^2 + 4x - 1 = 0$

e) $x^2 - \frac{5}{6}x + \frac{1}{6} = 0$ f) $x^2 - x - \frac{35}{2} = 0$

Q2   a) Multiply out $(x - 2 + \sqrt{5})(x - 2 - \sqrt{5})$.

b) Solve the equation $x^2 - 4x - 1 = 0$ using the quadratic formula.

c) How does your answer to b) relate to the expression given in a)?

Q3 Hint: Remember, the roots of the equation are the values of x that make the equation equal to 0.

Q3   The roots of the equation $x^2 + 8x + 13 = 0$ can be written in the form $x = A \pm \sqrt{B}$ where A and B are integers. Find A and B.

Q4   Solve the following equations, giving your answers in surd form where necessary.

a) $x^2 + x + \frac{1}{4} = 0$ b) $25x^2 - 30x + 7 = 0$

c) $60x - 5 = -100x^2 - 3$ d) $2x(x - 4) = 7 - 3x$

Completing the square

You could be asked to **solve** a quadratic equation by **completing the square** so you need to know this method just as well as the others. And what's more — it gives you loads of **useful information** about the quadratic.

> Completing the square just means writing a quadratic expression $ax^2 + bx + c$ in the form $a(x + \text{something})^2 + d$.
>
> - Basically, the '**square**' is this bit:
>
> $$a(x + \text{something})^2$$
>
>   The 'something' is chosen so that it will produce the correct x^2 and x terms when the square is multiplied out.
>
> - But this square won't always give the right constant term — so you need to '**complete**' it by adding a number to the square to make it the **same** as the original quadratic:
>
> $$a(x + \text{something})^2 + d$$

The method can seem complicated at first, but is actually very simple when you get it. As always, working through examples is the best way to learn it.

When $a = 1$

We'll start with the slightly easier case of $a = 1$...

Example 1

Rewrite $x^2 + 6x + 3$ by completing the square.

First, write down a square of the form $(x + \text{something})^2$. Choose it so that when you multiply it out you get the correct x^2 and x terms.

$$(x + 3)^2$$

> This number is just half the coefficient of x i.e. $\dfrac{b}{2}$.

Now complete the square:

$$(x + 3)^2 - 6$$

> This square multiplies out to give $x^2 + 6x + 9$ but we need the constant term to be $+3$...

> ...so subtract 6 from the square to match the original quadratic.

So...

$$x^2 + 6x + 3 = (x + 3)^2 - 6$$

Check that your answer multiplies out to give what you started with.

$$(x + 3)^2 - 6 = x^2 + 3x + 3x + 9 - 6 = x^2 + 6x + 3 \checkmark$$

Rewrite $x^2 - 5x - 1$ by completing the square.

Again, start by writing down the square:

This example has a negative coefficient of x — so make sure you have a minus sign in the brackets.

$$\left(x - \frac{5}{2}\right)^2$$

Now complete the square....

> Remember, this is just $\frac{b}{2}$.

$$\left(x - \frac{5}{2}\right)^2 - \frac{25}{4} - 1$$

> The square multiplies out to give $x^2 - 5x + \frac{25}{4}$ but we need the constant term to be -1.

> ...so subtract the $\frac{25}{4}$ and then 'add' -1.

Tip: You can always find the number that completes the square by subtracting off the number term you get from the bracket and adding on the number term from the original quadratic.

$$x^2 - 5x - 1 = \left(x - \frac{5}{2}\right)^2 - \frac{29}{4}$$

> Simplify the number.

Check your answer...

$$\left(x - \frac{5}{2}\right)^2 - \frac{29}{4} = x^2 - \frac{5}{2}x - \frac{5}{2}x + \frac{25}{4} - \frac{29}{4} = x^2 - 5x - 1 \checkmark$$

When $a \neq 1$

It's a little more complicated in cases where a is not 1. You have to put a outside of the squared bracket, and allow for this when choosing the number to go inside the bracket — basically by dividing by a.

Rewrite $2x^2 + 3x - 5$ by completing the square.

Start by writing the square —
$a = 2$ so it will be of the form $2(x + \text{something})^2$:

$$2\left(x + \frac{3}{4}\right)^2$$

> When a is not 1, this number will always be the coefficient of x divided by $2a$, i.e. $\frac{b}{2a}$.

Now complete the square:

$$2\left(x + \frac{3}{4}\right)^2 - \frac{9}{8} - 5$$

> The square multiplies out to give $2x^2 + 3x + \frac{9}{8}$, but we need the constant term to be -5...

> ...so subtract the $\frac{9}{8}$ and then 'add on' -5.

So...

$$2x^2 + 3x - 5 = 2\left(x + \frac{3}{4}\right)^2 - \frac{49}{8}$$ ← Simplify the number.

Check your answer...

$$2\left(x + \frac{3}{4}\right)^2 - \frac{49}{8} = 2\left(x^2 + \frac{3}{2}x + \frac{9}{16}\right) - \frac{49}{8}$$
$$= 2x^2 + 3x + \frac{9}{8} - \frac{49}{8} = 2x^2 + 3x - 5 \checkmark$$

Tip: If the constant terms are fractions, don't forget to put them over a common denominator before you try to add / subtract them.

Example 4

Rewrite $3 - 4x - x^2$ by completing the square.

Quadratics are easier to deal with when they're in the standard $ax^2 + bx + c$ form, so rewrite the expression as $-x^2 - 4x + 3$.

You'll need to take out the factor of a (= –1) when you write the square — so the first two terms will become $-(x^2 + 4x)$. So write the square:

$$-(x + 2)^2$$

This number is just $\frac{b}{2a}$ again.

Now complete the square:

$$-(x + 2)^2 + 7$$

The square multiplies out to give $-x^2 - 4x - 4$ but we want the constant to be +3...

...so add 7 to the square to make it match the original quadratic.

So...

$$3 - 4x - x^2 = -(x + 2)^2 + 7$$

Check your answer...

$$-(x + 2)^2 + 7 = -(x^2 + 4x + 4) + 7 = -x^2 - 4x - 4 + 7$$
$$= -x^2 - 4x + 3 \ (= 3 - 4x - x^2) \checkmark$$

Once you've completed the square, a quadratic equation becomes very easy to **solve**:

> - Take the **constant term** to the other side of the equals sign.
> - Square root both sides — don't forget the **negative** square root.
> - **Rearrange** to find the solutions.

Example 5

Solve $3 - 4x - x^2 = 0$ by completing the square.

From Example 4, you can write $3 - 4x - x^2$ as $-(x + 2)^2 + 7$ by completing the square.

So now all you need to do is set this equal to zero and rearrange.

$-(x + 2)^2 + 7 = 0$

$\quad -(x + 2)^2 = -7$ ← Take the constant to the other side.

$\quad\quad (x + 2)^2 = 7$ ← Take a square root — don't forget the $\pm$ sign.

$\quad\quad x + 2 = \pm\sqrt{7}$

$\quad\quad x = -2 \pm\sqrt{7}$ ← Subtract 2 from both sides.

So $x = -2 + \sqrt{7}$ or $x = -2 - \sqrt{7}$

Tip: When you take the square root of something, you need to put a $\pm$ sign in front of the $\sqrt{}$ sign.

Exercise 1.3

Q1 Hint: In these questions you don't need to complete the square — they'll just give you practice at the 'solving' bit.

Q1 Solve the following equations, leaving your answer in surd form where appropriate:

a) $(x + 4)^2 = 25$

b) $(5x - 3)^2 = 21$

Q2 Rewrite the following expressions in the form $p(x + q)^2 + r$:

a) $x^2 + 6x + 8$ b) $x^2 + 8x - 10$

c) $x^2 - 3x - 10$ d) $-x^2 + 20x + 15$

e) $x^2 - 2mx + n$ f) $3x^2 - 12x + 7$

Q3 Solve the following equations by completing the square:

a) $x^2 - 6x - 16 = 0$ b) $p^2 - 10p = 200$

c) $x^2 + 2x + k = 0$ d) $9x^2 + 18x = 16$

e) $x^2 + 4x - 8 = 0$ f) $2x^2 - 12x + 9 = 0$

g) $2x^2 - 12x - 54 = 0$ h) $5x^2 - 3x + \frac{2}{5} = 0$

Q4 By completing the square, show that the roots of $ax^2 + bx + c = 0$ are found at $x = \dfrac{-b \pm \sqrt{b^2 - 4ac}}{2a}$.

2. Quadratic Functions and Roots

The roots of a quadratic function f(x) are just the solutions to the equation f(x) = 0. But you don't actually need to solve the equation to find out how many roots there are.

Learning Objectives:

- Be able to calculate the discriminant of a quadratic function.
- Be able to identify the number of real roots of a quadratic function.
- Be able to use the discriminant to solve problems involving quadratics with unknown coefficients.

The roots of a quadratic function

Quadratic functions are just functions of the form $f(x) = ax^2 + bx + c$. Their graphs all have the same **general shape**, no matter what the values of a, b and c are — they are either '**u**'-shaped or '**n**'-shaped:

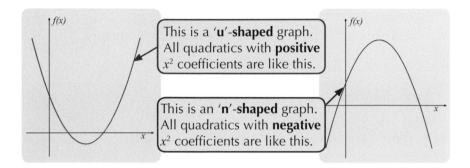

This is a '**u**'-shaped graph. All quadratics with **positive** x^2 coefficients are like this.

This is an '**n**'-shaped graph. All quadratics with **negative** x^2 coefficients are like this.

The **roots** of a quadratic function are the values of x where the function $f(x)$ is equal to **zero** — i.e. where the graph **crosses the x-axis**. They are the same as the **solutions** to the quadratic equation $f(x) = 0$. The functions shown above each have 2 roots because their graphs cross the x-axis twice.

A quadratic function may have **0**, **1** or **2 roots**. You'll see two methods for finding out which it is — **completing the square** and using the **discriminant**.

Using the completed square

If you've already **completed the square**, you can easily work out the number of roots by examining the completed square. The function will look like this:

$$f(x) = p(x + q)^2 + r$$

The key to this method is remembering that anything squared is ≥ 0.

So, let's assume for now that p is positive:

- Since p is positive, the graph will be u-shaped and have a minimum.
- The smallest value that $f(x)$ can take will occur when the bracket is 0 (since the square is ≥ 0). At that point $f(x)$ is just r, and x must be $-q$.
- So the minimum is $(-q , r)$.

Now the **value of r** tells us the number of roots...

- If $r < 0$, the minimum is below the x-axis, so the graph must cross the axis twice — meaning there are **two roots**.
- If $r > 0$, the graph is always above the x-axis — so there are **no roots**.
- If $r = 0$, the minimum point is on the x-axis, so there's **one root**.

So that covers cases where p is positive, i.e. u-shaped graphs.

Tip: Just picture what the graph looks like — remember, it's u-shaped. The number of times the graph crosses the x-axis depends on whether the minimum is above, below or on the axis.

Next, we'll see what happens when p is negative:

$$f(x) = p(x + q)^2 + r$$

- Since p is negative, the graph will be n-shaped and have a maximum.
- And also because p is negative, the highest value of $p(x + q)^2$ will be when the bracket is 0. At that point $f(x)$ is just r, and x is $-q$.
- So the maximum is $(-q, r)$.

Tip: The coordinates of the maximum are actually just the same as those we found for the minimum: $(-q, r)$.

Look at the **value of r** to work out the number of roots...

- If $r < 0$, the graph is always below the x-axis — so there are **no roots**.
- If $r > 0$, the maximum is above the x-axis, so the graph must cross the axis twice, meaning there are **two roots**.
- If $r = 0$, the maximum point is on the x-axis, so there's **one root**.

Let's see what this all means for a few real functions.

Tip: You'll see how to draw graphs of quadratic functions later in the chapter.

Two distinct real roots

$y = x^2 - 6x + 8$

- The completed square is $(x - 3)^2 - 1$.
- The minimum is $(3, -1)$, which is below the x-axis.
- So there are two roots ($x = 2$ and $x = 4$).

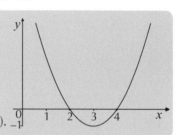

Tip: When you're factorising a quadratic equation, if both factors come out the same, in this case $(x - 3)$ $(x - 3)$, the function has two equal roots. We sometimes call this one **repeated** root.

Two equal roots

$y = x^2 - 6x + 9$

- The completed square is $(x - 3)^2$.
- The minimum is $(3, 0)$, so the graph just touches the x-axis.
- Solving $(x - 3)^2 = 0$ gives two roots at $x = 3$, so we say that $x = 3$ is the only root.

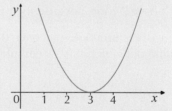

No real roots

$y = x^2 - 6x + 10$

- The completed square is $(x - 3)^2 + 1$.
- The minimum is $(3, 1)$, which is above the x-axis.
- So the graph never touches the x-axis, and there are no real roots.

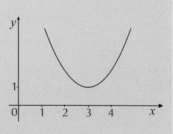

All the different cases we've covered can actually be summarised in these three simple rules:

> For a quadratic function of the form $f(x) = p(x + q)^2 + r$:
> - If p and r have **different signs**, the function has **two distinct** real roots.
> - If $r = 0$ then the function has **two equal** roots (one real root).
> - If p and r have the **same sign**, the function has **no** real roots.

How many roots does the quadratic function $f(x) = x^2 + 4x + 7$ have?

Completing the square, you can rewrite the function as
$f(x) = (x + 2)^2 + 3$ so $p = 1$ and $r = 3$ are of the same sign
and so the function has no real roots.

You can see why this works using the following argument:

$$f(x) = (x + 2)^2 + 3 \longleftarrow \text{This number's positive.}$$

The smallest this bit
can be is zero (at $x = -2$).

$(x + 2)^2$ is never less than zero
so $f(x)$ is never less than three.

This means that:

a) $f(x)$ can never be negative.
b) The graph of $f(x)$ never crosses the x-axis — so there are no real roots.

Exercise 2.1

Q1 How many real roots does each quadratic function have?

a)
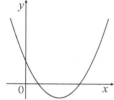

b)
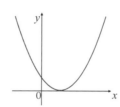

c)
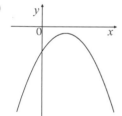

d)
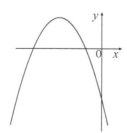

Q2 Express $f(x) = x^2 + 6x + 10$ in the form $f(x) = (x + q)^2 + r$,
where q and r are positive or negative constants.
Using your answer, state whether $f(x)$ has any real roots.

Q2 Hint: Complete the square.

Q3 The function $f(x) = -x^2 - 7x - 6$ can be expressed in the form
$$f(x) = -\left(x + \frac{7}{2}\right)^2 + \frac{25}{4}$$
Does this function have any real roots? Explain your answer.

Using the discriminant

Remember the **quadratic formula** for solving an equation of the form $ax^2 + bx + c = 0$:

$$x = \frac{-b \pm \sqrt{b^2 - 4ac}}{2a}$$

The $b^2 - 4ac$ bit is called the **discriminant**.

- If the discriminant is **positive**, the formula will give you **two** different values for x — when you **add** and **subtract** the $\sqrt{b^2 - 4ac}$ bit.

- If it's **zero**, you'll only get **one** value for x, since adding and subtracting zero gets the same value.

- If it's **negative**, you don't get any (real) values for x because you can't take the square root of a negative number.

Tip: In some areas of maths, you can actually take the square root of negative numbers and get 'imaginary' or 'complex' numbers. That's why we say no 'real' roots.

To picture what this means, recall the examples from p.28:

Two distinct real roots	Two equal roots	No real roots
$b^2 - 4ac > 0$	$b^2 - 4ac = 0$	$b^2 - 4ac < 0$

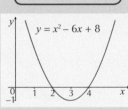

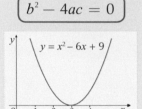

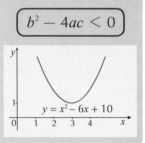

When working out the **discriminant**, the first thing you have to do is to work out what a, b and c are. Make sure you get them the right way round — it's easy to get mixed up if the quadratic's in a different order.

Example 1

Find the discriminant of $15 - x - 2x^2$.
How many real roots does the function $f(x) = 15 - x - 2x^2$ have?

- First, identify a, b and c:
    $a = -2$, $b = -1$ and $c = 15$ (NOT $a = 15$, $b = -1$ and $c = -2$).

- Then put these values into the formula for the discriminant:
    $b^2 - 4ac = (-1)^2 - (4 \times -2 \times 15) = 1 + 120 = \boxed{121}$

- The discriminant is > 0, so $15 - x - 2x^2$ has $\boxed{\text{two distinct real roots.}}$

You may need to work with a quadratic where one or more of a, b and c are given in terms of an **unknown**. This means that you'll end up with an equation or inequality for the discriminant in terms of the unknown — you might have to solve it to find the **value** or **range of values** of the unknown.

Example 2

Find the range of values of k for which the function $f(x) = 3x^2 + 2x + k$:
a) has 2 distinct roots, b) has 2 equal roots (1 root), c) has no real roots.

- First, decide what a, b and c are: $\boxed{a = 3, b = 2, c = k}$

- Then work out what the discriminant is: $b^2 - 4ac = 2^2 - 4 \times 3 \times k$
$$= \boxed{4 - 12k}$$

a) Two distinct roots means:
$$\boxed{b^2 - 4ac > 0} \Rightarrow 4 - 12k > 0$$
$$\Rightarrow 4 > 12k$$
$$\Rightarrow \boxed{k < \frac{1}{3}}$$

b) Two equal roots (or one root) means:
$$\boxed{b^2 - 4ac = 0} \Rightarrow 4 - 12k = 0$$
$$\Rightarrow 4 = 12k$$
$$\Rightarrow \boxed{k = \frac{1}{3}}$$

The working is exactly the same in all three cases. The only difference is the equality / inequality symbol.

c) No real roots means:
$$\boxed{b^2 - 4ac < 0} \Rightarrow 4 - 12k < 0$$
$$\Rightarrow 4 < 12k$$
$$\Rightarrow \boxed{k > \frac{1}{3}}$$

Tip: The discriminant often comes up in exam questions — but sometimes they'll be sneaky and not actually tell you that's what you have to find.
Any question that mentions **roots** of a quadratic will probably mean that you need to find the **discriminant**.

Example 3

The equation $x^2 + kx + 9 = 0$ has two distinct roots. Find k.

- First, decide what a, b and c are: $\boxed{a = 1, b = k, c = 9}$

- Then work out what the discriminant is: $b^2 - 4ac = k^2 - 4 \times 1 \times 9$
$$= \boxed{k^2 - 36}$$

- Two distinct roots means
$$\boxed{b^2 - 4ac > 0} \Rightarrow k^2 - 36 > 0$$
$$\Rightarrow k^2 > 36$$
$$\Rightarrow k^2 > 36 \Rightarrow \boxed{k > 6 \text{ or } k < -6}$$

Tip: You'll learn more about quadratic inequalities in Chapter 3 — but here you just need to notice that if $k^2 > 36$, then k must either be bigger than 6 or less than –6.

Q1 Find the discriminants of the following equations.

a) $x^2 + 8x + 15 = 0$

b) $x^2 + 2\sqrt{3}x + 3 = 0$

c) $(2x + 1)(5x - 3) = 0$

d) $-3x^2 - \frac{11}{5}x - \frac{2}{5} = 0$

e) $9x^2 + 20x = 0$

f) $\frac{19}{16}x^2 - 4 = 0$

Q1 Hint: Make sure the equation is written in the form $ax^2 + bx + c = 0$ before trying to calculate the discriminant.

Q2 The discriminant of the equation $15x^2 + bx = 2$ is 169, where b is a positive number. Find all possible values of b.

Q3 The equation $0 = ax^2 + 7x + \frac{1}{4}$ has two equal roots (i.e. one real root). Find a.

Q4 Determine the number of real roots of the following equations, without solving them:

a) $13x^2 + 8x + 2 = 0$

b) $\frac{x^2}{3} + \frac{5}{2}x + 3 = 0$

Q5 Find the range of values of p for which $x^2 - 12x + 27 + p = 0$ has two distinct real roots.

Q6 Find the range of values of q for which $10x^2 - 10x + \frac{q}{2} = 0$ has two distinct real roots

Q7 The equation $2x^2 + (10p + 1)x + 5 = 0$ has no real roots. Show that p satisfies:

$$p(5p + 1) < \frac{39}{20}$$

Q8 Find the range of values of k for which $-2x^2 - 2x + k = 0$ has:

a) two distinct real roots,   b) two equal roots (one real root),

c) no real roots.

Q9 The equation $x^2 + (k + 5)x + \frac{k^2}{4} = 0$, where k is a constant, has no real roots.

a) Show that k satisfies $10k + 25 < 0$

b) Find the range of possible values of k.

Q10 a) Find the discriminant of $(k - \frac{6}{5})x^2 + \sqrt{k}x + \frac{5}{4}$.

b) For what values of k would the equation $(k - \frac{6}{5})x^2 + \sqrt{k}x + \frac{5}{4} = 0$ have:

(i) two equal roots (one real root)?

(ii) no real roots?

(iii) two distinct real roots?

3. Quadratic Graphs

Using the methods you've learnt for finding roots of quadratic functions, you'll be able to draw the graph of any quadratic function at all.

Learning Objective:

- Be able to sketch graphs of quadratic functions accurately.

Sketching a quadratic graph

There are two pieces of information you **always need** to know about a quadratic function before you can sketch it.

- The **shape** — u-shaped or n-shaped.
- The coordinates of the **points of intersection** with the x- and y-axes.

Sometimes, there will be two **different** graphs which have the same points of intersection and shape — in this case you'll need to work out the location of the **vertex point** (maximum or minimum) to decide which graph is right.

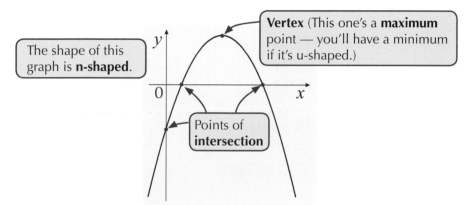

The shape of this graph is **n-shaped**.

Vertex (This one's a **maximum** point — you'll have a minimum if it's u-shaped.)

Points of **intersection**

Tip: The **vertex** of a quadratic graph is just the point where the graph changes direction. It is either a maximum point or a minimum point depending on the shape of the graph.

Shape

The first thing you need to decide is the **shape** of the graph — look at the coefficient of the x^2 term.

- If the coefficient of x^2 is **positive** — the graph will be **u-shaped**.
- If the coefficient of x^2 is **negative** — the graph will be **n-shaped**.

Intercepts

The next bit of information you need is where the graph **intersects the axes** — set x or y equal to zero and work out the other coordinate.

If you're sketching the function $y = ax^2 + bx + c$:

- To find the **y-intercept** — let **$x = 0$** and calculate the value of y.
- To find the **x-intercepts** — let **$y = 0$** and solve the equation $0 = ax^2 + bx + c$ to find the value or values of x.

Don't forget the x-intercepts correspond to the roots of the quadratic function — bear in mind that there may be **two repeated** roots, or **no** roots.

Tip: Use one of the methods of solving quadratics from earlier in the chapter to work out the x-intercepts — they're just the solutions of the equation.

Example 1

Draw the graph of the quadratic function f(x) = x^2 – 4x + 3, including any points of intersection with the axes.

- The coefficient of x^2 is positive...

  f(x) = x^2 – 4x + 3

  ...so the graph's u-shaped.

- Let $x = 0$ in the function to find the y-intercept.
  $$f(0) = (0)^2 - 4(0) + 3 = 3$$

  So the y-intercept is at 3.

- Solve f(x) = 0 to find the x-intercepts
  This equation will factorise:
  $$x^2 - 4x + 3 = 0$$
  $$\Rightarrow (x - 3)(x - 1) = 0$$
  $$\Rightarrow x - 3 = 0 \text{ or } x - 1 = 0$$
  $$\Rightarrow x = 3 \text{ or } x = 1$$

  So the x-intercepts are at 1 and 3.

- Put all this information together to draw the graph.

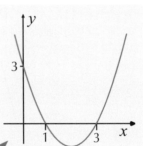

Vertex points

You'll sometimes need to find the minimum or maximum of the graph — which one it is depends on whether your graph is u-shaped or n-shaped.

One way to find the vertex is to **complete the square** and then interpret this. We actually did this back on pages 27-28 when finding the number of roots of a quadratic. Have a look back at those pages to remind yourself of the method. But here's the key result you need...

Tip: This comes from the fact that a square is always positive and so can never be less than 0.

A function of the form $y = p(x + q)^2 + r$ has a vertex at $(-q, r)$.
If $p > 0$, the graph is u-shaped, so the vertex is a minimum.
If $p < 0$, the graph is n-shaped, so the vertex is a maximum.

Quadratic graphs are always **symmetrical**, with a **vertical** line of symmetry that goes through the **vertex**. You can work out the **equation** of the line of symmetry by looking at the **coordinates** of the vertex points — for a quadratic with a vertex at (m, n), the line of symmetry has equation $x = m$. So if you've **completed the square** as above, the line of symmetry is $x = -q$.

Example 2

Find the vertex of $y = f(x)$, where $f(x) = 3x^2 - 6x - 7$, stating whether it is a maximum or minimum.

As it's a quadratic function and the coefficient of x^2 is positive, it's a **u-shaped** graph so it has a minimum.

Completing the square gives $f(x) = 3x^2 - 6x - 7 = 3(x - 1)^2 - 10$.

This is a square — it can never be negative. The smallest it can be is 0.

When the squared bit is zero, f(x) reaches its minimum value.
So find the value of x that makes the squared bit zero.

$f(x) = 3(x - 1)^2 - 10$ —— This bracket is 0 when $x = 1$...

Tip: f(1) means using $x = 1$ in the function

$f(1) = 3(1 - 1)^2 - 10$

$f(1) = 3(0)^2 - 10 = -10$ ◄—— ...so the minimum is –10.

The vertex is (1, –10).

Find where the graph of $y = f(x)$ crosses the axes and hence sketch the graph.

$y = f(x)$ crosses the y-axis when $x = 0$ which gives $y = -7$

$y = f(x)$ crosses the x-axis when $f(x) = 0$ so...

$$3x^2 - 6x - 7 = 0$$

$$\Rightarrow 3(x - 1)^2 - 10 = 0 \quad \longleftarrow \quad \text{Complete the square.}$$

$$\Rightarrow (x - 1)^2 = \frac{10}{3} \quad \longleftarrow \quad \text{Solve it to find where } y = f(x) \text{ crosses the } x\text{-axis.}$$

$$\Rightarrow x - 1 = \pm\sqrt{\frac{10}{3}}$$

$$\Rightarrow x = 1 \pm \sqrt{\frac{10}{3}}$$

So $y = f(x)$ crosses the x-axis when... $x = 1 + \sqrt{\frac{10}{3}}$ or $x = 1 - \sqrt{\frac{10}{3}}$

Now use this information to sketch the graph...

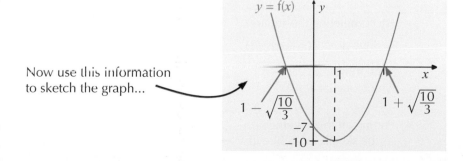

Tip: You can see from the graph that there's a line of symmetry at $x = 1$. You could have worked this out from the coordinates of the vertex.

If a function has **no real roots**, the shape and the axis intercepts won't be **enough** to draw the graph. In these cases you'll **have** to find the coordinates of the **vertex point**, even if the question doesn't ask you to.

Example 3

Sketch the graph of the function $y = 2x^2 - 4x + 3$, showing any intersection points with the axes.

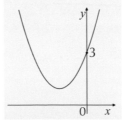

- The coefficient of x^2 here is positive...

  $$y = 2x^2 - 4x + 3$$

  ...so the graph's u-shaped.

- Now find the places where the graph crosses the axes (both the y-axis and the x-axis).

  (i) Put $x = 0$ to find where it meets the y-axis.

  $$y = 2x^2 - 4x + 3$$

  $$y = (2 \times 0^2) - (4 \times 0) + 3$$

  so $\boxed{y = 3}$ is where it crosses the y-axis.

  (ii) Solve $y = 0$ to find where it meets the x-axis (or show that it doesn't).

  Let $2x^2 - 4x + 3 = 0$

  $$b^2 - 4ac = -8 < 0$$

  So it has $\boxed{\text{no real roots,}}$ and doesn't cross the x-axis.

- Now the information we have so far isn't enough to say exactly what the graph will look like — it could be either of these...

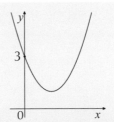

  ...so we need to find the minimum to tell us which it is.

  By completing the square...

  $$y = 2(x - 1)^2 + 1$$

  ...the minimum value is $y = 1$, which occurs at $x = 1$.

  Putting all this together — the sketch looks like this:

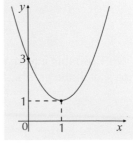

Tip: You could use the quadratic formula to try to solve the equation:

$$x = \frac{-b \pm \sqrt{b^2 - 4ac}}{2a}$$

But if you did you'd quickly realise that there will be no solutions.

So we've seen a couple of examples of finding the vertex by completing the square. But if you've already worked out the roots, and found that there are **one** or **two** real roots, you can work out the vertex more easily like this:

If the function has **two distinct roots** — use symmetry of quadratic graphs

- The graph of a quadratic function is **symmetrical**, so the x-coordinate of the vertex is **halfway** between the roots of the function.
- Work out the x-value halfway between the two roots and put it into the function to find the corresponding y-value of the vertex.

If the function has **two equal roots** (i.e. one root) — the vertex is at the root

- If a function has one root, then its graph just **touches** the x-axis at the root — this point will always be the vertex.

Example 4

Sketch a graph of the function $y = 8 - 2x - x^2$ showing all intersection points with the axes and the vertex point.

- The coefficient of x^2 is negative so the graph is n-shaped...
- Now find the places where the graph crosses the axes.

   (i) Putting $x = 0$ gives $y = 8$ as the y-intercept.

   (ii) Putting $y = 0$ gives: $8 - 2x - x^2 = 0$
   $$\Rightarrow (2 - x)(4 + x) = 0$$
   $$\Rightarrow x = 2 \text{ and } x = -4 \text{ as the } x\text{-intercepts}$$

- Now find the vertex.

   The graph is n-shaped so it has a maximum.
   The two distinct roots of the function are known, so you can work out the maximum by finding the x-value halfway between the two roots.

   The maximum point is at $x = -1$ ⟵ Halfway between 2 and –4
   $x = -1$ gives $y = 8 - (2 \times -1) - (-1)^2 = 9$

   So the graph has a maximum at the point (–1, 9).

   Putting all this together — the sketch looks like this:

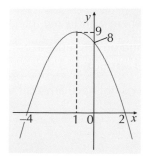

> **Tip:** If you find this factorisation confusing, rewrite the equation as $x^2 + 2x - 8 = 0$ and you'll get the factorisation $(x + 4)(x - 2) = 0$ which will give you the same answers.

> **Tip:** You could still find the vertex by completing the square, but this method is easier when you've already found the roots.

Q1　Sketch the following graphs on the same set of axes, indicating the x- and y-intercepts of each.

　　a) $y = x^2 - 1$　　　　　　　　　　b) $y = x^2 - 9$

Q2　a) Factorise the expression $f(x) = x^2 - 10x + 9$.

　　b) Use your answer to a) to sketch the graph of $f(x)$, showing the points where it crosses both axes.

　　c) Sketch the graph of $-f(x)$ on the same axes.

Q3　For each of the following quadratic functions:

　　(i)　　Describe its shape.

　　(ii)　Find the value of the y-intercept.

　　(iii)　Find the number of real roots.

　　(iv)　Find the values of x at which the graph intersects the x-axis — if it does.

　　(v)　Find the coordinates of the vertex.

　　(vi)　Sketch the graph of the function, marking on all the information you've found.

　　a) $y = -x^2 + 2x + 1$　　b) $y = x^2 - 7x + 15$　　c) $y = 2x^2 + 4x - 9$

Q4　The graph below shows the quadratic function $f(x)$.

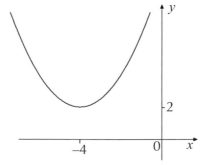

　　a) Use the sketch above to write down the function $f(x)$ in the form $f(x) = (x + q)^2 + r$ where q and r are integers.

　　b) Copy the sketch, and on the same axes, sketch the graph of the function $g(x) = (x + 4)^2$.

　　c) Which function does not have any real roots, $f(x)$ or $g(x)$?

Q5   a) Complete the square of the expression $x^2 - 6x + 5$.

b) Use part a) to solve the equation $x^2 - 6x + 5 = 0$.

c) Draw a graph of $y = x^2 - 6x + 5$ showing any intersections
with the axes and marking the vertex.

Q6   Sketch the following graphs, showing any intersections with the axes:

a) $y = x^2 - 2x + 1$ b) $y = x^2 + x - 1$

c) $y = x^2 - 8x + 18$ d) $y = -x^2 + 3$

Q7   a) What are the roots of the quadratic function shown
in the graph below?

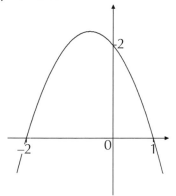

b) The quadratic can be written in the form $y = -x^2 + px + q$ where
p and q are integers. Use your answer to part a) to find p and q.

Q7b) Hint: If you know
the roots, you can find
the factors by working
backwards. This will
be covered in detail in
Chapter 4 when you do
the Factor Theorem.

Review Exercise — Chapter 2

Q1 Factorise the following expressions:

a) $x^2 + 2x + 1$

b) $x^2 - 13x + 30$

c) $x^2 - 4$

d) $3 + 2x - x^2$

e) $2x^2 - 7x - 4$

f) $5x^2 + 7x - 6$

Q2 Solve the following equations:

a) $x^2 - 3x + 2 = 0$

b) $x^2 + x - 12 = 0$

c) $2 + x - x^2 = 0$

d) $x^2 + x - 16 = x$

e) $3x^2 - 15x - 14 = 4x$

f) $4x^2 - 1 = 0$

g) $6x^2 - 11x + 9 = 2x^2 - x + 3$

Q3 Rewrite these quadratics by completing the square. Then state their maximum or minimum value and the value of x where this occurs. Also, say if and where their graphs cross the x-axis.

a) $x^2 - 4x - 3$

b) $3 - 3x - x^2$

c) $2x^2 - 4x + 11$

d) $4x^2 - 28x + 48$

Q4 How many roots do these quadratic equations have?
Sketch the graph of each quadratic function.

a) $x^2 - 2x - 3 = 0$

b) $x^2 - 6x + 9 = 0$

c) $2x^2 + 4x + 3 = 0$

Q5 Solve these quadratic equations, leaving your answers in surd form where necessary.

a) $3x^2 - 7x + 3 = 0$

b) $2x^2 - 6x - 2 = 0$

c) $x^2 + 4x + 6 = 12$

Q6 If the quadratic equation $x^2 + kx + 4 = 0$ has two distinct real roots, what are the possible values of k?

1   The equation $x^2 + 2kx + 4k = 0$, where k is a non-zero integer, has equal roots.

Find the value of k.

(4 marks)

2   The equation $px^2 + (2p + 3)x + p = 0$ has 2 distinct real solutions for x (p is a constant).

Find the range of possible values for p.

(4 marks)

3   Given that
$$5x^2 + nx + 14 \equiv m(x + 2)^2 + p \,,$$

find the values of the integers m, n and p.

(3 marks)

4   a)   Rewrite $x^2 - 12x + 15$ in the form $(x - a)^2 + b$, for integers a and b.

(2 marks)

b)   (i)   Find the minimum value of $x^2 - 12x + 15$.

(1 mark)

(ii)   State the value of x at which this minimum occurs.

(1 mark)

5   a)   Use the quadratic formula to solve the equation $x^2 - 14x + 25 = 0$.
         Leave your answers in simplified surd form.

         (3 marks)

    b)   Sketch the curve of $y = x^2 - 14x + 25$, giving the coordinates
         of the points where the curve crosses the x- and y-axis.

         (3 marks)

    c)   Hence solve the inequality $x^2 - 14x + 25 \leq 0$.

         (1 mark)

6   a)   (i)   Express $10x - x^2 - 27$ in the form $-(m - x)^2 + n$,
               where m and n are integers.

               (2 marks)

         (ii) Hence show that $10x - x^2 - 27$ is always negative.

               (1 mark)

    b)   (i)   State the coordinates of the maximum point
               of the curve $y = 10x - x^2 - 27$.

               (2 marks)

         (ii) Sketch the curve, showing where the curve crosses the y-axis.

               (2 marks)

1. Simultaneous Equations

Solving simultaneous equations just means finding the answers to two equations at the same time — i.e. finding values for x and y for which both equations are true.

Simultaneous equations — both linear

Solving by elimination

Simultaneous equations are just a pair of equations containing two unknown quantities, usually x and y.

This is how simultaneous equations are often shown:

$$3x + 5y = -4$$
$$-2x + 3y = 9$$

But they'll look different sometimes, maybe like this:

$$4 + 5y = -3x$$
$$-2x = 9 - 3y$$

You can solve two linear simultaneous equations by **elimination**. Before you can use the method, you need to **rearrange** them as '$ax + by = c$'.

$$4 + 5y = -3x \qquad\longrightarrow\qquad 3x + 5y = -4$$
$$-2x = 9 - 3y \qquad\qquad\qquad -2x + 3y = 9$$

The elimination method involves **four** steps:

1) Match the coefficients
   Multiply the equations by numbers that will make either the x's or the y's **match** in the two equations. (Ignoring minus signs.)

2) Eliminate to find one variable
   If the coefficients are the **same** sign, you'll need to **subtract** one equation from the other. If the coefficients are **different** signs, you need to **add** the equations.

3) Find the other variable (that you eliminated)
   When you've found one variable, put its value into one of the **original equations** so you can find the **other** variable.

4) Check your answer
   By putting these values into the **other original equation**.

Learning Objectives:

- Be able to solve two linear simultaneous equations using elimination or substitution.

- Be able to solve simultaneous equations where one is linear and one is quadratic using substitution.

Tip: You can also solve two linear simultaneous equations by substitution — see pages 46-49.

Solve the simultaneous equations $3x + 5y = -4$ and $-2x + 3y = 9$

- Number your equations 1 and 2.

  ① $\quad 3x + 5y = -4$

  ② $\quad -2x + 3y = 9$

- Match the coefficients:
  To get the x's to match, you need to multiply the first equation by 2 and the second by 3:

  ① $\times 2 \qquad 6x + 10y = -8 \quad$ —③ $\longleftarrow$ Number these

  ② $\times 3 \qquad -6x + 9y = 27 \quad$ —④ $\longleftarrow$ new equations.

- Eliminate to find one variable:
  Add the new equations together to eliminate the x's.

  ③ + ④ $\quad 19y = 19$

  $\boxed{y = 1}$

- Find the variable you eliminated:
  So $y = 1$. Now stick that value for y into one of the equations to find x:

  $y = 1$ in ① $\Rightarrow 3x + 5 = -4$

  $\qquad\qquad\qquad 3x = -9$

  $\qquad\qquad\qquad \boxed{x = -3}$

- So the solution is $\boxed{x = -3, \, y = 1.}$

- Check your answer:
  Putting these values into the other equation

  ② $\quad -2x + 3y = 9 \longleftarrow$ $\qquad$ If these two numbers are the

  $\qquad x = -3$ $\qquad\qquad\qquad\qquad$ same, then the values you've

  $\qquad y = 1$ $\qquad\qquad\qquad\qquad$ got for the variables are right.

  $\Rightarrow -2 \times (-3) + 3 \times 1 = 6 + 3 = 9$

If you drew the **graph** of each equation you'd get two straight lines.

- The point where these two lines **intersect** gives the **solution** to the two simultaneous equations.

- For the last example, the graph of the two lines $3x + 5y = -4$ and $-2x + 3y = 9$ would look like this:

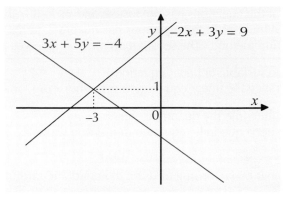

Tip: See Chapter 5 for more on straight line graphs.

Tip: In an exam, if they ask you to find the coordinates of the point of intersection, you should find them using one of the algebraic methods rather than using a graph.

- And the point where the two lines intersect is (–3, 1) — which is the same as the answer worked out on the previous page.

- However, **not all** simultaneous equations have solutions that work in both equations — for example, no values of x and y satisfy both $2x + 3y = 5$ and $4x + 6y = 7$. This would be obvious if you **sketched the graphs** — the lines are **parallel** so they never intersect.

Exercise 1.1

Q1 Solve the following simultaneous equations:

a) $2x - 3y = 3$
$x + 3y = 6$

b) $3x + 2y = 7$
$7x - y = -12$

c) $4x + 3y = -4$
$6x - 4y = 11$

d) $7x - 6y = 4$
$11x + 9y = -6$

e) $6x + 2y - 8 = 0$
$4x + 3 = -3y$

f) $2x + 18y - 21 = 0$
$-14y = 3x + 14$

g) $2x + 16y = 10$
$64y - 5 + 3x = 0$

Q1 Hint: Don't forget to rearrange the equations so they're in the form $ax + by = c$. It makes life much easier.

Q2 Find the point of intersection of each pair of straight lines.

a) $y = 2x - 3$
$y = \frac{1}{2}x + 3$

b) $y = -\frac{2}{3}x + 7$
$y = \frac{1}{2}x + \frac{21}{2}$

c) $x + 2y + 5 = 0$
$3x - 5y - 7 = 0$

d) $2x - 3y = 7$
$5x - \frac{15}{2}y = 9$

e) $8x = -3y + 10$
$9y = 3 - 6x$

f) $7x - 5y = 15$
$2x - 9 = 3y$

Q2 Hint: Although this question is phrased differently to Q1, it's still asking you to do the same thing — but remember, not all simultaneous equations have solutions (see above).

Simultaneous equations —
if one is quadratic

Solving by substitution

Elimination is great for simple equations, but it won't always work. Sometimes one of the equations has not just x's and y's in it — but bits with x^2 and y^2 as well. When one of the equations has quadratic terms, you can **only** use the **substitution** method. The substitution method involves **four** steps:

1) Isolate variable in linear equation
   Rearrange the linear equation to get either x or y on its own.

2) Substitute into the quadratic equation
   — to get a quadratic equation in just one variable.

3) Solve to get values for one variable
   — either by factorising or using the quadratic formula.

4) Stick these values in the linear equation
   — to find corresponding values for the other variable.

Tip: Always check your answer at the end too, by putting the values back into the original equations.

Example 1

Solve the simultaneous equations $-x + 2y = 5$ and $x^2 + y^2 = 25$.

- Start by labelling the two equations. Here the linear equation is labelled ①, and the equation with quadratic terms is labelled ②.

$$-x + 2y = 5 \quad \text{—①}$$
$$x^2 + y^2 = 25 \quad \text{—②}$$

Tip: The linear equation is the one with only x's and y's in. The quadratic is the one with x^2 or y^2 terms.

- Rearrange the linear equation so that either x or y is on its own on one side of the equals sign.

$$① \quad -x + 2y = 5$$
$$\Rightarrow x = 2y - 5$$

- Substitute this expression into the quadratic...

$$\text{Sub into } ②: \quad x^2 + y^2 = 25$$
$$\Rightarrow (2y - 5)^2 + y^2 = 25$$

- ...and then rearrange this into the form $ax^2 + bx + c = 0$, so you can solve it — either by factorising or using the quadratic formula.

$$\Rightarrow (4y^2 - 20y + 25) + y^2 = 25$$
$$\Rightarrow 5y^2 - 20y = 0$$
$$\Rightarrow 5y(y - 4) = 0$$
$$\Rightarrow y = 0 \text{ or } y = 4$$

- Finally put both these values back into the linear equation to find corresponding values for x:

When $y = 0$:

$$-x + 2y = 5 \quad ①$$
$$\Rightarrow x = -5$$

When $y = 4$:

$$-x + 2y = 5 \quad ①$$
$$\Rightarrow -x + 8 = 5$$
$$\Rightarrow x = 3$$

- So solving these simultaneous equations has actually produced a **pair** of solutions:

$$x = -5, y = 0 \quad \text{and} \quad x = 3, y = 4$$

Tip: You'll often, but not always, get a pair of solutions if one of the equations is quadratic.

- Now, **check your answers** by putting each set of values back into the original equations.

$$x = -5, y = 0: \ -(-5) + 2 \times 0 = 5 \ \checkmark$$
$$(-5)^2 + 0^2 = 25 \ \checkmark$$

$$x = 3, y = 4: \ -(3) + 2 \times 4 = 5 \ \checkmark$$
$$3^2 + 4^2 = 25 \ \checkmark$$

- The equation $x^2 + y^2 = 25$ is actually a circle about the origin with radius 5 and the linear equation is just a standard straight line.

Tip: Don't worry too much about circles for now — they're covered in Chapter 6.

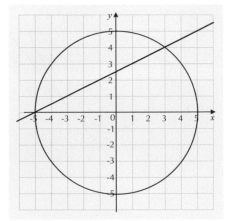

- So by solving the simultaneous equations you're actually finding the two points where the line passes through the circle — the points (–5, 0) and (3, 4).

Tip: The solutions to simultaneous equations are just the points where their graphs meet. If there are 2 solutions, the graphs will cross in 2 places. If there are no solutions, the graphs will never meet.

Example 2

Find any points of intersection of the following graphs:

a) $y = x^2 - 4x + 5$ and $y = 2x - 4$

- Label the two equations:

$$y = x^2 - 4x + 5 \ \text{———}①$$
$$y = 2x - 4 \ \text{———}②$$

- Substitute ② in ①:

$$2x - 4 = x^2 - 4x + 5$$

Tip: Look back at
Chapter 2 (pages 27-
29) for more on the
roots of quadratics.

- Rearrange and solve:

$$x^2 - 6x + 9 = 0$$
$$(x - 3)^2 = 0$$
$$\boxed{x = 3}$$

Two equal roots — i.e. you
only get 1 solution from
the quadratic equation.

- In Equation ② this gives:

$$y = 2 \times 3 - 4$$
$$\boxed{y = 2}$$

- So there's one solution: $\boxed{x = 3,\ y = 2}$

- Since the equations have only one solution, the
two graphs only meet at one point — (3, 2).

- The straight line is actually a tangent to the curve.

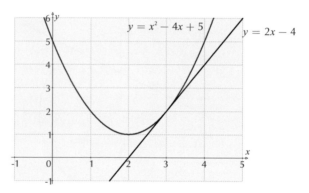

b) $y = x^2 - 4x + 5$ and $y = 2x - 5$

- Label the two equations:

$$y = x^2 - 4x + 5 \quad —①$$
$$y = 2x - 5 \quad —②$$

- Substitute ② in ① :

$$2x - 5 = x^2 - 4x + 5$$

- Rearrange and try to solve with the quadratic formula:

$$x^2 - 6x + 10 = 0$$
$$b^2 - 4ac = (-6)^2 - 4 \times 1 \times 10$$
$$= 36 - 40 = \boxed{-4}$$

- $b^2 - 4ac < 0$, so the quadratic has no real roots.

So the simultaneous equations have no solutions.

Tip: $b^2 - 4ac$ is called
the discriminant
— see page 30.

- This means the graphs never meet:

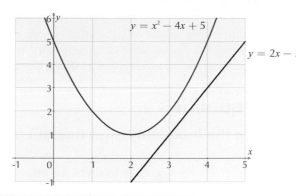

Observation: How sad.

Exercise 1.2

Q1 Solve the following simultaneous equations using substitution:

a) $y = 4x + 3$
$2y - 3x = 1$

b) $5x + 2y = 16$
$2y - x - 4 = 0$

Q2 Solve the following simultaneous equations:

a) $y = 2x + 5$
$y = x^2 - x + 1$

b) $y = 2x^2 - 3$
$y = 3x + 2$

c) $2x^2 - xy = 6$
$y - 3x + 7 = 0$

d) $xy = 6$
$2y - x + 4 = 0$

e) $y = x^2 - 2x - 3$
$y + x + 8 = 0$

f) $y = 2x^2 - 3x + 5$
$5x - y = 3$

g) $2x^2 + 3y^2 = 77$
$x + 3y = 14$

Q3 Find the points of intersection of the following curves and straight lines:

a) $y = \frac{1}{2}x^2 + 4x - 8$
$y = \frac{3}{2}x + 4$

b) $y = 2x^2 + x - 6$
$5x - y + 10 = 0$

c) $x^2 + y^2 = 50$
$x + 2y = 5$

d) $2x^2 - y + 3x + 1 = 0$
$y - x - 5 = 0$

Q4 a) Solve the simultaneous equations $x^2 + y^2 = 10$ and
$x - 3y + 10 = 0$.

b) Say what your answer to part a) means geometrically.

Q4 b) Hint: Here, you don't even need to draw a graph, just describe what your answer to part a) means.

Q5 Without drawing the graphs, determine whether the following curves and lines intersect at one or two points, or do not intersect at all:

a) $y = x^2 + 6x - 7$ and $y = 2x - 3$

b) $3x^2 + 4y^2 = 7$ and $3x + 4y = 7$

c) $xy + 2x - y = 8$ and $x + y = 1$

2. Inequalities

Learning Objectives:

- Be able to solve linear inequalities, e.g. $ax + b > cx + d$.
- Be able to solve quadratic inequalities, e.g. $ax^2 + bx + c \geq 0$.

Solving an inequality is very similar to solving an equation. But when multiplying or dividing both sides of an inequality, you've got to make sure that you keep the inequality sign pointing the right way.

Linear inequalities

Solving where the inequality sign doesn't change direction

Solve inequalities like you'd solve equations — whatever you do to one side, you have to do to the other.

- If you **add** or **subtract** something from both sides of an inequality, the inequality sign **doesn't** change direction.

- Multiplying or dividing both sides of an inequality by a **positive** number **doesn't** affect the direction of the inequality sign.

Tip: Solve an inequality just like you would an equation, by getting x (or whatever letter you're looking for) on its own.

Example 1

Find the set of values for x which satisfy:

a) $x - 3 < -1 + 2x$

$\Rightarrow x - 3 + 1 < -1 + 2x + 1$ ← Adding 1 to both sides leaves the inequality sign pointing in the same direction.

$\Rightarrow \qquad x - 2 < 2x$

$\Rightarrow x - 2 - x < 2x - x$ ← Subtracting x from both sides doesn't affect the direction of the inequality sign.

$\Rightarrow \boxed{-2 < x}$ And this is the same as... $\boxed{x > -2}$

b) $8x + 2 \geq 2x + 17$

$\Rightarrow 8x + 2 - 2 \geq 2x + 17 - 2$ ← Subtracting 2...

$\Rightarrow \qquad 8x \geq 2x + 15$

$\Rightarrow \qquad 8x - 2x \geq 2x + 15 - 2x$ ← ...and then $2x$, from both sides...

$\Rightarrow \qquad 6x \geq 15$

$\Rightarrow \qquad \dfrac{6x}{6} \geq \dfrac{15}{6}$ ← ...and dividing both sides by 6...

$\Rightarrow \boxed{x \geq \dfrac{5}{2}}$ ← ...leaves the inequality sign pointing in the same direction.

Solving where the inequality sign does change direction

When solving inequalities, multiplying or dividing by **negative** numbers **changes** the direction of the inequality sign.

Example 2

Find the set of values of x for which $4 - 3x \leq 16$.

$\Rightarrow 4 - 3x - 4 \leq 16 - 4$ ⬅ Subtract 4 from both sides.

$\Rightarrow \qquad -3x \leq 12$

$\Rightarrow \qquad \dfrac{-3x}{-3} \geq \dfrac{12}{-3}$ ⬅ Then divide both sides by –3 — but change the direction of the inequality sign.

$\Rightarrow \boxed{x \geq -4}$

Tip: The reason for the sign changing direction is because it's just the same as swapping everything from one side to the other:

$$-3x \leq 12$$

$$\Rightarrow -12 \leq 3x$$

$$\Rightarrow \quad -4 \leq x$$

$$\Rightarrow \qquad x \geq -4$$

Example 3

Find the set of values of x for which $\dfrac{2 - 4x}{3} > \dfrac{5 - 3x}{4}$.

$\Rightarrow \quad 4(2 - 4x) > 3(5 - 3x)$ ⬅ Multiply both sides by 12 to remove the fractions.

$\Rightarrow \quad 8 - 16x > 15 - 9x$ ⬅ Multiply out the brackets.

$\Rightarrow \qquad -16x > 7 - 9x$ ⬅ Subtract 8 from both sides.

$\Rightarrow \qquad -7x > 7$ ⬅ Add $9x$ to both sides.

$\Rightarrow \qquad \boxed{x < -1}$ ⬅ Then divide both sides by –7 and change the direction of the inequality sign.

Finding the solution to two inequalities

You may be given two inequalities and be asked to find a solution which satisfies **both** of them.

Example 4

Find the set of values for x which satisfy both the inequalities $x - 5 < -3 + 2x$ and $2x > 4x - 6$.

- Solve both inequalities separately.

$$x - 5 < -3 + 2x \qquad\qquad 2x > 4x - 6$$

$$\Rightarrow x - 2 < 2x \qquad\qquad \Rightarrow 2x + 6 > 4x$$

$$\Rightarrow \boxed{-2 < x} \qquad\qquad \Rightarrow \qquad 6 > 2x$$

$$\Rightarrow \qquad \boxed{3 > x}$$

Tip: You can write these solutions as $x > -2$ and $x < 3$ if you prefer.

- Show both solutions on a number line.
- Each line has an open circle at the end to show that this number isn't equal to x.

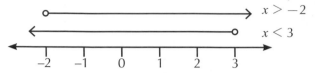

- Look where the two lines overlap to find the set of values that satisfy **both** inequalities.
- They overlap between –2 and 3, so:

$$-2 < x < 3$$

Exercise 2.1

Q1 Find the set of values for x which satisfy:

a) $2x - 1 < x + 4$ b) $4 - 3x \geq 10 - 5x$

c) $5x + 7 > 3x + 1$ d) $3 - 2x \leq 5x - 4$

e) $9 - x \geq 7x + 5$

Q2 Find the set of values for x which satisfy:

a) $2(x + 3) > 3(x + 2)$ b) $5(1 + 3x) \leq 7$

Q3 Find the set of values for x which satisfy:

a) $\dfrac{6 - 5x}{2} < \dfrac{4 - 8x}{3}$ b) $\dfrac{3x - 1}{4} \geq 2x$

c) $\dfrac{x - 2}{2} - \dfrac{2x + 3}{3} < 7$

Q4 Find the set of values for x which satisfy:

a) $-5 < 2x - 3 < 15$ b) $-5 \leq 4 - 3x < 19$

Q5 Solve the following inequalities, and represent the solutions on a number line:

a) $2x \geq 3 - x$ b) $5x - 1 < 3x + 5$

c) $2x + 1 \geq 3x + 2$ d) $3x - 1 \leq 5x - 7$

e) $9 - x \leq 3 - 4x$ f) $\dfrac{2(x - 3)}{3} + 1 < \dfrac{2x - 1}{2}$

Q6 a) Find the set of values of x for which $7 \leq 3x - 2 < 16$.

b) Show your solution to part a) on a number line.

Q7 Find the set of values for x which satisfy **both** $4 - 2x < 10$ and $3x - 1 < x + 7$. Draw the solutions to both inequalities on a number line to help you.

Q8 Find the values of x which satisfy both inequalities:

a) $2x \geq 3x - 5$ and $3x - 2 \geq x - 6$

b) $5x + 1 \leq 11$ and $2x - 3 < 5x - 6$

c) $2x - 1 \leq 3x - 5$ and $5x - 6 > x + 22$

d) $3x + 5 < x + 1$ and $6x - 1 \geq 3x + 5$

Quadratic inequalities

When solving inequalities, it's important that you **don't divide** or **multiply** by **variables** (anything you don't know the value of, e.g. x or y).

- The variable might be **negative** — so the inequality sign may end up pointing in the wrong direction.
- The variable could be equal to **zero** — you can't divide something by zero.

Example 1

$36x < 6x^2$

- Start by dividing by 6.
- Dividing by 6 is okay because 6 is definitely positive.

$$\Rightarrow 6x < x^2$$

- It's tempting to divide both sides by x now — but x could be negative (or zero).
- So instead take $6x$ from both sides.

$$\Rightarrow \boxed{0 < x^2 - 6x} \quad \text{Which is...} \quad \boxed{x^2 - 6x > 0}$$

Method for solving quadratic inequalities

The best way to solve a quadratic inequality is to do the following:

- Rewrite the inequality with zero on one side.
- Sketch the graph of the quadratic function.
- Use the graph to find the solution.

Example 2

Find the values of x which satisfy $-x^2 + 2x + 4 \geq 1$.

- First rewrite the inequality with zero on one side.

$$-x^2 + 2x + 3 \geq 0$$

- Then you need to draw the graph of $y = -x^2 + 2x + 3$.
- So find where it crosses the x-axis (i.e. where $y = 0$), by factorising to find the roots:

$$-x^2 + 2x + 3 = 0 \Rightarrow x^2 - 2x - 3 = 0$$

$$\Rightarrow (x + 1)(x - 3) = 0$$

$$\Rightarrow x = -1 \quad \text{or} \quad x = 3$$

Tip: See pages 16-19 if you need a refresher on how to factorise a quadratic.

Tip: See pages 33-37 for more on drawing graphs of quadratic functions.

Tip: Look at the inequality sign to tell you which bit of the graph you want — it'll either be the range(s) of x where the graph is below the x-axis or the range(s) where it's above.

Tip: Here you're looking for when it's positive **or** zero because the inequality sign in the quadratic equation tells us it's "greater than or equal to" zero.

- And the coefficient of x^2 is negative, so the graph is n-shaped. So it looks like this:

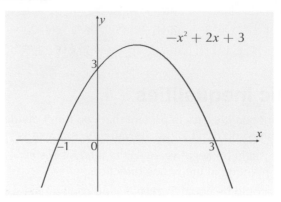

- Now you're trying to solve the inequality $-x^2 + 2x + 3 \geq 0$, so you're interested in when the graph is positive or zero, i.e. when it's above the x-axis.
- From the graph, this is when x is between -1 and 3 (including those points).
- So the solution is: $\boxed{-1 \leq x \leq 3}$

Example 3

Find the values of x which satisfy $2x^2 + 2x - 5 > 3x - 2$.

- First rewrite the inequality with zero on one side.
$$2x^2 - x - 3 > 0$$

- Then draw the graph of $y = 2x^2 - x - 3$
- So factorise the quadratic equation to find where it crosses the x-axis:
$$2x^2 - x - 3 = 0$$
$$\Rightarrow (2x - 3)(x + 1) = 0$$
$$\Rightarrow \boxed{x = \tfrac{3}{2} \text{ or } x = -1}$$

- And the coefficient of x^2 is positive, so the graph is u-shaped. And it looks like this:

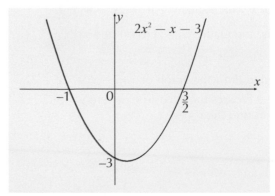

- Now you're trying to solve $2x^2 - x - 3 > 0$, so you need to say when the graph is positive.
- Looking at the graph, there are two parts of the x-axis where this is true — when x is less than -1 and when x is greater than $\frac{3}{2}$.
- So the solution is:

$$x < -1 \text{ or } x > \tfrac{3}{2}$$

Tip: You're only looking for when it's positive (rather than zero too) because the inequality sign in the quadratic inequality is a "greater than" sign.

Example 1 revisited

- On page 53 you had to solve $\mathbf{36x < 6x^2}$.

$$36x < 6x^2$$
$$\Rightarrow 6x < x^2$$
$$\Rightarrow 0 < x^2 - 6x$$

- So draw the graph of $y = x^2 - 6x = x(x - 6)$:

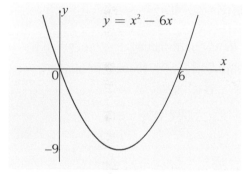

- You're looking for when it is positive.
- And this is positive when:

$$x < 0 \quad \text{or} \quad x > 6$$

Tip: If you'd divided the inequality $6x < x^2$ by x you'd only get half the solution — you'd miss the $x < 0$ part.

You may be asked to find the set of values for x which satisfy **both** a quadratic inequality and a linear inequality. To do this, you just work out the solution of each inequality separately and then use a **graph** to help you find the solution that satisfies both.

Example 4

Find the set of values of x which satisfy:
a) $5x - 10 > 4x - 7$

- Solve in the usual way.

$$\Rightarrow 5x - 10 > 4x - 7$$
$$\Rightarrow \quad 5x > 4x + 3$$
$$\Rightarrow \quad \boxed{x > 3}$$

b) $2x^2 - 11x + 5 < 0$

- You've already got zero on one side, so just factorise the quadratic to find where the graph crosses the x-axis:

$$2x^2 - 11x + 5 = 0$$
$$\Rightarrow (2x - 1)(x - 5) = 0$$
$$\Rightarrow \boxed{x = \tfrac{1}{2} \text{ or } x = 5}$$

- The coefficient of x^2 is positive, so the graph is u-shaped. And looks like this:

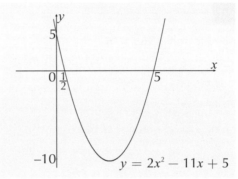

Tip: You're looking for when it is negative as the inequality sign tells us it is less than zero.

- You're interested in when this is negative, i.e. when it's below the x-axis.
- From the graph, this is when x is between $\tfrac{1}{2}$ and 5.
- So $2x^2 - 11x + 5 < 0$ when:

$$\boxed{\tfrac{1}{2} < x < 5}$$

c) both $5x - 10 > 4x - 7$ **and** $2x^2 - 11x + 5 < 0$

- You already know the solutions to both inequalities — and the graph above shows the solution to the quadratic inequality.
- So add the line $x = 3$ to your graph.
- You're now interested in when the curve is negative, **and** when the x values are greater than 3.

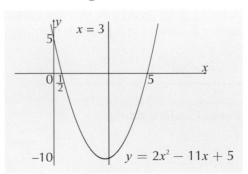

- So both inequalities are satisfied when:

$$\boxed{3 < x < 5}$$

Solving a quadratic inequality to find k

On page 31 we covered questions where the quadratic contained an **unknown constant** (k), and by using the formula for the discriminant we ended up with linear inequalities in terms of the unknown. We'll now take a look at a similar example that results in a **quadratic inequality**.

Tip: The discriminant is just the $b^2 - 4ac$ part of the quadratic formula — see page 30 for more.

Example 5

The equation $kx^2 + (k + 3)x + 4 = 0$ has two distinct real solutions. Show that $k^2 - 10k + 9 > 0$, and find the set of values of k which satisfy this inequality.

Tip: This question doesn't mention finding the discriminant — but that's what you've got to do first, to get that quadratic inequality in terms of k.

- Identify a, b and c: $a = k$, $b = (k + 3)$ and $c = 4$
- Then put these values into the formula for the discriminant:

$$b^2 - 4ac = (k + 3)^2 - (4 \times k \times 4) = k^2 + 6k + 9 - 16k = k^2 - 10k + 9$$

- The original equation has two distinct real solutions, so the discriminant must be > 0.
- So:

$$k^2 - 10k + 9 > 0.$$

- Now, to find the set of values for k, you have to factorise the quadratic:

$$k^2 - 10k + 9 = (k - 1)(k - 9)$$

- So, the graph of the quadratic will cross the horizontal axis at $k = 1$ and $k = 9$ and it's u-shaped.
- Sketching the graph, you can see that the quadratic is > 0 when:

   $k < 1$ or when $k > 9$

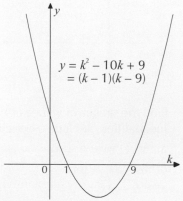

$$y = k^2 - 10k + 9$$
$$= (k - 1)(k - 9)$$

Exercise 2.2

Q1   Use the graphs given to solve the following quadratic inequalities:

a) $x^2 + 2x - 3 < 0$

b) $4x - x^2 < 0$

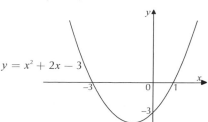

$y = x^2 + 2x - 3$

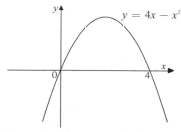

$y = 4x - x^2$

c) $2x^2 \geq 5 - 9x$

$y = 2x^2 + 9x - 5$

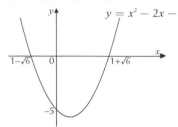

d) $x^2 - 2x - 5 > 0$

$y = x^2 - 2x - 5$

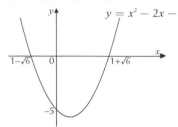

Q2 Hint: Here, you're given the graphs but you'll have to calculate where the x-intercepts are yourself.

Q2   Use the graphs given to help you solve the following quadratic inequalities:

a) $x^2 \leq 4$

$y = x^2 - 4$

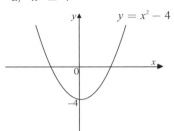

b) $13x < 3x^2 + 4$

$y = -3x^2 + 13x - 4$

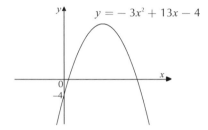

c) $x^2 + 4 < 6x$

$y = x^2 - 6x + 4$

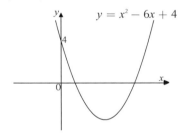

Q3   Find the ranges of values of x which satisfy the following quadratic inequalities. Include a sketch of the graph for each answer.

a) $x^2 + 5x - 6 \geq 0$ b) $x^2 - 3x + 2 < 0$

c) $6 - 5x > 6x^2$ d) $x^2 - 5x + 24 \leq 5x + 3$

e) $36 - 4x^2 \leq 0$ f) $x^2 - 6x + 3 > 0$

g) $x^2 - x + 3 > 0$ h) $6 \geq 5x^2 + 13x$

Q4   The sides of a rectangle are $(x - 9)$ m and $(x - 6)$ m respectively. Find the values of x for which the area of the rectangle is greater than 28 m².

Q5   By using the discriminant, find the set of values of k for which $x^2 - 6x + k = 0$ has two distinct real solutions.

Q6   Find the set of values for k which gives the equation $x^2 - kx + k = 0$ no real roots.

Q7   Find the values of x which satisfy both $4(3 - x) \geq 13 - 5x$ and $7x + 6 \geq 3x^2$.

Review Exercise — Chapter 3

Q1 Solve these sets of simultaneous equations:

a) $3x - 4y = 7$ and $-2x + 7y = -22$

b) $2x - 3y = \frac{11}{12}$ and $x + y = -\frac{7}{12}$

Q2 Find where the following lines meet:

a) $y = 3x - 4$ and $y = 7x - 5$

b) $y = 13 - 2x$ and $7x - y - 23 = 0$

c) $2x - 3y + 4 = 0$ and $x - 2y + 1 = 0$

Q3 Find where possible the solutions to these sets of simultaneous equations. Interpret your answers geometrically.

a) $y = x^2 - 7x + 4$
   $2x - y - 10 = 0$

b) $y = 30 - 6x + 2x^2$
   $y = 2(x + 11)$

c) $2x^2 + 2y^2 - 3 = 0$
   $y = x + 4$

> **Q3 Hint:** The "where possible" bit of this question is a bit of a clue.

Q4 Without drawing the graphs, decide whether the curve $y = x^2 - 2x - 3$ and line $y = 3x + 11$ intersect at one or two points, or do not intersect at all.

Q5 Solve:

a) $7x - 4 > 2x - 42$

b) $12y - 3 \le 4y + 4$

c) $9y - 4 \ge 17y + 2$

d) $x + 6 < 5x - 4$

e) $4x - 2 > x - 14$

f) $7 - x \le 4 - 2x$

Q6 Find the set of values for x that satisfy the following inequalities:

a) $3x^2 - 5x - 2 \le 0$

b) $x^2 + 2x + 7 > 4x + 9$

c) $3x^2 + 7x + 4 \ge 2(x^2 + x - 1)$

d) $x^2 + 3x - 1 \ge x + 2$

e) $2x^2 > x + 1$

f) $3x^2 - 12 < x^2 - 2x$

> **Q6 Hint:** Watch that you use the right kind of inequality sign in your answers.

1   Find the set of values of x that satisfy the following inequalities:

   a) $3x + 2 \leq x + 6$,

   (2 marks)

   b) $20 - x - x^2 > 0$,

   (4 marks)

   c) $3x + 2 \leq x + 6$ and $20 - x - x^2 > 0$.

   (1 mark)

2   Solve the simultaneous equations:

   $2x + 3y = 5$
   $5x + 4y = 2.$

   (3 marks)

3   Solve the inequalities:

   a) $3 \leq 2p + 5 \leq 15$,

   (3 marks)

   b) $q^2 - 9 > 0$.

   (4 marks)

4   a)   Factorise $3x^2 - 13x - 10$.

   (1 mark)

   b)   Hence, or otherwise, solve $3x^2 - 13x - 10 \leq 0$.

   (3 marks)

5   Solve the simultaneous equations:

   $y = -5x + 6$
   $7x + 2y - 6 = 0.$

   (4 marks)

6   a)   Eliminate x from the following equations:
$$x^2 + y^2 = 13$$
$$x - 5y + 13 = 0$$
to show that:
$$y^2 - 5y + 6 = 0$$
(3 marks)

b)   Hence, or otherwise, solve the simultaneous equations:
$$x^2 + y^2 = 13$$
$$x - 5y + 13 = 0$$
(3 marks)

7   Find the coordinates of any points of intersection for the following curve and line:
$$x^2 + 2y^2 = 36, \quad x + y = 6$$
(5 marks)

8   The curve C has equation $y = -x^2 + 3$ and the line l has equation $y = -2x + 4$.

a)   Find the coordinates of the point (or points) of intersection of C and l.
(4 marks)

b)   Sketch the graphs of C and l on the same axes, clearly showing where the graphs intersect the x- and y- axes.
(5 marks)

9   The line l has equation $y = 2x - 3$ and the curve C has equation $y = (x + 2)(x - 4)$.

a)   Sketch the line l and the curve C on the same axes, showing the coordinates of the x- and y- intercepts.
(5 marks)

b)   Show that the x-coordinates of the points of intersection of l and C satisfy the equation $x^2 - 4x - 5 = 0$.
(2 marks)

c)   Hence, or otherwise, find the points of intersection of l and C.
(3 marks)

Chapter 4

1. Algebraic Division

Learning Objectives:

- Know what the terms divisor, quotient and remainder mean.
- Be able to carry out simple algebraic division of quadratic or cubic polynomials by $(x + a)$ or $(x - a)$.

Algebraic division means dividing one expression by another. It's just one way to simplify a fraction that has letters in it. Below we will look at one method you can use — long division.

Algebraic division

Important terms

There are a few words that come up a lot in algebraic division, so make sure you know what they all mean.

> - **Divisor** — this is the thing you're dividing by. For example, if you divide $x^2 + 4x - 3$ by $x + 2$, the divisor is $x + 2$.
> - **Quotient** — the bit that you get when you divide by the divisor (not including the **remainder**).
> - **Remainder** — the bit that's **left over** after the division (it can't be divided by the divisor). If the remainder is 0, it means the polynomial divides exactly by the divisor. So the divisor is a factor of the polynomial.

Tip: The degree is the highest power of the variable.

For algebraic division to work, the **degree** of the **divisor** has to be less than (or equal to) the **degree** of the **original polynomial** (for example, you couldn't divide $x^2 + 2x + 3$ by $x^3 + 4$ as $3 > 2$, but you could do it the other way around).

In C1, you will only be expected to divide by algebraic expressions no trickier than $(x + a)$ or $(x - a)$ — these are **linear divisors**.

Algebraic long division

You can use **long division** to divide two algebraic expressions, using the same method as you'd use for numbers.

> **Example 1**
>
> **Divide $(x^3 + 3x^2 - 5x + 2)$ by $(x + 2)$.**
>
> - Start by dividing the first term in the polynomial by the first term of the divisor: $x^3 \div x = x^2$. Write this answer above the polynomial:
>
> $$\begin{array}{r} x^2 \\ x + 2 \overline{) x^3 + 3x^2 - 5x + 2} \end{array}$$
>
> - Multiply the divisor $(x + 2)$ by this answer (x^2) to get $x^3 + 2x^2$:
>
> $$\begin{array}{r} x^2 \\ x + 2 \overline{) x^3 + 3x^2 - 5x + 2} \\ x^3 + 2x^2 \end{array}$$

- Subtract this from the main expression to get x^2. Bring down the $-5x$ term just to make things clearer for the next subtraction.

$$\begin{array}{r} x^2 \\ x+2\overline{\smash{\big)}x^3 + 3x^2 - 5x + 2} \\ -\underline{x^3 + 2x^2} \\ x^2 - 5x \end{array}$$

Tip: Note that we only divide each term by the 'x' term, not the '$x + 2$'. The $+2$ bit is dealt with in the steps in between.

- Now divide the first term of the remaining polynomial (x^2) by the first term of the divisor (x) to get x (the second term in the answer).

$$\begin{array}{r} x^2 + x \\ x+2\overline{\smash{\big)}x^3 + 3x^2 - 5x + 2} \\ -\underline{x^3 + 2x^2} \\ x^2 - 5x \end{array}$$

- Multiply ($x + 2$) by x to get $x^2 + 2x$, then subtract again and bring down the $+2$ term.

$$\begin{array}{r} x^2 + x \\ x+2\overline{\smash{\big)}x^3 + 3x^2 - 5x + 2} \\ -\underline{x^3 + 2x^2} \\ x^2 - 5x \\ -\underline{x^2 + 2x} \\ -7x + 2 \end{array}$$

- Divide $-7x$ by x to get -7 (the third term in the answer). Then multiply ($x + 2$) by -7 to get $-7x - 14$.

$$\begin{array}{r} x^2 + x - 7 \\ x+2\overline{\smash{\big)}x^3 + 3x^2 - 5x + 2} \\ -\underline{x^3 + 2x^2} \\ x^2 - 5x \\ -\underline{x^2 + 2x} \\ -7x + 2 \\ -\underline{-7x - 14} \\ 16 \end{array}$$

- After subtracting, this term (16) has a degree that's **less** than the degree of the divisor, ($x + 2$), so it can't be divided. This is the **remainder**.

- So $(x^3 + 3x^2 - 5x + 2) \div (x + 2) = x^2 + x - 7$ remainder 16.

Tip: So this means
$x^3 + 3x^2 - 5x + 2 =$
$(x^2 + x - 7)(x + 2) + 16.$

Example 2

Divide $(2x^3 - 2x + 3)$ by $(x - 3)$.

Tip: You can do this for any missing term in a polynomial — just add a term into the right place with a coefficient of 0.

- This polynomial doesn't have an x^2 term, so add a $0x^2$ to where the x^2 term would be. This means you won't miss any terms out when doing the division.

$$x - 3 \,)\overline{2x^3 + 0x^2 - 2x + 3}$$

Tip: This method is exactly the same as the one used in Example 1.

- Then divide the first term in the polynomial by the first term of the divisor.

$$\begin{array}{r} 2x^2 \\ x - 3 \,)\overline{2x^3 + 0x^2 - 2x + 3} \end{array}$$

- Multiply the divisor by this answer and subtract this from the original expression. Bring down the next term.

$$\begin{array}{r} 2x^2 \\ x - 3 \,)\overline{2x^3 + 0x^2 - 2x + 3} \\ -\ \underline{2x^3 - 6x^2} \\ 6x^2 - 2x \end{array}$$

- Divide the first term of the remaining polynomial by the first term of the divisor.

$$\begin{array}{r} 2x^2 + 6x \\ x - 3 \,)\overline{2x^3 + 0x^2 - 2x + 3} \\ -\ \underline{2x^3 - 6x^2} \\ 6x^2 - 2x \end{array}$$

- Multiply the divisor by this answer and subtract this from the original expression. Bring down the next term.

$$\begin{array}{r} 2x^2 + 6x \\ x - 3 \,)\overline{2x^3 + 0x^2 - 2x + 3} \\ -\ \underline{2x^3 - 6x^2} \\ 6x^2 - 2x \\ -\ \underline{6x^2 - 18x} \\ 16x + 3 \end{array}$$

- Divide the first term of the remaining polynomial by the first term of the divisor. Multiply the divisor by this answer and subtract this from the original expression.

$$\begin{array}{r}
2x^2 + 6x + 16 \\
x - 3 \overline{)2x^3 + 0x^2 - 2x + 3} \\
- \ 2x^3 - 6x^2 \\
\hline
6x^2 - 2x \\
- \ 6x^2 - 18x \\
\hline
16x + 3 \\
- \ 16x - 48 \\
\hline
51
\end{array}$$

- So we get a remainder of 51.
- Therefore $(2x^3 - 2x + 3) \div (x - 3) = 2x^2 + 6x + 16$ remainder 51.

Tip: So this means
$2x^3 - 2x + 3 =$
$(2x^2 + 6x + 16)(x - 3) + 51$.

Exercise 1.1

Q1 Use long division to solve the following.
In each case state the quotient and remainder.
a) $(x^3 - 2x^2 - 4x + 8) \div (x - 3)$
b) $(x^3 - x^2 - 11x - 10) \div (x + 2)$
c) $(x^3 - x^2 - 3x + 3) \div (x - 2)$
d) $(x^3 - 2x^2 - 5x + 6) \div (x + 3)$
e) $(x^3 - 9x^2 + 7x + 33) \div (x + 2)$

Q2 Divide $(x^3 - 5x + 4)$ by $(x - 1)$ using long division.

Q3 Divide $(x^3 - x^2 - 11)$ by $(x - 3)$ using long division.

Q2, 3 Hint: Remember, you can add in any missing terms — just give them a coefficient of 0.

Q4 Divide the cubic $(2x^3 + 3x^2 - 11x - 6)$ by the expressions below:
a) $x + 1$
b) $x + 2$
c) $x - 1$

Q5 $f(x) = x^3 + 2x^2 - 7x - 2$
Express $f(x)$ in the form $(x - 2)g(x)$, where $g(x)$ is a quadratic.

Q5 Hint: $g(x)$ is the quotient when you divide $f(x)$ by $(x - 2)$.

2. The Remainder and Factor Theorems

Learning Objectives:

- Be able to use the Remainder Theorem.
- Know that if f(x) = 0 when x = a, then (x – a) is a factor of f(x) (the Factor Theorem).

The Remainder Theorem and Factor Theorem are useful tools. The Remainder Theorem gives an easy way to work out remainders and the Factor Theorem is an extension of the Remainder Theorem that helps you to factorise polynomials.

The Remainder Theorem

The Remainder Theorem gives you a quick way of **working out** the **remainder** from an algebraic division, but **without** actually having to do the division.

The Remainder Theorem says:

> When you divide **f(x)** by **(x – a)**, the remainder is **f(a)**.

So just stick $x = a$ into the polynomial.

Tip: Be careful if you're dividing by something like $(x + 7)$, as a will be negative. In this case, you'd get $a = -7$.

Example

Use the Remainder Theorem to work out the remainder when $(2x^3 - 3x^2 - 3x + 7)$ is divided by $(x - 2)$.

- So: $f(x) = 2x^3 - 3x^2 - 3x + 7$
- You're dividing by $(x - 2)$, so $a = 2$
- So the remainder must be:

$$f(a) = f(2) = (2 \times 8) - (3 \times 4) - (3 \times 2) + 7 = 5$$

If you want the remainder after dividing by something like $(ax - b)$, there's an extension to the Remainder Theorem:

Tip: You probably won't have to divide by $(ax - b)$ in the exam, but it'll be useful in later modules.

> When you divide **f(x)** by **(ax – b)**, the remainder is $f\left(\frac{b}{a}\right)$.

All this does is find the value of x that would make the bracket 0.

Example

Find the remainder when you divide $(2x^3 - 3x^2 - 3x + 7)$ by $(2x - 1)$.

- So: $f(x) = 2x^3 - 3x^2 - 3x + 7$
- You're dividing by $(2x - 1)$, so comparing it to $(ax - b)$ we get:

$$a = 2 \quad \text{and} \quad b = 1$$

- So the remainder must be:

$$f\left(\frac{b}{a}\right) = f\left(\frac{1}{2}\right) = 2\left(\frac{1}{8}\right) - 3\left(\frac{1}{4}\right) - 3\left(\frac{1}{2}\right) + 7 = 5$$

Fact: This page breaks the UK record for the most appearances of the word "remainder" on a single page. The title had previously been held by page 12 of "The Remainder Theorem Annual 1983".

If you're given the remainder when a polynomial is divided by something, you can use the Remainder Theorem to work **backwards** to find an **unknown coefficient** in the original polynomial.

Example

When $(x^3 + cx^2 - 7x + 2)$ is divided by $(x + 2)$, the remainder is –4. Use the Remainder Theorem to find the value of c.

- The polynomial was divided by $(x + 2)$, so: $a = -2$

- When you divide f(x) by $(x - a)$, the remainder is f(a), so:

$$f(-2) = -4 \quad \Rightarrow \quad (-2)^3 + c(-2)^2 - 7(-2) + 2 = -4$$
$$-8 + 4c + 14 + 2 = -4$$
$$4c = -12$$
$$c = -3$$

Exercise 2.1

Q1 Use the Remainder Theorem to work out the remainder in each of the following divisions:

a) $2x^3 - 3x^2 - 39x + 20$ divided by $(x - 1)$

b) $x^3 - 3x^2 + 2x$ divided by $(x + 1)$

c) $6x^3 + x^2 - 5x - 2$ divided by $(x + 1)$

d) $x^3 + 2x^2 - 7x - 2$ divided by $(x + 3)$

e) $4x^3 - 6x^2 - 12x - 6$ divided by $(2x + 1)$

f) $x^3 - 3x^2 - 6x + 8$ divided by $(2x - 1)$

Q2 The remainder when $x^3 + px^2 - 10x - 19$ is divided by $(x + 2)$ is 5. Use the Remainder Theorem to find the value of p.

Q3 When $x^3 - dx^2 + dx + 1$ is divided by $(x + 2)$ the remainder is –25. Use the Remainder Theorem to find the value of d.

Q4 When $x^3 - 2x^2 + 7x + k$ is divided by $(x + 1)$ the remainder is –8. Find the value of k.

Q5 f(x) = $x^4 + 5x^3 + px + 156$. The remainder when f(x) is divided by $(x - 2)$ is the same as the remainder when f(x) is divided by $(x + 1)$. Use the Remainder Theorem to find the value of p.

Q5 Hint: Find the remainder from both divisions in terms of p.

The Factor Theorem

If you get a **remainder of zero** when you divide f(x) by ($x - a$), then ($x - a$) must be a **factor** of f(x). This is the **Factor Theorem**.

Example

Use the Remainder Theorem to work out the remainder from the algebraic division: ($x^3 - 5x^2 + x + 10$) ÷ ($x - 2$).

- So: $a = 2$

- Work out the remainder: $f(a) = f(2) = 8 - (5 \times 4) + 2 + 10 = \boxed{0}$

- The remainder is 0, so that means ($x - 2$) divides into $x^3 - 5x^2 + x + 10$ **exactly**. So ($x - 2$) must be a **factor** of $x^3 - 5x^2 + x + 10$.

The **Factor Theorem** states:

> If **f(x)** is a polynomial, and **f(a) = 0**, then **($x - a$)** is a factor of **f(x)**.

Tip: In other words: If you know the roots, you also know the factors — and vice versa.

Example

Show that ($2x + 1$) is a factor of f(x) = $2x^3 - 3x^2 + 4x + 3$.

- The question's giving you a big hint here. Notice that $2x + 1 = 0$ when $x = -\frac{1}{2}$. So plug this value of x into f(x).

- If you show that $f(-\frac{1}{2}) = 0$, then the Factor Theorem says that $(x + \frac{1}{2})$ is a factor — which means that $2 \times (x + \frac{1}{2}) = (2x + 1)$ is also a factor.

$$f(x) = 2x^3 - 3x^2 + 4x + 3$$

- And so: $f\left(-\frac{1}{2}\right) = 2\left(-\frac{1}{8}\right) - 3\left(\frac{1}{4}\right) + 4\left(-\frac{1}{2}\right) + 3 = \boxed{0}$

- So, by the Factor Theorem, $(x + \frac{1}{2})$ is a factor of f(x), and so ($2x + 1$) is also a factor.

Just one more useful thing to mention about polynomials and factors:

> If the **coefficients** in a polynomial **add up to 0**, then **($x - 1$)** is a **factor**.

This works for **all polynomials** — there are no exceptions.

Tip: If you put $x = 1$ into a polynomial f(x), x^2, x^3 etc. are all just 1, so f(1) is the sum of the coefficients.

Example

Factorise the polynomial f(x) = $6x^2 - 7x + 1$.

- The coefficients (6, –7 and 1) add up to 0.
- That means $f(1) = 0$, and so ($x - 1$) is a factor.
- Then just factorise it like any quadratic to get this:

$$f(x) = 6x^2 - 7x + 1 = \boxed{(6x - 1)(x - 1)}$$

Q1 Use the Factor Theorem to show that:

a) $(x - 1)$ is a factor of $x^3 - x^2 - 3x + 3$

b) $(x + 1)$ is a factor of $x^3 + 2x^2 + 3x + 2$

c) $(x + 2)$ is a factor of $x^3 + 3x^2 - 10x - 24$

Q2 Use the Factor Theorem to show that:

a) $(2x - 1)$ is a factor of $2x^3 - x^2 - 8x + 4$

b) $(3x - 2)$ is a factor of $3x^3 - 5x^2 - 16x + 12$

Q2 Hint: Be careful with the fractions here.

Q3 a) Use the Factor Theorem to show that $(x - 3)$ is a factor of $x^3 - 2x^2 - 5x + 6$.

b) Show, by adding the coefficients, that $(x - 1)$ is also a factor of this cubic.

Q4 $f(x) = 3x^3 - 5x^2 - 58x + 40$. Use the Factor Theorem to show that the following are factors of $f(x)$:

a) $(x + 4)$ b) $(3x - 2)$

Q5 The cubic $qx^3 - 4x^2 - 7qx + 12$ has a factor of $(x - 3)$. Find the value of q.

Q5-6 Hint: Use the same method as on page 67 but with remainder 0.

Q6 The polynomial $f(x) = x^3 + cx^2 + dx - 2$ has factors $(x - 1)$ and $(x - 2)$. Using the Factor Theorem, find the values of c and d.

3. Factorising Cubics

Some cubic equations can be solved using factorisation, just like some quadratics. Factorising cubics will also help you to draw their graphs later in the module.

Factorising $ax^3 + bx^2 + cx$

Factorising a **cubic** means exactly what it meant with a quadratic — putting **brackets** in.

To factorise a cubic of the form $ax^3 + bx^2 + cx$ (i.e. with an x in every term), just **take out** x as your first factor as follows:

$$ax^3 + bx^2 + cx = x(ax^2 + bx + c)$$

Now you can just factorise the **quadratic** inside the brackets to get the other factors (see pages 16-19). Once you've factorised, you can **solve** a cubic equation just as you would with a quadratic.

Example 1

Factorise and solve the following cubic equations.

a) $x^3 - 2x^2 - 24x = 0$

Start by taking out a factor of x...

$x^3 - 2x^2 - 24x = x(x^2 - 2x - 24)$ This quadratic will factorise.

$= x(x \quad)(x \quad)$

$= x(x \quad 6)(x \quad 4)$ Put in the x's, work out the numbers then choose the signs.

$= x(x - 6)(x + 4)$

$\Rightarrow x(x - 6)(x + 4) = 0$

So either $x = 0$, $x - 6 = 0$ or $x + 4 = 0$

$\Rightarrow x = 0$, $x = 6$ or $x = -4$

b) $-x^3 - 2x^2 + 3x = 0$

If the x^3 coefficient is negative, take out a factor of $-x$...

...but don't forget these signs change.

$-x^3 - 2x^2 + 3x = -x(x^2 + 2x - 3)$

$= -x(x \quad)(x \quad)$

$= -x(x \quad 3)(x \quad 1)$ Factorise the quadratic in the brackets using the normal method.

$= -x(x + 3)(x - 1)$

$\Rightarrow -x(x + 3)(x - 1) = 0$

So either $x = 0$, $x + 3 = 0$ or $x - 1 = 0$

$\Rightarrow x = 0$, $x = -3$ or $x = 1$

Tip: Cubic equations have one, two or three solutions. So, unlike quadratics, they always have at least one real solution.

You might come across cubics of the form $ax^3 + bx^2 + cx$ which **won't fully factorise**. In these cases you can use the quadratic formula, as shown below.

Tip: See pages 20-22 for a reminder on the quadratic formula.

Example 2

Solve the cubic equation $-4x^3 - 4x^2 + x = 0$

- The first thing you need to do is factorise.

- The x^3 coefficient is negative, so take out a factor of $-x$ again...

$$-4x^3 - 4x^2 + x = 0$$

$$-x(4x^2 + 4x - 1) = 0$$

- Now $-x(4x^2 + 4x - 1) = 0$, so either $x = 0$ or $4x^2 + 4x - 1 = 0$. $x = 0$ is one solution and solving the quadratic equation will give the other two.

- This quadratic $4x^2 + 4x - 1$ **won't factorise** so use the quadratic formula.

$$x = \frac{-b \pm \sqrt{b^2 - 4ac}}{2a}$$

$$= \frac{-4 \pm \sqrt{4^2 - 4 \times 4 \times (-1)}}{2 \times 4}$$

$$= \frac{-4 \pm \sqrt{32}}{8}$$

$$= \frac{-4 \pm 4\sqrt{2}}{8}$$

$$= -\frac{1}{2} \pm \frac{1}{2}\sqrt{2}$$

So the solutions are $x = 0$, $x = -\frac{1}{2} + \frac{1}{2}\sqrt{2}$ and $x = -\frac{1}{2} - \frac{1}{2}\sqrt{2}$.

Exercise 3.1

Q1 Factorise the following cubic expressions:

a) $x^3 + 5x^2 + 6x$

b) $x^3 + 6x^2 - 7x$

c) $x^3 - 18x^2 + 81x$

d) $x^3 + 7x^2 + 10x$

e) $-x^3 + 4x^2 - 3x$

f) $2x^3 + 15x^2 + 25x$

g) $x^3 - 49x$

h) $x^3 - \frac{9}{4}x$

Q2 Solve the following cubic equations:

a) $-x^3 + 2x^2 + 24x = 0$

b) $x^3 - \frac{7}{9}x^2 + \frac{10}{81}x = 0$

c) $2x^3 + 9x^2 + 4x = 0$

d) $3x^3 - 3x^2 + 4x = 0$

e) $x^2(4x + 3) = x$

f) $2x^3 + 8x^2 = -3x$

Q2 Hint: Some of the quadratics may not factorise — use the quadratic formula to get the remaining solutions.

Factorising $ax^3 + bx^2 + cx + d$

You may be asked to **factorise** a cubic of the form $ax^3 + bx^2 + cx + d$.
That constant term at the end means you can't just take out x as a factor.

Sometimes you'll be **given one of the factors** to start you off. If so, you can use the following method to find the other factors.

Equating coefficients method

1) Write down the **factor** you know $(x - k)$, and a **general quadratic**: $(x - k)(px^2 + qx + r)$, where p, q and r are constants to be found.

2) Expand the brackets to get a **cubic** containing all your unknowns: $px^3 + (q - pk)x^2 + (r - qk)x - kr$.

3) Then **equate** this expression to the cubic you're trying to factorise.

4) To find the values of p, q and r, **equate the coefficients** on either side of your equation. Start by equating the **coefficients of x^3** to find p, and then equate the **constant terms** to find r. Finally, equating the x^2 **or x terms** will let you find q.

5) Put the values of p, q and r **back into the quadratic** from step 1).

6) The last step is to **factorise** this quadratic — if you can. Otherwise leave it as it is or use the quadratic formula to find any roots.

Tip: You could also find the quadratic using long division — see pages 62-65. You might find one way easier than another, so do it the way you prefer.

Example 1

$(x - 3)$ is a factor of $f(x) = x^3 - x^2 - 5x - 3$. Find the other factors.

- Start by writing down the factor you know and a **general quadratic**.
$$(x - 3)(px^2 + qx + r)$$

- **Expand the brackets** to get a cubic containing your unknowns:
$$= px^3 + (q - 3p)x^2 + (r - 3q)x - 3r$$

- **Equate** this expression to $f(x)$:
$$px^3 + (q - 3p)x^2 + (r - 3q)x - 3r = x^3 - x^2 - 5x - 3$$

- Equating the **coefficients of x^3** gives you $px^3 = x^3 \Rightarrow p = 1$.
Equating the **constant terms** gives you $-3r = -3 \Rightarrow r = 1$.
Equating the **coefficients of x^2** gives you $(q - 3p)x^2 = -x^2 \Rightarrow q - 3 = -1$
$$\Rightarrow q = 2.$$

- Putting p, q and r **back in the quadratic** gives:
$$f(x) = (x - 3)(x^2 + 2x + 1)$$

- The quadratic factorises, so $f(x) = (x - 3)(x + 1)(x + 1) = (x - 3)(x + 1)^2$

- So, the other factor is $(x + 1)$ — it's squared in the above factorisation because it's a repeated root.

Tip: If you'd been asked to solve $f(x) = 0$, you'd just set each bracket to 0 to give roots of $x = 3$ and $x = -1$.

If you're not given any factors, you can use the **Factor Theorem** to find one:

- First, **add up** the **coefficients** to check if $(x - 1)$ is a factor.
- If that doesn't work, keep trying small numbers (find $f(-1)$, $f(2)$, $f(-2)$, $f(3)$, $f(-3)$ and so on) until you find a number that gives you **zero** when you put it in the **cubic**. Call that number k. $(x - k)$ is a **factor of the cubic**.
- Then **finish factorising** the cubic, either by algebraic long division or using the equating coefficients method.

Tip: Flick back to page 68 for the Factor Theorem.

Example 2

Solve $x^3 - 5x^2 - 4x + 20 = 0$.

- Check to see if the coefficients **add up to 0**: $1 - 5 - 4 + 20 = 12$. They don't — so $(x - 1)$ is **not** a factor.

- Try **different values of x** in $f(x)$ until you find a number that gives you $f(x) = 0$:

  $$f(-1) = (1 \times -1) - (5 \times 1) - (4 \times -1) + 20 = 18$$ So $(x + 1)$ isn't a factor...

  $$f(2) = (1 \times 8) - (5 \times 4) - (4 \times 2) + 20 = 0$$ ... but $(x - 2)$ is.

  So $(x - 2)$ is a factor.

Tip: If you've added the coefficients and they don't add up to zero, then you don't need to do $f(1)$, as you already know that $(x - 1)$ isn't a factor.

- You can now **factorise the cubic** by taking $(x - 2)$ out as a factor, leaving a quadratic. You can either **divide** the cubic by $(x - 2)$ using long division, or use the **equating coefficients** method on the previous page.

  Either way, you'll end up with: $(x - 2)(x^2 - 3x - 10)$

- The quadratic will factorise: $(x - 2)(x - 5)(x + 2)$

- The last step is to **solve** $(x - 2)(x - 5)(x + 2) = 0$, so the solutions are: $x = 2$, $x = 5$ and $x = -2$.

Exercise 3.2

Q1   Fully factorise $2x^3 + 3x^2 - 11x - 6$, given that $(x - 2)$ is one factor.

Q2   Fully factorise $x^3 - 3x^2 + 3x - 1$, given that $(x - 1)$ is a factor.

Q3 $f(x) = x^3 - 2x^2 - 4x + 8$
    a) Factorise $f(x)$.
    b) Find the solutions of $f(x) = 0$.

Q4   Find the roots of the cubic $f(x) = x^3 - x^2 - 3x + 3$.

Q4 Hint: "Find the roots" just means the same as "Find the solution to $f(x) = 0$".

Q5 $f(x) = x^3 - px^2 + 17x - 10$, and $(x - 5)$ is a factor of $f(x)$.
    a) Find the value of p.
    b) Factorise $f(x)$.
    c) Find all the solutions to $f(x) = 0$.

Review Exercise — Chapter 4

Q1   Use long division to divide the cubics below.
In each case show your working, and state the quotient and remainder.
a) $x^3 - x^2 - 3x + 3$ by $(x + 3)$
b) $x^3 - 3x^2 - 5x + 6$ by $(x - 2)$
c) $x^3 + 2x^2 + 3x + 2$ by $(x + 2)$

Q2   Using long division, write the following functions f(x) in the form
$f(x) = (x + 2)g(x) +$ remainder (where g(x) is a quadratic):
a) $f(x) = 3x^3 - 4x^2 - 5x - 6$ b) $f(x) = x^3 + 2x^2 - 3x + 4$ c) $f(x) = 2x^3 + 6x - 3$

Q3   Find the remainder when the following are divided by:
     (i) $(x + 1)$,   (ii) $(x - 1)$,   (iii) $(x - 2)$
a) $f(x) = 6x^3 - x^2 - 3x - 12$
b) $f(x) = x^4 + 2x^3 - x^2 + 3x + 4$
c) $f(x) = x^5 + 2x^2 - 3$

Q4   Find the remainder when $f(x) = x^4 - 3x^3 + 7x^2 - 12x + 14$ is divided by:
a) $x + 2$ b) $2x + 4$ c) $x - 3$ d) $2x - 6$

Q5   The remainder when $x^3 + cx^2 + 17x - 10$ is divided by $(x + 3)$ is -16.
Use the Remainder Theorem to find the value of c.

Q6   Work out whether the following are factors of $f(x) = x^5 - 4x^4 + 3x^3 + 2x^2 - 2$.
a) $x - 1$ b) $x + 1$ c) $x - 2$ d) $2x - 2$

Q7 $f(x) = (x + 5)(x - 2)(x - 1) + k$. If $(x + 2)$ is a factor of f(x), find the value of k.

Q8   a) Find the coordinates of the points of intersection of the graphs
       of $y = f(x)$ and $y = g(x)$, where $f(x) = 5x^3 - 13x^2 + 6x$
       and $g(x) = -5x^3 + 7x^2 + 6x$.

      b) Using your answer to part a) or otherwise, express
       $f(x) = 5x^3 - 13x^2 + 6x$ as the product of three factors.

> **Q8 Hint:** The points where the graphs intersect are found by setting the functions equal to each other and solving to find x.

Q9   a) Show that the x-coordinates of the points where the curves $y = x(x - 6)^2$
       and $y = -x(2x - 31)$ intersect are given by the solutions to
       the equation $x^3 - 10x^2 + 5x = 0$.

      b) Find the x-coordinates of the points where the two curves meet.
       Where appropriate, express your answers in surd form.

> **Q9 Hint:** The quadratic formula will come in handy here.

Q10 Given that $(x - 3)$ is a factor of the cubic $f(x) = x^3 - 9x^2 + 7x + 33$,
find all the solutions of $f(x) = 0$.

Q11 Find the roots of $f(x) = x^3 + 6x^2 + 11x + 6$.

1    $f(x) = 2x^3 - 5x^2 - 4x + 3$

     a)   Find the remainder when $f(x)$ is divided by

         (i) $(x - 1)$

                (2 marks)

         (ii) $(2x + 1)$

                (2 marks)

     b)   Show using the Factor Theorem that $(x + 1)$ is a factor of $f(x)$.

                (2 marks)

     c)   Factorise $f(x)$ completely.

                (4 marks)

2    $f(x) = (4x^2 + 3x + 1)(x - p) + 5$, where p is a constant.

     a)   State the value of $f(p)$.

                (1 mark)

     b)   Find the value of p, given that when $f(x)$ is divided by $(x + 1)$,
         the remainder is -1.

                (2 marks)

     c)   Find the remainder when $f(x)$ is divided by $(x - 1)$.

                (1 mark)

3    $f(x) = 3x^3 + 8x^2 + 3x - 2$

     a)   Use the Factor Theorem to show that $(x + 2)$ is a factor of $f(x)$.

                (2 marks)

     b)   Factorise $f(x)$ completely.

                (4 marks)

     c)   Write down all the solutions to the equation:

$$3x^3 + 8x^2 + 3x - 2 = 0$$

                (1 mark)

1. The Equation of a Straight Line

Learning Objectives:

- Be able to find the equation of a straight line passing through two given points, or though one point with a certain gradient.

- Write straight line equations in any of the three forms:
$y - y_1 = m(x - x_1)$,
$y = mx + c$ and
$ax + by + c = 0$.

- Be able to find the midpoint and length of a line segment between two points.

Any straight line can be described by an equation made up of an x term, y term and constant term (though one of these may actually be zero). There are three standard ways of arranging straight line equations that you need to learn.

$$y - y_1 = m(x - x_1)$$

This is the first form you need to know.

$$\boxed{y - y_1 = m(x - x_1)}$$

m is the **gradient** (the steepness of the line)
x_1 and y_1 are the **coordinates** of one of the points on the line.

If you're told **two points** that a straight line passes through, this is probably the easiest one to use. You do need to be a little careful using the formula, so here's a method to follow:

> 1) **LABEL** the points (x_1, y_1) and (x_2, y_2).
>
> 2) **GRADIENT** — find this using $m = \dfrac{y_2 - y_1}{x_2 - x_1}$.
>
> 3) **WRITE DOWN THE EQUATION** $y - y_1 = m(x - x_1)$.
>
> 4) **SUBSTITUTE** in your values for m, x_1 and y_1.

Example

Find the equation of the line that passes through the points (–3, 10) and (1, 4), and write it in the form $y - y_1 = m(x - x_1)$.

- Label the points.

$$\text{Point 1 —} \quad (x_1, y_1) = (-3, 10)$$
$$\text{Point 2 —} \quad (x_2, y_2) = (1, 4)$$

- Find the gradient of the line using $m = \dfrac{y_2 - y_1}{x_2 - x_1}$.

$$m = \frac{4 - 10}{1 - (-3)} = \frac{-6}{4} = \boxed{-\frac{3}{2}}$$

Tip: Make sure you subtract the same way round on the top and bottom of the fraction.

In other words, **don't** do this: $\dfrac{y_2 - y_1}{x_1 - x_2}$

- Write down the equation of the line.

$$y - y_1 = m(x - x_1)$$

- Now just substitute in the values for m, x_1 and y_1.

$$x_1 = -3, y_1 = 10, m = -\frac{3}{2} \longrightarrow y - 10 = -\frac{3}{2}(x - (-3))$$

$$\boxed{y - 10 = -\frac{3}{2}(x + 3)}$$

Tip: This would work fine if you used x_2 and y_2 instead. The equation would look different, but still represent the line.

$y = mx + c$

This form for the straight line equation is probably the most popular — it's certainly the easiest form to make sense of.

$$y = mx + c$$

m is the **gradient** of the line

c is the **y-intercept** (where it crosses the y-axis).

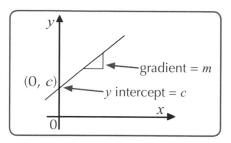

When in $y = mx + c$ form, you can simply read off the values of m and c — and together these give you a fairly good idea of what the graph will look like.

Tip: This diagram shows a straight line with positive values for m and c. A negative value for m would make the graph slope downwards.

As well as being easy to interpret, it's fairly easy to find the equation of a line in $y = mx + c$ form. Here are a couple of examples — you're given different information in each case.

Examples

A straight line has a gradient of –2 and passes through the point (3, 1). Find the equation of the line.

- To find c, sub in the values of m, x and y given in the question.

$$y = mx + c$$
$$1 = (-2 \times 3) + c$$
$$7 = c$$

- Then put your values of m and c into the equation $y = mx + c$.

$$y = -2x + 7$$

Tip: It's a good idea to put the x- and y-values of your given point into your final equation to check it's right.

Find the equation of the straight line that passes through the points (–18, 16) and (10, 2).

- Start by finding m.

$$m = \frac{2 - 16}{10 - (-18)} = \frac{-14}{28} = -\frac{1}{2}$$

- Write down the equation with $m = -\frac{1}{2}$.

$$y = -\frac{1}{2}x + c$$

- Using one of the given points, substitute in values for x and y — this will find c.

$x = 10$, $y = 2$ gives: $\quad 2 = -\frac{1}{2}(10) + c$
$$c = 7$$

- So the equation is: $\quad y = -\frac{1}{2}x + 7$

Tip: This method is very similar to that on the previous page — find the gradient, then put in the x and y values of one of the points...

Q1 Give the gradient and y-intercept of the following straight lines:

a) $y = -4x + 11$ b) $y = 4 - x$ c) $y = 1.7x - 2.3$

Q2 Give equations for the following straight lines in the form $y = mx + c$:

a) gradient -3, y-intercept $(0, 2)$

b) gradient 5, y-intercept $(0, -3)$

c) gradient $\frac{1}{2}$, y-intercept $(0, 6)$

d) gradient 0.8, y-intercept $(0, 1.2)$

Q3 Use the information in the diagrams to the find the equation of each straight line in the form $y = mx + c$.

a)

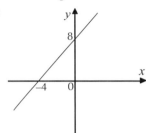

b)

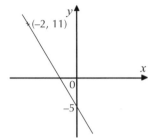

c)

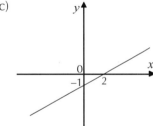

Q4 Find the equations of the lines that pass through the following pairs of points. Give each answer in these forms:

(i) $y - y_1 = m(x - x_1)$ (ii) $y = mx + c$.

a) $(4, 1), (0, -3)$ b) $(12, -3), (14, 1)$

c) $(5, 7), (-2, 5)$ d) $(-3, 6), (4, -2)$

Q5 Find the equation of the straight line which passes through the point $(-4, -3)$ and has a gradient of $\frac{1}{4}$. Give your answer in the form $y = mx + c$.

Q6 Hint: Find the equation of the line first, then see if the given x- and y-values fit.

Q6 A straight line has gradient 3 and passes through the point $(2, -7)$. State which of the following coordinates are points on the line.

a) $(1, -10)$ b) $(-2, -7)$

c) $(5, 2)$ d) $(0.5, 2.5)$

e) $(7, 8)$ f) $(0, -12)$

$ax + by + c = 0$

This is the last form you need to know for straight line equations.

$$ax + by + c = 0$$ Where a, b and c are **integers**.

Note that this form doesn't involve m. As a result, it's not as easy to work with. So if you're asked to give an equation in this form, it's often easiest just to find it in one of the previous two forms, then rearrange it at the end.

One important thing to remember when using this form is that a, b and c are integers, so you must get rid of any fractions.

Example 1

Find the gradient and y-intercept of the line $5x + 2y - 10 = 0$.

- The easiest way to answer this question is to rearrange the equation into the form $y = mx + c$.

$$5x + 2y - 10 = 0$$
$$\Rightarrow 2y = -5x + 10$$
$$\Rightarrow y = -\frac{5}{2}x + 5$$

- Now compare the equation with $y = mx + c$.
- So for the line $5x + 2y - 10 = 0$:

$$\text{gradient} = -\frac{5}{2} \text{ and the } y\text{-intercept is } (0, 5)$$

Example 2

Find the equation of the line that passes through the point $(2, -15)$ and has gradient $-\frac{3}{2}$, giving your answer in the form $ax + by + c = 0$, where a, b and c are integers.

- Start by finding the equation in one of the easier forms. We'll use $y - y_1 = m(x - x_1)$ this time, but $y = mx + c$ would be just as easy...

$$m = -\frac{3}{2} \text{ gives: } y - y_1 = -\frac{3}{2}(x - x_1)$$

- Now sub in $x_1 = 2$ and $y_1 = -15$:

$$y + 15 = -\frac{3}{2}(x - 2)$$

- Now you can start rearranging into $ax + by + c = 0$ form:

$$y + \frac{3}{2}x + 15 - 3 = 0$$
$$y + \frac{3}{2}x + 12 = 0$$
$$\Rightarrow 3x + 2y + 24 = 0$$

Tip: If you end up with an equation like $\frac{3}{2}x - \frac{4}{3}y + 6 = 0$, where you've got a 2 and a 3 on the bottom of the fractions — multiply everything by the lowest common multiple of 2 and 3, i.e. 6.

Q1 Write the following equations in the form $ax + by + c = 0$, where a, b and c are integers.

a) $y = 5x + 2$

b) $3y = -\frac{1}{2}x + 3$

c) $2(x - 1) = 4y - 1$

d) $7x - 3 = 2y + 6$

e) $\frac{1}{2}(4x + 3) = 3(y - 2)$

f) $3(y - 4) = 4(x - 3)$

Q2 Hint: You'll need to convert to a different form so that you can interpret the equations.

Q2 Find the gradient and y-intercept of the following lines:

a) $6x - 2y + 3 = 0$

b) $-9x + 3y - 12 = 0$

c) $-x - 4y - 2 = 0$

d) $7x + 8y + 11 = 0$

Q3 Find the equation of the line that passes through the following points. Write your answer in the form $ax + by + c = 0$, where a, b and c are integers.

a) $(5, 2)$, $(3, 4)$

b) $(9, -1)$, $(7, 2)$

c) $(-6, 1)$, $(4, 0)$

d) $(-12, 3)$, $(5, 7)$

Q4 Hint: Again, it's easiest to find the equation in a different form, then convert it at the end.

Q4 Find the equation of the lines below in the form $ax + by + c = 0$, where a, b and c are integers.

a)

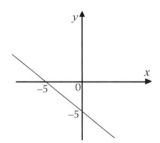

b)

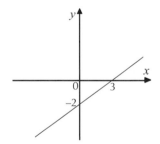

Finding the midpoint of a line segment

The **midpoint** of a line segment is the point exactly halfway between the two endpoints. To find it, all you have to do is **add** the coordinates of the **endpoints** of the line segment together, then **divide** by two.

Example 1

Points A and B are given by the coordinates (7, 4) and (–1, –2) respectively. M is the midpoint of the line segment AB. Find the coordinates of M.

- **Add** together the x-coordinates of A and B, and the y-coordinates of A and B, as shown:

$$(x_A, y_A) + (x_B, y_B) = (x_A + x_B, y_A + y_B)$$

$$(7, 4) + (-1, -2) = (7 + (-1), 4 + (-2)) = (6, 2)$$

- Now **divide** each coordinate by **two**:

$$\left(\frac{6}{2}, \frac{2}{2}\right) = (3, 1)$$

- So the M has coordinates (3, 1)

Tip: You're just averaging the endpoints when you add them together and divide by two.

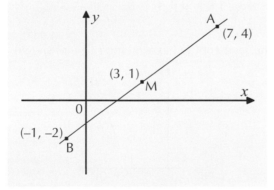

Tip: It can help to sketch a graph of the line segment so you can roughly check that your answer is what you expect it to be.

Example 2

The line segment XY has a midpoint M. Y has the coordinates (6, –6) and M has the coordinates (4, 0). Find the coordinates of X.

- To work out the **x-coordinate** of the midpoint, you'd have done the calculation $\frac{x_X + x_Y}{2}$.

- But you know the x-coordinate of the midpoint is 4, so put what you know into the calculation as follows:

$$\frac{x_X + 6}{2} = 4$$

$$\Rightarrow x_X + 6 = 8 \Rightarrow x_X = 2$$

- You can work out the **y-coordinate** of X in the same way:

$$\frac{y_X + (-6)}{2} = 0$$

$$\Rightarrow y_X + (-6) = 0 \Rightarrow y_X = 6$$

- So the point X has coordinates (2, 6).

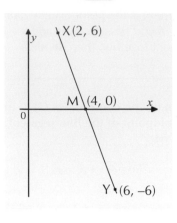

Exercise 1.3

Q1 Hint: Drawing a sketch of each line segment can sometimes help.

Q1   Find the coordinates of the midpoint of the line segment AB when:

a) A is (2, 4) and B is (5, 2)   b) A is (0, –5) and B is (–1, 6)

c) A is (0, 0) and B is (10, 4)   d) A is (–20, –56) and B is (–1, 6)

e) A is (–3, –12) and B is (7, 8)   f) A is (–2, –1) and B is (3, 0)

Q2   The line segment CD has a midpoint M, as shown.

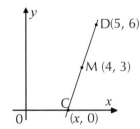

Find the x-coordinate of C.

Q3   The line segment PQ has a midpoint M, as shown.

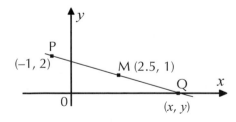

Find the coordinates of Q.

Q4   The midpoint of a line segment, AB, is (1, 1).
Give the coordinates for B when A is:

a) (1, 4)   b)   (3, 0)

c) (6, 2)   d)   (–1, –4)

Finding the distance between two points

The **distance** between two points is the same as the **length** of the line segment drawn between them. This length can be found using Pythagoras' theorem:

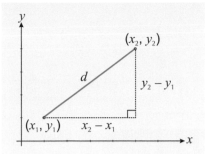

The distance, d, between two points (x_1, y_1) and (x_2, y_2) is the hypotenuse of the right-angled triangle with sides $(x_2 - x_1)$ and $(y_2 - y_1)$. So:

$$d = \sqrt{(x_2 - x_1)^2 + (y_2 - y_1)^2}$$

Example 1

Find the distance between the points P (6, 2) and Q (–1, 0).

- Take point P as (x_1, y_1) and Q as (x_2, y_2).

  So $x_1 = 6$, $x_2 = -1$, $y_1 = 2$ and $y_2 = 0$.

- Plugging these into the formula gives:

$$d = \sqrt{(-1 - 6)^2 + (0 - 2)^2}$$

$$= \sqrt{(-7)^2 + (-2)^2}$$

$$= \sqrt{49 + 4}$$

$$= \boxed{\sqrt{53}}$$

> This is the length of the line segment PQ.

Tip: You'd get exactly the same answer if you took Q as (x_1, y_1) and P as (x_2, y_2).

Tip: You can't use a calculator in the exam, so it's fine to leave your answer in surd form.

Example 2

The point U has coordinates (3, k), and the point V has coordinates (15, 6). UV has a length of 13. Find all the possible values of k.

- Take point U as (x_1, y_1) and V as (x_2, y_2).

  So $x_1 = 3$, $x_2 = 15$, $y_1 = k$ and $y_2 = 6$.

- Substituting into the equation gives:

$$13 = \sqrt{(15 - 3)^2 + (6 - k)^2}$$
$$13 = \sqrt{12^2 + (6 - k)^2}$$

Tip: You can also find the solutions for k another way:
$25 = (6 - k)^2$
$\pm 5 = 6 - k$
$k = 6 \pm 5$
$k = 1$ or 11

- Square both sides to remove the square root:

$$13^2 = 12^2 + (6 - k)^2$$

$$169 = 144 + (6 - k)^2$$

$$25 = (6 - k)^2$$

$$25 = 36 - 12k + k^2$$

$$k^2 - 12k + 11 = 0$$

$$(k - 1)(k - 11) = 0 \qquad \text{So } k = 1 \text{ or } k = 11$$

Exercise 1.4

Q1 Hint: Look back at pages 10-13 to recap on surds.

Q1 Find the distance between the following points A and B, giving your answers in surd form where necessary:

a) A (3, 4) and B (−2, 6)   b) A (7, 12) and B (8, 1)

c) A (6, 2) and B (−3, −2)   d) A (0, 0) and B (−6, −8)

e) A (2, −4) and B (−6, −3)   f) A (10, 20) and B (20, −10)

Q2 and Q3 Hint: 'All the possible values' is a clue that there may be more than one answer.

Q2 X has coordinates (4, 10) and Y has coordinates $(x, 6)$. XY has length 5. Find all the possible values of x.

Q3 N has coordinates (−5, 8) and P has coordinates $(0, y)$. NP has length 13. Find all the possible values of y.

Q4 Four line segments, AB, CD, EF and GH, are given below. Work out the length of each one.

a) A (4, 6) and B (1, 2)   b) C (3, 7) and D (0, 0)

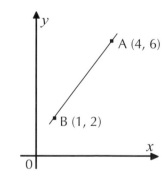

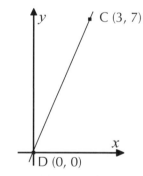

c) E (−8, 3) and F (2, 5)   d) G (20, −10) and H (12, −5)

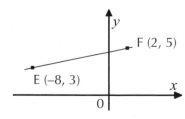

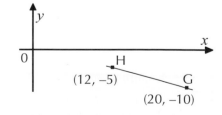

2. Parallel and Perpendicular Lines

You can work out the equation of a line if 1) it is parallel or perpendicular to a line you already know the equation of, and 2) you know a point that the line passes through. The first thing you need to do is find the gradient of the line.

Learning Objectives:

- Be able to find the equation of a line parallel or perpendicular to a given line through a given point.
- Know the conditions for two straight lines to be parallel or perpendicular to each other.

Parallel lines

Parallel lines have **equal gradient** — that's what makes them parallel. So when finding the equation of a line parallel to a line with a given equation, you know the gradient will be the same for both.

Example 1

Find the line parallel to $y = \frac{3}{4}x - \frac{7}{4}$ that:

a) **has a y-intercept of (0, 4)**

- Parallel lines have the same gradient, so the gradient of the line you want is also $\frac{3}{4}$.
- You then need to find c — this is just the y-intercept which we already know is at 4.
- So putting m and c into the equation $y = mx + c$ gives: $\boxed{y = \frac{3}{4}x + 4}$

b) **passes through the point (3, –1).**

- The gradient is $\frac{3}{4}$. So the new equation will be: $\boxed{y = \frac{3}{4}x + c}$
- You then need to find c. We know that the line passes through point (3, –1), so stick $x = 3$ and $y = -1$ into the equation to find c:
$$-1 = \frac{3}{4}(3) + c \quad \Rightarrow \quad c = -\frac{13}{4}$$
- So the equation of the line is: $\boxed{y = \frac{3}{4}x - \frac{13}{4}}$

Example 2

Find the line parallel to $2x - 8y + 11 = 0$ that passes through the point (3, –1). Give your equation in the form $ax + by + c = 0$, where a, b and c are integers.

- First, put the given line in a more useful form, i.e. $y = mx + c$...
$$2x - 8y + 11 = 0$$
$$-8y = -2x - 11$$
$$y = \frac{1}{4}x + \frac{11}{8}$$

- The gradient of the given line is $\frac{1}{4}$, so that's also the gradient of the parallel line you want.
$$y = \frac{1}{4}x + c$$
$$x = 3 \text{ and } y = -1 \longrightarrow \quad -1 = \frac{1}{4}(3) + c \quad \Rightarrow \quad c = -\frac{7}{4}$$

So $y = \frac{1}{4}x - \frac{7}{4}$ which rearranges to $\boxed{x - 4y - 7 = 0}$

Tip: Look back at pages 76-79 if you need a recap on rearranging equations of straight lines.

You may be asked whether two lines are parallel or not. To work this out you need to **compare** their gradients. This is easiest when both equations are in the **same form** — so one or both equations may need **rearranging**.

Example 3

Line l_1 is given by the equation $y = \frac{1}{2}x + 6$ and line l_2 is given by the equation $3x + 6y - 1 = 0$. Find out whether the lines are parallel.

- To compare the gradients you want both lines in the form $y = mx + c$. So rearrange line l_2 into this form:

$$3x + 6y - 1 = 0$$
$$\Rightarrow 6y = -3x + 1$$
$$\Rightarrow y = -\frac{3}{6}x + \frac{1}{6}$$
$$\Rightarrow y = -\frac{1}{2}x + \frac{1}{6}$$

Tip: Rearranging the equations into the form $y = mx + c$, rather than $ax + by + c = 0$, makes it a hundred million times* easier to compare the gradients.   *Approximately.

- Then compare the two equations:

$$y = \frac{1}{2}x + 6 \quad \longleftarrow \quad \text{Line } l_1$$
$$y = -\frac{1}{2}x + \frac{1}{6} \quad \longleftarrow \quad \text{Line } l_2$$

- You are only concerned about the gradient so look at the bit before the x. Here line l_1 has a gradient of $\frac{1}{2}$ and line l_2 has a gradient of $-\frac{1}{2}$.
- So: The lines l_1 and l_2 are NOT parallel.

Exercise 2.1

Q1 State which of the following straight lines are parallel to $y = -3x - 1$.

a) $2y = -6x + 2$

b) $y - 3x - 1 = 0$

c) $6y + 18x = 7$

d) $\frac{1}{3}(y + 1) = x$

e) $-9y - 2 = 27x$

f) $4y = 12x$

Q2 Find the equations of the parallel lines shown in blue.
Write them in the form $ax + by + c = 0$, where a, b and c are integers.

a) $y = 4x - 1$

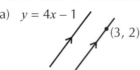

(3, 2)

b) $(-4, -5)$

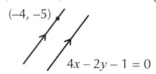

$4x - 2y - 1 = 0$

Q3 State whether the following pairs of lines are parallel.

a) $y = 2x + 1$
$y + \frac{1}{2}x = 1$

b) $2x - 3y + 1 = 0$
$y = \frac{2}{3}x + 2$

c) $-5x + 4y + 3 = 0$
$8y = 10x$

Q4 Line A passes through the point (4, 3) and is parallel to the line $2x - 4y + 3 = 0$. Find the equation of line A in the form:

a) $y = mx + c$,

b) $ax + by + c = 0$.

Perpendicular lines

Finding the equations of **perpendicular** lines (or '**normals**') is just as easy as finding the equations of parallel lines — you just need to know one key fact:

> The gradients of perpendicular lines **multiply to give –1**.

Which means:
> Gradient of the perpendicular line =
> **–1 ÷ the gradient of the other one**.

Tip: Remember, 'perpendicular' just means 'at right angles'.

Tip: So if a line has a gradient of m, a line perpendicular to it will have a gradient of $-\frac{1}{m}$.

Example 1

Find the equation of the line perpendicular to $y = \frac{1}{3}x - 1$ that passes through (–2, 4).

- Use the gradient rule:

  Gradient of perpendicular line $= -1 \div$ gradient of the other one
  $$= -1 \div \frac{1}{3} = -3$$

  So: $\quad y = -3x + c$

Tip: Remember, to divide by a fraction, turn it upside down and then multiply by it.

- To find c, put the coordinates (–2, 4) into the equation
  $$4 = (-3) \times (-2) + c$$
  $$\Rightarrow c = 4 - 6 = -2$$

- So the equation of the line is: $\quad y = -3x - 2$

Example 2

Find the equation of the line perpendicular to $7x - 3y + 5 = 0$ that passes through the point (–3, –11).

- Start by converting the equation into a more useful form:
  $$7x - 3y + 5 = 0$$
  $$-3y = -7x - 5$$
  $$y = \frac{7}{3}x + \frac{5}{3} \quad \longleftarrow \text{ So the gradient is } \frac{7}{3}.$$

- Now use the gradient rule:
  $$\text{Gradient of perpendicular line} = -1 \div \frac{7}{3} = -\frac{3}{7}$$

  So we have: $\quad y = -\frac{3}{7}x + c$

- Substitute in the coordinates (–3, –11) to find c:
  $$-11 = -\frac{3}{7}(-3) + c$$
  $$c = -11 - \frac{9}{7} = -\frac{86}{7}$$

- So the perpendicular line has equation:
  $$y = -\frac{3}{7}x - \frac{86}{7} \Rightarrow 3x + 7y + 86 = 0$$

You can use the fact that the gradients of perpendicular lines **multiply** to **–1** to work out whether two lines are perpendicular.

Example 3

Show that the line $2x + 5y + 3 = 0$ is perpendicular to $y = \frac{5}{2}x + 5$.

- To work out if they are perpendicular, first find the gradient of both lines.
- Rearrange $2x + 5y + 3 = 0$ into the form $y = mx + c$ to find its gradient:

$$2x + 5y + 3 = 0$$
$$\Rightarrow 5y = -2x - 3$$
$$\Rightarrow y = -\frac{2}{5}x - \frac{3}{5}$$

- So the gradient of this line is $-\frac{2}{5}$.

- Comparing $y = \frac{5}{2}x + 5$ to $y = mx + c$, its gradient is $\frac{5}{2}$.

- The two lines are perpendicular if the gradients of the two lines **multiply** together to make **–1**.

$$-\frac{2}{5} \times \frac{5}{2} = -1$$

The two lines are perpendicular.

Example 4

The points A (2, 5) and B (6, 0) lie on the line l_1. The line l_2 is perpendicular to l_1 and passes through point A.

a) Find an equation for l_2 in the form $ax + by + c = 0$, where a, b and c are integers.

- To find the equation of l_2 we need to find its gradient. We know two points on the line l_1, so work out its gradient first.

$$(x_1, y_1) = (2, 5), (x_2, y_2) = (6, 0)$$

$$m = \frac{0 - 5}{6 - 2} = -\frac{5}{4}$$

- The gradient of a perpendicular line is: $-1 \div$ the other one. So the gradient of l_2 is:

$$m = -1 \div -\frac{5}{4}$$

$$\Rightarrow m = \frac{4}{5}$$

- So l_2 is: $y = \frac{4}{5}x + c$

Tip: Look back at page 76 for more on finding the gradient from two points.

- To find c, put the coordinates for point A (2, 5) into $y = \frac{4}{5}x + c$.

$$5 = \frac{4}{5} \times 2 + c$$
$$\Rightarrow c = \frac{17}{5}$$

- So the equation of the l_2 is:

$$y = \frac{4}{5}x + \frac{17}{5} \Rightarrow \boxed{4x - 5y + 17 = 0}$$

b) **Find the coordinates of point C, the y-intercept of line l_2.**

- At C, $x = 0$. So put $x = 0$ into the equation $y = \frac{4}{5}x + \frac{17}{5}$:

$$\Rightarrow y = \frac{4}{5} \times 0 + \frac{17}{5} = \frac{17}{5}$$

Tip: This is actually the value of c you just found.

So the coordinates of point C are $(0, \frac{17}{5})$.

Exercise 2.2

Q1 Find the equations of the dotted lines.
Give your answers in the form $y = mx + c$.

a) 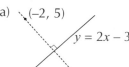 (−2, 5)

$y = 2x - 3$

b) (5, 2)

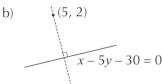

$x - 5y - 30 = 0$

Q2 Find the equations of the lines which are perpendicular to each of the following lines and pass through the points given. Give your answers in the form $ax + by + c = 0$, where a, b, and c are integers.

a) $y = \frac{1}{4}x - 1$ (−1, 2)   b) $2x + 3y - 1 = 0$ (−3, −1)

c) $5x - 10y + 1 = 0$ (6, −5)   d) $y = \frac{3}{2}x + 2$ (2, 1)

Q3 Work out which of the following pairs of lines are perpendicular.

a) $y = \frac{4}{3}x - 2$ and $3x + 4y - 1 = 0$

b) $y = \frac{3}{2}x - 1$ and $3x + 2y - 3 = 0$

c) $4x - y + 3 = 0$ and $2x + 8y + 1 = 0$

Q4 Triangle ABC has vertices at A(0, 2), B(4, 3) and C(5, −1).
a) Find the equations of the lines AB, BC and AC in the form $y = mx + c$.
b) What type of triangle is ABC? Explain why.

Q4 b) Hint: Check to see if any of the sides are perpendicular, and think how this affects the type of triangle.

Q5 Line A passes through the point (a, b) and is perpendicular to the line $3x - 2y = 6$. Find an equation of line A in terms of a and b.

3. Curve Sketching

Learning Objective:

- Be able to sketch and interpret graphs of simple cubic functions.

Being able to sketch the graph of a curve is an important skill at A-Level. It can help you get your head round tricky questions. You've already seen how to sketch quadratic graphs, and now it's time to look at cubic functions.

Sketching cubic functions

Cubic functions have an x^3 term in them — as the highest power of x. They can be written $y = ax^3 + bx^2 + cx + d$ (for $a \neq 0$).

The graphs of cubic functions all have a characteristic 'wiggle'. This happens when the curve changes direction — from bending clockwise to bending anticlockwise, or vice versa.

Here are the graphs for the two **simplest** cubic functions.

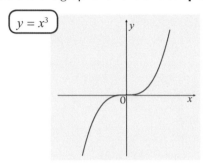

$y = x^3$

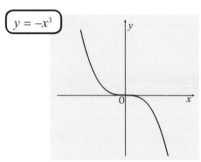

$y = -x^3$

- A **positive** coefficient of x^3 gives a '**bottom-left to top-right**' shape.

- A **negative** coefficient of x^3 gives a '**top-left** to **bottom-right**' shape.

Tip: The 'flat bit' on $y = x^3$ and $y = -x^3$ is called a point of inflection. It's a type of stationary point — see page 128.

The graphs of $y = x^3$ and $y = -x^3$ briefly '**flatten out**' at the point where the curve starts bending the other way. Other cubics can have an actual dip in the graph as shown below:

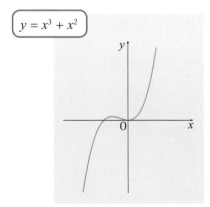

$y = x^3 + x^2$

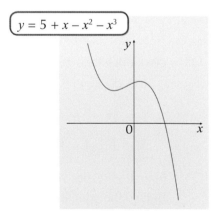

$y = 5 + x - x^2 - x^3$

- If the cubic has x^2 terms there'll be more of a '**wiggle**'.

- You can tell that this graph has a **negative** x^3 term because it's got the '**top-left** to **bottom-right**' shape.

As well as knowing the shapes, you may need to sketch some simple cubics. The key is finding where the graphs **cross the axes**, particularly the x-axis.

Example

Sketch the graphs of the following cubic functions.

a) $f(x) = x(x - 1)(2x + 1)$

- If you multiplied out the brackets, you'd get $2x^3 - x^2 - x$. But it's just the $2x^3$ term we're interested in for deciding the rough shape.

- The coefficient of x^3 is positive — so the graph will have a **bottom-left** to **top-right** shape.

- Now we need to find where the graph crosses the x-axis, i.e. where the function is zero. The cubic is actually given in factorised form here, so we can simply read off the solutions.

$$x(x - 1)(2x + 1) = 0 \implies \boxed{x = 0, 1 \text{ or } -\tfrac{1}{2}}$$

- So the curve crosses the x-axis **three times** and will look like this:

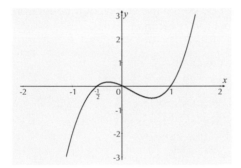

Tip: For all cubics, it's the x^3 term that gives the **overall cubic** shape, i.e. corner-to-corner with a 'wiggle'.

The other terms just affect how much it bends and where.

Tip: This graph has a much more pronounced wiggle than $y = x^3$, creating an actual dip in the graph. The dip makes the graph cross the x-axis 3 times, creating the 3 roots.

b) $g(x) = (x - 3)^2(x + 1)$

- Multiplying out the brackets gives $x^3 - 5x^2 + 3x + 9$.

- The coefficient of x^3 is positive — so the graph will have a **bottom-left** to **top-right** shape.

- Now find where it crosses both axes:

- $x = 0$ gives $y = (-3)^2 = 9$, so the y-intercept is $(0, 9)$.

- For the x-intercepts, find where $g(x) = 0$. Again, the function is helpfully factorised...

$$(x - 3)^2(x + 1) = 0 \implies \boxed{x = 3, \text{ or } -1}$$

- So the graph only crosses the x-axis **twice** and looks like this:

Tip: Again you don't actually need to multiply out the whole function — you only need to know what the x^3 term will be.

The cubic has a 'double root' at $x = 3$ — the result of this is that the graph **just touches** the x-axis there but doesn't go through.

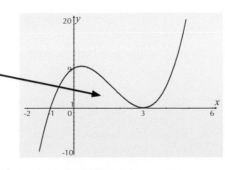

c) $h(x) = (2 - x)^3$

- Expanding the brackets gives $h(x) = 8 - 12x + 6x^2 - x^3$.
- Here the coefficient of x^3 is negative — so the graph will have a **top-left** to **bottom-right** shape.
- $x = 0$ gives a y-intercept of 8.
- The function is zero **only once**, at $x = 2$ — this is a **triple root**.
- The graph looks like this:

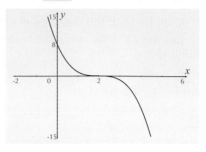

Tip: This graph is actually just the graph of $y = -x^3$ shifted 2 to the right. Graph transformations like this are covered on the next page.

Exercise 3.1

Hint: If you're not sure exactly what the graph will do, stick some values for x into the function, especially around the roots.

For Questions 1-3, sketch the graphs of the functions showing clearly where they meet the coordinate axes.

Q1 a) $y = x(x + 2)(x - 3)$
  b) $y = x(x + 1)(2 - x)$
  c) $y = 3x(4 - x)(1 - 2x)$

Q2 a) $y = (1 - x)(2 - x)^2$ b) $y = -3x(2x - 7)^2$

Q3 a) $y = (7 - x)(9 - 2x)(3 - x)$ b) $y = (4 + x)^3$

Q4 a) Factorise completely $x^3 - 7x^2 + 12x$.
  b) Use your answer to a) to sketch the graph of $y = x^3 - 7x^2 + 12x$, showing clearly where the graph meets the coordinate axes.

Q5 Sketch the graphs of these functions, showing clearly where the graph meets the coordinate axes.
  a) $y = x^3 - 16x$ b) $y = 2x^3 - 12x^2 + 18x$

Q6 a) Use graph paper to draw the graphs of $y = x(x^2 + 3)$ and $y = 5 - 3x$ on the same axes for $-0.5 \leq x \leq 1.5$.
  b) Show that any solutions of $x^3 + 6x - 5 = 0$ are given by the x-coordinates of the points of intersection of $y = x(x^2 + 3)$ and $y = 5 - 3x$.
  c) Use the graphs from part a) to estimate the solution to $x^3 + 6x - 5 = 0$. Note — there is only one real solution.

Q7 Hint: Work out if the quadratic factor has real roots — if it doesn't, the graph will only cross the x-axis once.

Q7 Sketch the graphs of the following cubics:
  a) $y = x(x^2 - 3x + 12)$
  b) $y = (2 - 3x)(4x^2 + 5x + 4)$
  c) $y = x(2x^2 - 5x + 5)$

4. Transformations

If you have a function f(x), you can transform the graph by adding or subtracting constant terms. This will translate the graph of f(x) either vertically or horizontally.

Learning Objectives:

- Know the effect of the translations
  $y = f(x) + a$ and
  $y = f(x + a)$.
- Apply these translations to linear, quadratic and cubic functions.
- Given the graph of a function f(x), sketch the graph resulting from the above translations.

Translations

Translating the graph of a function means **moving it** either horizontally or vertically. The shape of the graph itself doesn't change, it just moves. There are two types of translation:

$y = f(x) + a$

Adding a number to the **whole function** translates the graph in the **y-direction**.

- If $a > 0$, the graph goes **upwards**.
- If $a < 0$, the graph goes **downwards**.

$y = f(x + a)$

Writing '$x + a$' instead of 'x' means the graph moves **sideways** ("translated in the **x-direction**").

- If $a > 0$, the graph goes to the **left**.
- If $a < 0$, the graph goes to the **right**.

Tip: Function notation is used a lot in this section — don't get confused, it's quite simple.
E.g. if $f(x) = 3x^2$ then...
$f(5)$ means $3(5)^2 = 75$
$f(x - 2)$ means $3(x - 2)^2$
$f(x) + 4$ means $3x^2 + 4$.

Example 1

Shown below is the graph of $y = f(x)$, where $f(x) = x(x + 2)(x - 2)$.

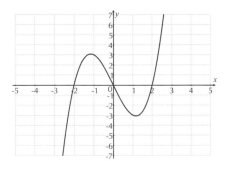

a) **Sketch the graph $y = f(x) + 2$.**

- Here 2 has been added to the **whole function**, i.e. $a = 2$.
- So the graph will be translated 2 units in the positive y-direction, i.e. shifted upwards by 2.

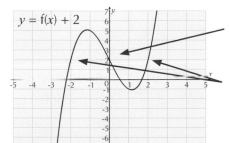

The point (0, 0) on f(x) has become the point (0, 2).

The other roots of f(x), (−2, 0) and (2, 0), have become (−2, 2) and (2, 2).

Tip: The equation of the transformed function is:
$y = x(x + 2)(x - 2) + 2$,
$= x^3 - 4x + 2$.

But you don't need to know this to sketch the transformed function.

Tip: When sketching a transformed graph, you need to show what happens to its **key points**, e.g. where it crosses the axes, max / min points, etc.

Exactly how much info to give will depend on the question.

b) Sketch the graph $y = f(x) - 4$.

- Here −4 has been added to the whole function, so $a = -4$
- The graph will be translated 4 units in the negative y-direction, i.e. down 4.

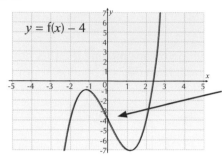

$y = f(x) - 4$

The point (0, 0) on $f(x)$ has become the point (0, −4).

c) Sketch the graph $y = f(x + 2)$.

- It's of the form $y = f(x + a)$ so it's translation in the x-direction.
- $a = 2$ — so as a is positive, it's a translation to the **left**, and it's by 2 units.

Tip: If you wanted to know the equation of the new curve, replace the x's in the original equation with $x + 2$:

Original equation is:
$f(x) = x(x - 2)(x + 2)$

So...
$f(x + 2) = (x + 2)(x)(x + 4)$
$\qquad\quad = x(x + 2)(x + 4)$

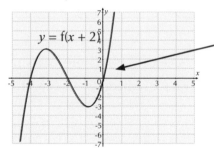

$y = f(x + 2)$

The x-coordinate of every point becomes 2 less.

E.g. the three roots of $f(x)$, (−2, 0), (0, 0) and (0, 2) are now (−4, 0), (−2, 0) and (0, 0).

d) Sketch the graph $y = f(x - 1)$.

- Again, it's of the form $y = f(x + a)$ so it's a translation in the x-direction.
- $a = -1$ which is negative, so it's a translation to the **right** by 1 unit.

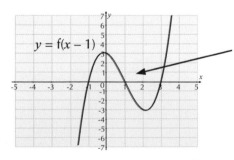

$y = f(x - 1)$

1 is added to the x-coordinate of every point.

E.g. (−2, 0) becomes (−1, 0).

You can use the **equation** of the transformed function to find **intercepts**, as shown in the next example.

Example 2

A function f(x) = x² is transformed into g(x) = (x + 3)² – 2.

a) Describe the transformation from f(x) to g(x).

- Comparing the equation of g(x) with f(x) gives g(x) = f(x + 3) – 2.
- This shows that **two translations** are needed to get from f(x) to g(x):

> A translation of **3 units** in the **negative x-direction**.
> A translation of **2 units** in the **negative y-direction**.

(i.e. 3 left and 2 down)

Tip: You could also give this in vector notation — it's a translation by $\begin{pmatrix} -3 \\ -2 \end{pmatrix}$.

- You can show this transformation on a sketch:

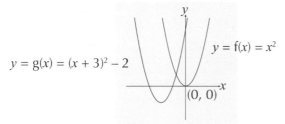

Tip: Sketching a graph helps you to see where the key points of the graph have moved to.

b) Give the coordinates of the vertex and the x- and y-intercepts of g(x).

- f(x) has a **vertex** at (0, 0), as shown on the graph above. This will be translated 3 left and 2 down, so take 3 from the x-coordinate and 2 from the y-coordinate, to give g(x) a vertex at (–3, –2).

- To find the intercepts, just put x = 0 and y = 0 into the equation for g(x).

  When x = 0, y = 3² – 2 = 7, so the y-intercept is (0, 7).

  When y = 0, $(x + 3)^2 - 2 = 0$
  $$(x + 3)^2 = 2$$
  $$x + 3 = \pm\sqrt{2}$$
  $$x = -3 + \sqrt{2} \text{ or } -3 - \sqrt{2}$$

- So the two x-intercepts are $(-3 + \sqrt{2}, 0)$ and $(-3 - \sqrt{2}, 0)$.

Exercise 4.1

Q1 The diagram shows the graph of y = f(x). The curve has a maximum at (2, 4) and meets the x-axis at (0, 0) and (5, 0).

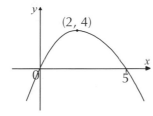

a) Sketch the graph of y = f(x) + 2, labelling the coordinates of the maximum and where the curve meets the y-axis.

b) Sketch the graph of y = f(x + 2) labelling the points where the curve meets the x-axis and the maximum.

Q2 The diagram below shows the graph of $y = g(x)$ and two other graphs.
Which graph represents $y = g(x - 1)$?

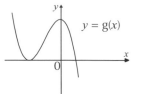

$y = g(x)$

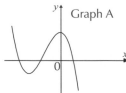

Graph A

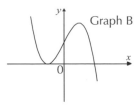

Graph B

Q3 Given that $y = x^2(x - 4)$, describe how would you translate
the graph to give the graph of $y = (x - 2)^2(x - 6)$.

Q4 Explain how the graph of $y = x^3 + 3x + 7$ can be translated
to give the graph of $y = x^3 + 3x + 2$.

Q5 The graph of $y = x^2 - 3x + 7$ is translated 1 unit in the negative x-direction.
Write down the equation of the new graph.
Give your answer in as simple a form as possible.

Q6 The diagram shows the graph of $y = f(x)$.

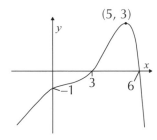

The graph has a maximum at (5, 3), crosses the x-axis
at (3, 0) and (6, 0) and crosses the y-axis at (0, −1).
a) Sketch the graph of $y = f(x) - 2$.
b) Label the coordinates of the maximum and
the point where the graph meets the y-axis.

Q7 a) Sketch the graph of $y = (x - 1)(2x - 3)(4 - x)$ and label the points
where the graph meets the coordinate axes.
b) The graph in part a) is translated 2 units in the positive x-direction.
Give the equation of the translated graph in its simplest form.
c) On separate axes sketch the graph of the equation from part b),
labelling all the points where the graph meets the x-axis.

Review Exercise — Chapter 5

Q1 Find the equations of the straight lines that pass through the points

a) $(2, -1)$ and $(-4, -19)$,   b) $\left(0, -\frac{1}{3}\right)$ and $\left(5, \frac{2}{3}\right)$.

Write each of them in the forms:

  (i) $y - y_1 = m(x - x_1)$,

  (ii) $y = mx + c$,

  (iii) $ax + by + c = 0$, where a, b and c are integers.

Q2 Point A has coordinates $(2, 5)$ and point B has coordinates $(12, -1)$. M is the midpoint of the line segment AB. Find:

a) The coordinates of M.

b) The distance, d, between A and M, leaving your answer in surd form.

Q3 Point A has coordinates $(1, k)$ and point B has coordinates $(6, 3)$. The line AB has equation $5y - x = 9$.

a) Find the value of k.

b) Find the length and the midpoint of AB. Leave your answer for the length in surd form.

c) Point C has coordinates $(-1, 0)$. Given that the line BC passes through $(2p + 3, p + 1)$, where p is a constant, find p.

Q4 a) The line l_1 has equation $y = \frac{3}{2}x - \frac{2}{3}$. Find the equation of the line parallel to l_1 passing through the point with coordinates $(4, 2)$.

b) The line l_2 passes through the point $(6, 1)$ and is perpendicular to $2x - y - 7 = 0$. What is the equation of l_2?

Q5 The coordinates of points R and S are $(1, 9)$ and $(10, 3)$ respectively. Find the equation of the line perpendicular to RS passing through the point $(1, 9)$.

Q6 Sketch these cubic graphs:

a) $y = (x - 4)^3$,   b) $y = (3 - x)(x + 2)^2$,

c) $y = (1 - x)(x^2 - 6x + 8)$,   d) $y = (x - 1)(x - 2)(x - 3)$.

Q7 Use the graph of f(x) below to sketch these transformed graphs:

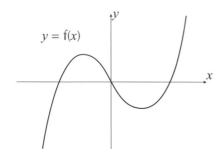

$y = f(x)$

a)   (i) $y = f(x+a)$,   (ii) $y = f(x-a)$, where $a>0$,
b)   (i) $y = f(x)+a$,   (ii) $y = f(x)-a$, where $a>0$.

Q8 The diagram shows the graph of $y = f(x)$.
The curve has a maximum at (2, 4) and meets the x-axis at (0, 0) and (5, 0).

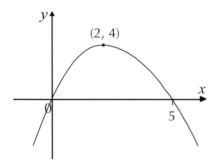

(2, 4)

5

Sketch the graphs of these functions, labelling clearly the coordinates of the maximum and any known points of intersection with the x- or y-axes:

a) $y = f(x) + 1$ b) $y = f(x - 1)$

1   The line PQ has equation $4x + 3y = 15$.

    a)   Find the gradient of PQ.

        (2 marks)

    b)   The point R lies on PQ and has coordinates $(3, 1)$. Find the equation of the line which passes through the point R and is perpendicular to PQ, giving your answer in the form $y = mx + c$.

        (3 marks)

2   The curve C has the equation
$$y = (2x + 1)(x - 2)^2.$$

Sketch C, clearly showing the points where the curve meets the x- and y-axes.

        (4 marks)

3

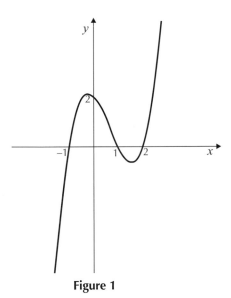

Figure 1

Figure 1 shows a sketch of the function $y = f(x)$. The function crosses the x-axis at $(-1, 0)$, $(1, 0)$ and $(2, 0)$, and crosses the y-axis at $(0, 2)$.

On separate diagrams, sketch the following:

    a) $y = f(x) + 1$

        (2 marks)

    b) $y = f(x - 4)$.

        (2 marks)

On each diagram, label any known points of intersection with the x- or y-axes.

4   a)   Sketch the curve $y = f(x)$, where $f(x) = x^2 - 4$, showing clearly the points
         of intersection with the x- and y-axes.

                                                                                    (2 marks)

    b)   Describe fully the transformation that transforms the
         curve $y = f(x)$ to the curve $y = f(x + 1) - 3$.

                                                                                    (2 marks)

    c)   The curve $y = f(x)$ is translated two units in the positive y-direction.
         State the equation of the curve after it has been transformed, in term of $f(x)$.

                                                                                    (1 mark)

5   The line l passes through the point $S(7, -3)$ and has gradient -2.

    a)   Find an equation of l, giving your answer in the form $y = mx + c$.

                                                                                    (3 marks)

    b)   The point T has coordinates $(5, 1)$. Show that T lies on l.

                                                                                    (1 mark)

6

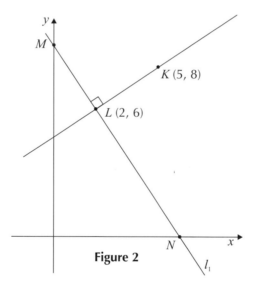

Figure 2

The points L and K have coordinates $(2, 6)$ and $(5, 8)$ respectively. The line l_1 passes
through the point L and is perpendicular to the line LK, as shown in **Figure 2**.

    a)   Find an equation for l_1 in the form $ax + by + c = 0$,
         where a, b, and c are integers.

                                                                                    (4 marks)

The line l_1 intersects the y-axis at the point M and the x-axis at the point N.

    b)   Find the coordinates of M.

                                                                                    (1 mark)

    c)   Find the coordinates of N.

                                                                                    (1 mark)

    d)   What are the coordinates of the midpoint of the line segment LN?

                                                                                    (2 marks)

1. Equation of a Circle

*If you've survived maths this long, you'll be very familiar with circles —
you're probably a dab hand at working out their circumference and area.
Now we're going to have a look at using equations to describe a circle.
An equation of a circle can tell you its radius and where its centre is.*

Equation of a circle with centre (0, 0)

The diagram to the right shows a circle centred on the origin $(0, 0)$ and with radius r.

You can describe a circle centred on the origin, with radius r, using the equation:

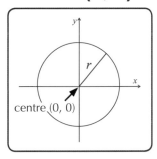

$$x^2 + y^2 = r^2$$

Even though you're dealing with circles, you get the equation above using **Pythagoras' theorem**. Here's how:

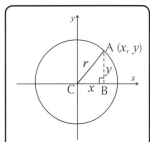

- The **centre** of the circle is at the origin, labelled **C**.

- **A** is any point on the circle, and has the coordinates **(x, y)**.

- **B** lies on the x-axis and has the same x-coordinate as A.

- So the length of line **CB** = x, and **AB** = y.

- Therefore, using Pythagoras' theorem to find the radius r, we get:

$$CB^2 + AB^2 = r^2$$

Which is... $\quad x^2 + y^2 = r^2$

If you're given the equation of a circle in the form $x^2 + y^2 = r^2$,
you can work out the radius of the circle in the following way:

Example

A circle has the equation $x^2 + y^2 = 4$. Calculate the radius of the circle.

- **Compare** the equation $x^2 + y^2 = 4$ to $x^2 + y^2 = r^2$.
- Equating the two equations gives: $\quad r^2 = 4$

$$r = 2$$

Tip: Ignore the negative square root as the radius will be positive.

Equation of a circle with centre (a, b)

Unfortunately, circles aren't always centred on the origin. This means we need a general equation for circles that have a centre somewhere else — the point (a, b).

The general equation for circles with **radius r** and **centre (a, b)** is:

$$(x - a)^2 + (y - b)^2 = r^2$$

Tip: A circle with the centre (a, b) is just a translation of a circle with the centre (0, 0) by a units in the positive x-direction and b units in the positive y-direction.

Notice that if the circle had a centre at (0, 0), then you'd get $a = 0$ and $b = 0$, so you'd just get $x^2 + y^2 = r^2$ (the equation for a circle centred at the origin).

The example below shows how you get the equation of a circle centred at (a, b) and with radius r using Pythagoras' theorem, as before.

Example 1

Find the equation of the circle with centre (6, 4) and radius 3.

- If we add a point P (x, y) on the **circumference** of the circle and join it to the centre (6, 4), we can create a **right-angled triangle**.

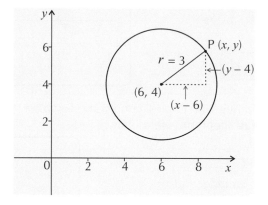

Tip: For the circle centred at the origin, the side lengths were r, x and y. Make sure you're happy with why the side lengths here are r, ($x - 6$) and ($y - 4$).

- The **sides** of this right-angled triangle are made up of the radius r (the hypotenuse), and sides of length ($x - 6$) and ($y - 4$).
- Now let's see what happens if we use **Pythagoras' theorem**:

$$(x - 6)^2 + (y - 4)^2 = 3^2$$
or: $$(x - 6)^2 + (y - 4)^2 = 9$$

This is the equation for the circle.

Once you know the general equation of a circle though you can just use it to work out the centre and radius of other circles, as shown here:

Example 2

What is the centre and radius of the circle with equation $(x - 2)^2 + (y + 3)^2 = 16$?

- **Compare** $(x - 2)^2 + (y + 3)^2 = 16$ with the general form:

$$(x - a)^2 + (y - b)^2 = r^2$$

- So, $a = 2$, $b = -3$ and $r = 4$.

  > So the centre (a, b) is $(2, -3)$ and the radius, r, is 4.

- On a set of axes, the circle would look like this:

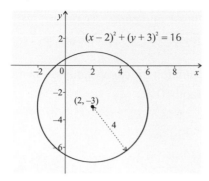

Tip: You're not actually asked to draw the circle, but it might help you to visualise the question.

If you're given the centre and radius of a circle and you're asked to find the equation of the circle, just put the values of a, b and r into the equation $(x - a)^2 + (y - b)^2 = r^2$.

Example

Write down the equation of the circle with centre (–4, 2) and radius 6.

- The question says, 'Write down...', so you know you **don't** need to do any working.
- The **centre** of the circle is $(-4, 2)$, so $a = -4$ and $b = 2$.
- The **radius** is 6, so $r = 6$.
- Using the **general equation** for a circle $(x - a)^2 + (y - b)^2 = r^2$ you can write:

  > $(x + 4)^2 + (y - 2)^2 = 36$

- On a set of axes, the circle would look like this:

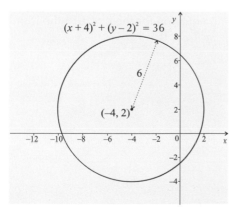

Q1 A circle has centre (0, 0) and radius 5.
Write down an equation for the circle.

Q2 A circle C has radius 7 and centre (0, 0).
Write down an equation for C.

Q3 Hint: Be careful here with the +/ – signs.

Q3 Write down the equation for each of the following circles:
a) centre (2, 5), radius 3
b) centre (–3, 2), radius 5
c) centre (–2, –3), radius 7
d) centre (3, 0), radius 4

Q4 Write down the centre and radius of the circles with the following equations:
a) $(x – 1)^2 + (y – 5)^2 = 4$
b) $(x – 3)^2 + (y – 5)^2 = 64$
c) $(x – 3)^2 + (y + 2)^2 = 25$

Q5 A circle has centre (5, 3) and radius 8. Give an equation for the circle, and describe the transformation that maps the circle with centre (0, 0) and the same radius onto this circle.

Q6 A circle has centre (3, 1) and a radius of $\sqrt{31}$.
Give an equation for the circle.

Q7 The equation of the circle C is $(x – 6)^2 + (y – 4)^2 = 20$.
a) Give the coordinates of the centre of the circle.
b) Find the radius of the circle and give your answer in the form $p\sqrt{5}$.

Q8 Hint: Find the equation in the usual form, then expand the brackets and rearrange.

Q8 A circle has radius $\sqrt{5}$ and centre (–3, –2).
Write down an equation for the circle in the form
$x^2 + y^2 + ax + by + c = 0$.

Rearranging circle equations

Sometimes you'll be given an equation for a circle that doesn't look much like $(x - a)^2 + (y - b)^2 = r^2$, for example, $x^2 + y^2 + ax + by + c = 0$.

- This means you can't immediately tell what the **radius** is or where the **centre** is.
- All you'll need to do is a bit of **rearranging** to get the equation into the familiar form.
- To do this, you'll normally have to **complete the square**.

Tip: Completing the square was covered on pages 23-26.

Example 1

The equation of a circle is $x^2 + y^2 - 6x + 4y + 4 = 0$.
Find the coordinates of the centre of the circle and the radius.

- We need to get the equation $x^2 + y^2 - 6x + 4y + 4 = 0$ into the form: $(x - a)^2 + (y - b)^2 = r^2$.

- To do this, we need to **complete the square**.

- So, first **rearrange** the equation to group the x's and the y's together:

$$x^2 + y^2 - 6x + 4y + 4 = 0$$
$$x^2 - 6x + y^2 + 4y + 4 = 0$$

- Then **complete the square** for the x-terms and the y-terms:

$$x^2 - 6x + y^2 + 4y + 4 = 0$$

$(x - 3)^2 = x^2 - 6x + 9$
So $x^2 - 6x = (x - 3)^2 - 9$

$(y + 2)^2 = y^2 + 4y + 4$
So $y^2 + 4y = (y + 2)^2 - 4$

- So you can write the equation as:

$$(x - 3)^2 - 9 + (y + 2)^2 - 4 + 4 = 0$$

- Then **rearrange** to get it into the form $(x - a)^2 + (y - b)^2 = r^2$.

$$(x - 3)^2 + (y + 2)^2 = 9$$

Tip: Collect all the number terms to find r^2.

- This is the recognisable form, so we can use this equation to find:

the centre is $(3, -2)$ and the radius is $\sqrt{9} = 3$

Example 2

The equation of a circle is $x^2 + y^2 - 5x - 5y + 10 = 0$.
Find the coordinates of the centre of the circle and the radius.

- Get the equation $x^2 + y^2 - 5x - 5y + 10 = 0$
  into the form: $(x - a)^2 + (y - b)^2 = r^2$.

- **Rearrange** the equation to group the x's and the y's together:

$$x^2 + y^2 - 5x - 5y + 10 = 0$$
$$x^2 - 5x + y^2 - 5y + 10 = 0$$

- Then **complete the square** for the x-terms and the y-terms.

$$x^2 - 5x + y^2 - 5y + 10 = 0$$
$$(x - \tfrac{5}{2})^2 - \tfrac{25}{4} + (y - \tfrac{5}{2})^2 - \tfrac{25}{4} + 10 = 0$$

Tip: This is pretty tricky because of the fractions.

- Then **rearrange** to get it into the form $(x - a)^2 + (y - b)^2 = r^2$.

$$(x - \tfrac{5}{2})^2 + (y - \tfrac{5}{2})^2 = \tfrac{5}{2}$$

- So: the centre is $\left(\tfrac{5}{2}, \tfrac{5}{2}\right)$ and the radius is $\sqrt{\tfrac{5}{2}}$.

Exercise 1.2

Q1 For each of the following circles find the radius
and the coordinates of the centre.
a) $x^2 + y^2 + 2x - 6y - 6 = 0$
b) $x^2 + y^2 - 2y - 4 = 0$
c) $x^2 + y^2 - 6x - 4y = 12$
d) $x^2 + y^2 - 10x + 6y + 13 = 0$

Q2 A circle has the equation $x^2 + y^2 + 2x - 4y - 3 = 0$.
a) Find the coordinates of the centre of the circle.
b) Find the radius of the circle. Give your answer in the form $k\sqrt{2}$.

Q3 A circle has the equation $x^2 + y^2 - 3x + 1 = 0$.
a) Find the coordinates of the centre of the circle.
b) Find the radius of the circle.
Simplify your answer as much as possible.

2. Circle Properties

You'll have seen the circle rules at GCSE. But it's important to keep them fresh in your mind as some are useful at A-Level too. You need to be able to look at a circle question and work out which of the rules apply to it.

Circle properties

Here is a reminder of some of the most useful properties of circles.

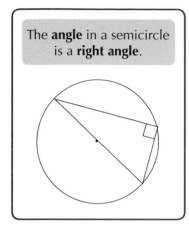

The **angle** in a semicircle is a **right angle**.

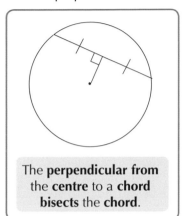

The **perpendicular from** the **centre** to a **chord bisects** the **chord**.

A **tangent** to the circle is **perpendicular** to the **radius** at its point of contact.

Learning Objectives:

- Know and use the following facts about circles:
  — the angle in a semicircle is a right angle.
  — the perpendicular from the centre of a circle to a chord bisects the chord.
  — when the radius of a circle meets a tangent to the circle at a point, the two will be perpendicular.

Tip: A chord is a line joining two points which lie on the circumference of a circle.

Using circle properties

When using the rules above about perpendicularity, you've also got to remember the **gradient rule** for perpendicular lines from Chapter 5:

Tip: Perpendicularity is a real word.

> The gradients of perpendicular lines **multiply to give –1**.

Which means:

> Gradient of the perpendicular line =
> **–1 ÷ the gradient of the other one**.

Remember that to find the gradient of any line segment between (x_1, y_1) and (x_2, y_2) you work out: $\frac{y_2 - y_1}{x_2 - x_1}$.

On the next page are some examples which rely on knowing the circle rules above and the gradient rule.

Example 1

The circle shown is centred at C. Points A and B lie on the circle. Point B has coordinates (6, 3). The midpoint, M, of the line AB has coordinates (4, 4). Line _l_ passes through both C and M.

Find an equation for the line _l_.

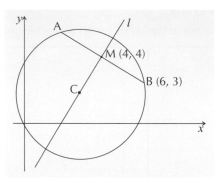

Tip: In the exam, after a question like this, they might then give you a bit more info and ask you to work out the equation for the circle.

- AB is a **chord**. _l_ goes through the centre of the circle and **bisects** the chord. So we can say that the line _l_ is **perpendicular** to the chord because of the 2nd property of circles on the previous page.

- We know two points on AB, so start by finding its **gradient**: $\dfrac{3-4}{6-4} = -\dfrac{1}{2}$

- Use the **gradient rule** to work out the gradient of _l_:

$$\text{Gradient of } l = \frac{-1}{\left(-\dfrac{1}{2}\right)} = 2$$

Tip: $y - y_1 = m(x - x_1)$ is one of the ways of writing the equation of a straight line (see pages 76-79).

- Then sub the gradient (2) and the point on _l_ that you know ((4, 4)) into one of the equations for a **straight line** to work out the equation:

$$y - y_1 = m(x - x_1)$$
$$y - 4 = 2(x - 4)$$
$$y - 4 = 2x - 8$$
$$\boxed{y = 2x - 4}$$

Example 2

Point A (6, 4) lies on a circle with the equation $x^2 + y^2 - 4x - 2y - 20 = 0$.

a) Find the centre and radius of the circle.

- Get the equation into the form: $(x - a)^2 + (y - b)^2 = r^2$.
  First, **rearrange** the equation to group the x's and the y's together:

$$x^2 + y^2 - 4x - 2y - 20 = 0$$
$$x^2 - 4x + y^2 - 2y - 20 = 0$$

- Then **complete the square** for the x-terms and the y-terms, and **rearrange** to get it into the form $(x - a)^2 + (y - b)^2 = r^2$.

$$(x - 2)^2 - 4 + (y - 1)^2 - 1 - 20 = 0$$
$$(x - 2)^2 + (y - 1)^2 = 25$$

- This shows: the centre is (2, 1) and the radius is 5.

b) Find the equation of the tangent to the circle at A.

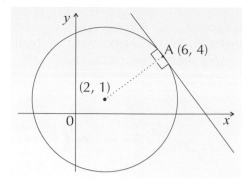

- The **tangent** is always **perpendicular** to the radius, so you can find the gradient of the tangent from the gradient of the radius using the gradient rule.

- Gradient of radius at $(6, 4) = \dfrac{4 - 1}{6 - 2} = \dfrac{3}{4}$

- Gradient of tangent $= \dfrac{-1}{\left(\dfrac{3}{4}\right)} = -\dfrac{4}{3}$

- Using $y - y_1 = m(x - x_1)$

$$y - 4 = -\frac{4}{3}(x - 6)$$
$$3y - 12 = -4x + 24$$
$$\boxed{3y + 4x - 36 = 0}$$

Tip: The question doesn't ask for the equation in a particular form, so pick whatever's easiest.

Example 3

The points A $(-2, 4)$, B $(n, -2)$ and C $(5, 5)$ all lie on the circle shown below. AB is a diameter of the circle.

Show that $n = 6$.

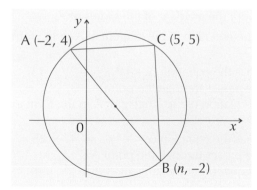

- The line AB is a **diameter** of the circle. So the angle ACB is an angle in a semicircle and must be a **right angle**.
- This means the lines AC and BC are **perpendicular** to each other.
- The **gradient rule** states that the gradients of two perpendicular lines multiply to give **−1**, so use this to work out n.

- First, find the gradient of AC: $m_1 = \dfrac{5 - 4}{5 - (-2)} = \dfrac{1}{7}$

- Then find the gradient of BC: $m_2 = \dfrac{-2 - 5}{n - 5} = \dfrac{-7}{n - 5}$

- Use the gradient rule: $m_1 \times m_2 = -1$

$$\frac{1}{7}\left(\frac{-7}{n - 5}\right) = -1 \quad \longleftarrow \boxed{\text{Cancel the 7s.}}$$

$$\frac{-1}{n - 5} = -1$$

$$1 = n - 5$$

$$n = 6$$

Tip: In an exam question, you might then be asked to use this information to find the equation for the circle.

Exercise 2.1

Q1 The circle shown below has the equation $(x - 3)^2 + (y - 1)^2 = 10$. The line shown is a tangent to the circle and touches it at point A (4, 4).

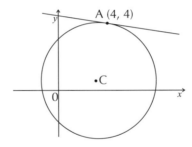

a) Write down the coordinates of the centre of the circle, C.

b) Work out the gradient of the radius at A.

c) Find the equation of the tangent at A in the form $ax + by = c$.

Q2 Hint: Do this in the same way as Q1. First find the centre of the circle, then the gradients of the radius and tangent.

Q2 A circle has the equation $(x + 1)^2 + (y - 2)^2 = 13$. The circle passes through the point A $(-3, -1)$. Find the equation of the tangent at A in the form $ax + by + c = 0$.

Q3 A circle has the equation $(x - 3)^2 + (y - 4)^2 = 25$. The circle passes through the point A (7, 1). Find the equation of the tangent at A in the form $ax + by = c$.

Q4 The circle C has the equation $x^2 + y^2 + 2x - 7 = 0$. Find the equation of the tangent to the circle at the point $(-3, 2)$.

Q5 A circle has the equation $x^2 + y^2 + 2x + 4y = 5$. The point A $(0, -5)$ lies on the circle. Find the tangent to the circle at A in the form $ax + by = c$.

Q6   The circle shown is centred at C. Points A and B lie on the circle. Point A has coordinates (−3, 7). The midpoint of the line AB, M, has coordinates (−1, 1). Line *l* passes through both C and M.

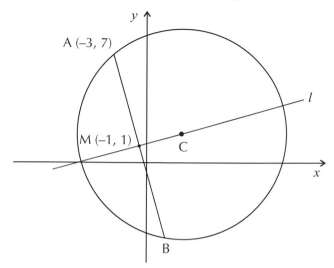

Q6 Hint: AB is a chord.

a)   Use the information above to find an equation for the line *l*.

b)   The coordinates of C are (2, 2).
    Find an equation for the circle.

Q7   The points A (−2, 12), B (4, 14) and C (8, 2) all lie on the circle shown below. Prove that the line AC is a **diameter** of the circle.

Q7 Hint: Think about the properties of an angle in a triangle in a semicircle.

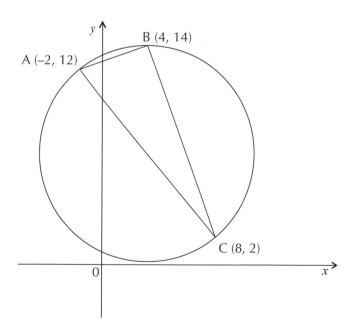

Review Exercise — Chapter 6

Q1 Give the radius and the coordinates of the centre of the circles
with the following equations:
a) $x^2 + y^2 = 9$
b) $(x - 2)^2 + (y + 4)^2 = 4$
c) $x(x + 6) = y(8 - y)$

Q2 Give the equation for the circles with the following properties:
a) centre (3, 2), radius 6
b) centre (−4, −8), radius 8
c) centre (0, −3), radius $\sqrt{14}$

Q3 A circle has the equation $x^2 + y^2 - 4x + 6y - 68 = 0$.
Find the coordinates of the centre of the circle and its radius.

Q4 A circle is shown below with equation $(x - 2)^2 + (y - 1)^2 = 100$ and centre C.
A, B and D are all points on the circle.

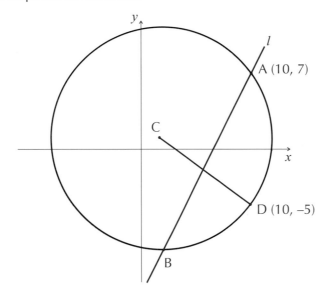

CD bisects AB. Find the equation of the line *l*, which passes through A and B, in the
form $ax + by + c = 0$.

Q5 The circle C has equation $x^2 + y^2 - 12x + 2y + 11 = 0$.
The point A (1, −2) lies on the circle.
Find the equation of the tangent at A.

1   C is a circle with the equation: $x^2 + y^2 - 2x - 10y + 21 = 0$.

 a) Find the centre and radius of C.

(4 marks)

 The line joining $P(3, 6)$ and $Q(q, 4)$ is a diameter of C.

 b) Show that $q = -1$.

(3 marks)

 c) Find the equation of the tangent to C at Q, giving your answer in the form $ax + by + c = 0$, where a, b and c are integers.

(4 marks)

2   A circle C is shown here. M is the centre of C, and J lies on C.

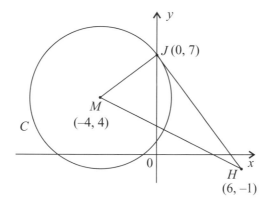

 a) Write down the equation of C in the form $(x - a)^2 + (y - b)^2 = r^2$.

(3 marks)

 The line JH is a tangent to circle C at point J.

 b) Show that angle $JMH = \tan^{-1} 2$.

(4 marks)

3   The diagram shows a circle C, with centre P. M is the midpoint of AB, a chord.

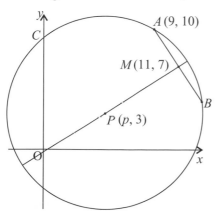

 a) Show that $p = 5$.

(4 marks)

 b) Find the equation of circle C.

(3 marks)

1. The Gradient of a Curve

Learning Objectives:

- Understand that the derivative of f(x) is the gradient of $y = f(x)$, which is the gradient of the tangent at any point.
- Understand that the gradient of the tangent at any point on the curve can be found as a limit.

Differentiation is an algebraic process that finds the gradient of a curve. It is useful for finding out how fast one thing changes with respect to another.

Finding the gradient of a curve

The **gradient** of a curve is just how **steep** it is. Unlike a straight line, the steepness of a curve **changes** as you move along it — you can only give an **exact value** for the gradient at a **particular point** on the curve.

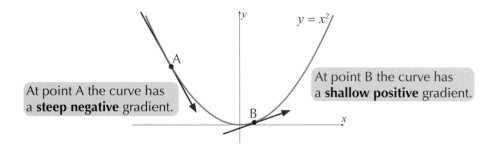

$y = x^2$

At point A the curve has a **steep negative** gradient.

At point B the curve has a **shallow positive** gradient.

Tip: For a reminder about gradients of straight lines, see p.76.

At a **point**, the gradient of a curve is the same as the gradient of the **tangent line** to the curve at that point.

- The tangent line is a **straight line** which **just touches** the curve at that point, without going through it.

- Sadly, you can't work out the gradient of this tangent using the normal method of picking **two points** and finding the change in y ÷ change in x. This is because you only know **one point** on the line — the point where the tangent **meets the curve**.

- So we need another method to find the gradient of a curve — it's known as **differentiation**.

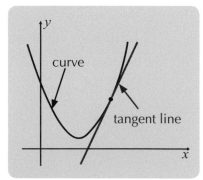

curve

tangent line

Differentiating produces an **algebraic expression** for the gradient as a **function of x** — its numerical value **changes** as you move along the curve.

Before we get started with differentiation, there's some important **notation** to learn:

- The function you get from differentiating y with respect to x is called the derivative of y with respect to x and it's written $\frac{dy}{dx}$.

- $\frac{dy}{dx}$ represents the rate of change of y with x or the gradient of the curve.

- The notation $f'(x)$ means the derivative of $y = f(x)$ with respect to x. It's sometimes used instead of $\frac{dy}{dx}$.

Tip: $\frac{dy}{dx}$ is **not** a fraction, it is just notation for a derivative.

Differentiating from first principles

To find the derivative of a function you need to find its gradient as a function of x.

You can get **close** to the gradient of the tangent (and so the curve) at a point $(x, f(x))$, by finding the gradient of the line joining $(x, f(x))$ and another point **close to** it on the curve.

- On the diagram, the point $(x + h, f(x + h))$ is a small distance further along the curve from $(x, f(x))$.

- As h gets smaller, the distance between the two points gets smaller.

- The closer the points, the **closer** the line joining them will be **to the tangent line**.

Tip: You won't be specifically asked to differentiate from first principles in the exam — but it's good to know as an introduction to differentiation.

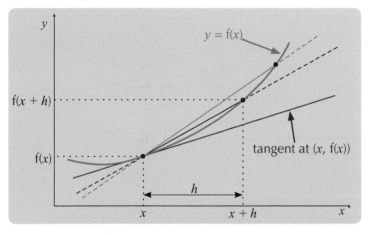

Now you can write an expression for the gradient of the **straight line** joining the two points $(x, f(x))$ and $(x + h, f(x + h))$ like this:

$$\frac{f(x + h) - f(x)}{(x + h) - x}$$

And you know that as h gets **smaller**, the gradient of the straight line gets **closer and closer** to the gradient of the **curve** at $(x, f(x))$.
So you can write an expression for the gradient of the curve $y = f(x)$ like this:

$$f'(x) = \lim_{h \to 0}\left[\frac{f(x + h) - f(x)}{(x + h) - x}\right]$$

Tip: Remember the gradient of a line which passes through points (x_1, y_1) and (x_2, y_2) is given by:
$$\frac{y_2 - y_1}{x_2 - x_1}$$

Tip: $\lim_{h \to 0}$ in front of the function just means 'what the function goes towards as h goes towards zero'.

This method of differentiation is known as differentiating from **first principles** and the formula can be used to find the gradient of a curve as a function of x.

Examples

Find an expression for the gradient of the function $f(x) = x^2$ by differentiating from first principles.

- Write down the formula for differentiating from first principles. $\longrightarrow$ $f'(x) = \lim\limits_{h \to 0}\left[\dfrac{f(x+h) - f(x)}{(x+h) - x}\right]$

- Use the fact that $f(x) = x^2$. $\longrightarrow$ $= \lim\limits_{h \to 0}\left[\dfrac{(x+h)^2 - x^2}{(x+h) - x}\right]$

- Multiply out and simplify. $\longrightarrow$ $= \lim\limits_{h \to 0}\left[\dfrac{x^2 + 2xh + h^2 - x^2}{x + h - x}\right]$

  $= \lim\limits_{h \to 0}\left[\dfrac{2xh + h^2}{h}\right]$

- Now decide what will happen as h gets close to 0. $\longrightarrow$ $= \lim\limits_{h \to 0}[2x + h]$

- In this case $2x + h$ gets close to $2x$. $\longrightarrow$ $= \boxed{2x}$

Find the gradient of the curve $y = 0.5x$ by differentiating from first principles.

$$\dfrac{dy}{dx} = \lim\limits_{h \to 0}\left[\dfrac{f(x+h) - f(x)}{(x+h) - x}\right]$$

- Use the fact that $y = f(x)$ with $f(x) = 0.5x$. $\longrightarrow$ $= \lim\limits_{h \to 0}\left[\dfrac{0.5(x+h) - 0.5x}{(x+h) - x}\right]$

  $= \lim\limits_{h \to 0}\left[\dfrac{0.5h}{h}\right]$

Tip: A straight line will always have a constant gradient.

- Decide what will happen as h gets close to 0. There are no h's so the limit is just 0.5. $\longrightarrow$ $= \lim\limits_{h \to 0}[0.5] = \boxed{0.5}$

Exercise 1.1

Q1 Hint: It's OK to use a calculator for this question.

Q1 The curve C is given by $y = f(x)$ where $f(x) = x^3$.

a) Find the gradient of the straight line joining the point on the curve where $x = 1$ and the point on the curve where:

(i) $x = 2$

(ii) $x = 1.5$

(iii) $x = 1.1$

b) The gradient of the curve at the point $(1, 1)$ is 3. What do you notice about the gradient of the straight lines in part a) as the value of x moves closer to 1?

Q2 Hint: Remember — you won't have to differentiate from first principles in the exam.

Q2 Derive from first principles expressions for the gradients of the following curves:

a) $y = x$ b) $f(x) = x^3$ c) $f(x) = 2x$

2. Differentiating $y = f(x)$

Differentiating from first principles can take a long time, especially if there are large powers involved. Luckily, there's a formula that will do it quickly for you.

Differentiating x^n

You can use this **formula** to differentiate powers of x:

$$\text{If } y = x^n, \text{ then } \frac{dy}{dx} = nx^{n-1}$$

It comes from differentiating x^n from **first principles**, like on the page before.

Example 1

Differentiate each of the following using the formula for powers of x.

a) $y = x^2$

For 'normal' powers, n is just the power of x. Here $n = 2$.

$$\frac{dy}{dx} = nx^{n-1}$$
$$= 2x^1$$
$$= \boxed{2x}$$

Tip: When it says 'differentiate', it actually means 'differentiate **with respect to** x' as it's a function of x you're differentiating.

b) $y = 4x^3$

This is just a normal power with $n = 3$, but there's a constant (a number) in front of it.

$$y = 4x^3$$
$$\frac{dy}{dx} = 4(nx^{n-1})$$
$$= 4(3x^2)$$
$$= \boxed{12x^2}$$

If there's a number in front of the x^n term — multiply the derivative by it. Formally:

$$\text{If } y = ax^n, \ \frac{dy}{dx} = anx^{n-1}$$

c) $y = -6x$

Don't worry if the constant is negative — just treat it the same as a positive constant.

$$x = x^1$$
$$y = -6x$$
$$\frac{dy}{dx} = -6(1x^0)$$
$$x^0 = 1$$
$$= \boxed{-6}$$

Tip: Differentiating $y = a$ where a is just a constant (i.e. a number) always gives zero, because the line has a gradient of 0.

Example 2

Differentiate $y = 5$ using the formula for powers of x.

There are no powers of x in this expression for y so multiply by $x^0 = 1$.

$\longrightarrow$ $y = 5x^0$, $n = 0$

$\dfrac{dy}{dx} = 5\,(nx^{n-1})$

$= 5\,(0x^{-1})$

$= \boxed{0}$

You could be asked to **use** your gradient function to work out the **numerical value** of the gradient at a **particular point** on the curve.

Example 3

Find the gradient of the curve $y = x^2$ at $x = 1$ and $x = -2$.

You need the gradient of the graph of $y = x^2$, so differentiate this function to get $\dfrac{dy}{dx} = 2x$.

Now when $x = 1$, $\dfrac{dy}{dx} = 2$,

And so the gradient of the graph at $x = 1$ is 2.

And when $x = -2$, $\dfrac{dy}{dx} = -4$.

So the gradient of the graph at $x = -2$ is -4.

Exercise 2.1

Q1 Differentiate to find $\dfrac{dy}{dx}$ for:

a) $y = x^6$ b) $y = x^3$ c) $y = x^0$ d) $y = 3x^2$

e) $y = 7x$ f) $y = 3$ g) $y = 5x^3$ h) $y = 11x^1$

Q2 Differentiate to find $f'(x)$ for:

a) $f(x) = x^5$ b) $f(x) = x^7$ c) $f(x) = x^4$ d) $f(x) = 4x^3$

e) $f(x) = 8x$ f) $f(x) = 3x^5$ g) $f(x) = -7$ h) $f(x) = 4x^2$

Q3 Find the gradient of each of the following functions:

a) $y = 2x^2$ when $x = 4$ b) $y = x$ when $x = 2$

c) $y = -4x^5$ when $x = 1$ d) $f(x) = 2x^2$ at the point $(9, 162)$

e) $f(x) = x^4$ at the point $(-2, 16)$ f) $f(x) = -2x^3$ when $f(x) = -250$

Differentiating functions

Even if there are **loads** of terms in the expression, it doesn't matter.

Differentiate each bit **separately** and you'll be fine.

Formally, this means:

$$f'(x^m + x^n) = f'(x^m) + f'(x^n)$$

Example 1

a) **Differentiate** $y = 3x^2 + 2x.$

Differentiate each bit separately.

$$y = 3x^2 + 2x$$

$$\frac{dy}{dx} = 3(2x) + 2 = \boxed{6x + 2}$$

> **Tip:** Remember — if there's a number in front of the function, multiply the derivative by the same number.

b) **Differentiate** $f(x) = x^4 + 6x - 2.$

Differentiate each bit separately.

$$f(x) = x^4 + 6x - 2$$

$$f'(x) = 4x^3 + 6 - 0 = \boxed{4x^3 + 6}$$

You'll often need to **simplify** a function before you can differentiate it by multiplying out **brackets** or simplifying **fractions**.

Example 2

a) **Differentiate** $y = x(x + 3)(x - 4) + 4(2 - x^2).$

- Multiply out all brackets and simplify to powers of x.

$$y = x(x + 3)(x - 4) + 4(2 - x^2)$$
$$= x(x^2 - x - 12) + 8 - 4x^2$$
$$= x^3 - x^2 - 12x + 8 - 4x^2$$
$$= x^3 - 5x^2 - 12x + 8$$

- Differentiate term-by-term.

$$\frac{dy}{dx} = 3x^2 - 10x - 12 + 0$$
$$= \boxed{3x^2 - 10x - 12}$$

---

b) Find f'(x) for the function $f(x) = (\frac{1}{2}x + 5)(\frac{1}{2}x - 1)$.

$$f(x) = (\tfrac{1}{2}x + 5)(\tfrac{1}{2}x - 1)$$

$$= \tfrac{1}{4}x^2 - \tfrac{1}{2}x + \tfrac{5}{2}x - 5$$

$$= \tfrac{1}{4}x^2 + \tfrac{4}{2}x - 5$$

- x^2 is multiplied by $\frac{1}{4}$ so multiply the derivative by $\frac{1}{4}$ as well and simplify.

$$= \tfrac{1}{4}x^2 + 2x - 5$$

$$f'(x) = \tfrac{1}{4}(2x) + 2 - 0$$

$$= \tfrac{1}{2}x + 2$$

Example 3

Tip: If the denominator is an expression instead of just one term, chances are the numerator will have a factor that cancels with the denominator.

Differentiate $y = \dfrac{x^3 - 5x^2 + 6x}{x - 2}$.

The numerator of this fraction will factorise and then one of the factors will cancel with the denominator.

$$y = \frac{x^3 - 5x^2 + 6x}{x - 2}$$

$$= \frac{x(x^2 - 5x + 6)}{x - 2}$$

$$= \frac{x(x - 3)(x - 2)}{x - 2}$$

$$= x(x - 3)$$

$$= x^2 - 3x$$

$$\frac{dy}{dx} = 2x - 3$$

Exercise 2.2

Q1 Differentiate these functions:

a) $y = 4x^3 - x^2$

b) $y = x + 1$

c) $y = 3x^2 + x - 5$

d) $f(x) = -2x^5 + 4x - 6$

e) $f(x) = x^4 - x$

f) $f(x) = 5x - 2x^3 + 21$

Q2 Hint: Remember that $\frac{d}{dx}(\ \ )$ means the derivative with respect to x of the thing in brackets.

Q2 Find:

a) $\dfrac{d}{dx}(x(x^6 - 1))$

b) $\dfrac{d}{dx}((x - 3)(x + 4))$

c) $\dfrac{d}{dx}(x(x - 1)(x - 2))$

d) $\dfrac{d}{dx}((x - 3)(x + 4)(x - 1))$

e) $\dfrac{d}{dx}(x^2(x - 4)(3 - x^3))$

f) $\dfrac{d}{dx}((x - 3)^2(x^2 - 2))$

Q3 Find the gradient of each of the following curves:

a) $y = x^4 - x^2 + 2$ when $x = 3$

b) $y = 2x^5 + 4$ when $x = -2$

c) $y = x(x - 1)(x - 2)$ when $x = -3$

d) $y = 5(x^2 - 1)(3 - x)$ when $x = 0$

e) $y = x(x - 1)$ at $(4, 12)$

f) $f(x) = x^3(x^2 - 5)$ at $(-1, 4)$

g) $f(x) = \dfrac{1}{3x^2}(x^5 - 3x^3)$ at $x = 5$

h) $f(x) = \dfrac{3x^3 + 18x^2 + 24x}{x + 4}$ at $(-2, 0)$

Q4
a) Find the coordinates of the point on the curve $y = (x + 3)(x + 4)$ where $\dfrac{dy}{dx} = 3$.

b) Find the coordinates of the point on the curve $y = (x + 3)(x - 5)$ where $\dfrac{dy}{dx} = 2$.

c) Find the coordinates of the point on the curve $y = x^2 + 8x$ where $\dfrac{dy}{dx} = 4$.

d) Find the coordinates of the point on the curve $y = \dfrac{x^3 - 3x^2 + 2x}{x - 1}$ where $\dfrac{dy}{dx} = -6$.

Q5 For each of the following functions, find the coordinates of the point or points where the gradient is 0:

a) $y = x^2 - 2x$

b) $y = 3x^2 + 4x$

c) $y = 5x^2 - 3x$

d) $y = 9x - 3x^3$

e) $y = 2x^3 - x^2$

f) $y = 2x^3 + 3x^2 - 12x$

Q6 Differentiate these functions:

a) $y = \dfrac{x^2 - 3x - 4}{x + 1}$

b) $f(x) = \dfrac{x^4 - 9}{x^2 + 3}$

Q6 Hint: Where there's a fraction with an expression in the denominator, try to take the denominator out of the numerator as a factor.

Finding tangents and normals

Differentiation can be used to find the gradient at a point on a curve. When you've done this it's easy to find the equation for the **tangent** or **normal** at that point.

- You already know that a **tangent** is a straight line that just **touches** the curve and has the **same gradient** as the curve at that point.

- A **normal** is a straight line that is **perpendicular** (at right angles) to the curve at a particular point.

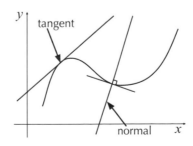

Now, there's one key fact to remember for normals — tangents and normals are perpendicular, and as a result, their **gradients multiply to give –1**:

> gradient of tangent × gradient of normal = –1
>
> gradient of normal = $\dfrac{-1}{\text{gradient of tangent}}$

Tip: This rule for the gradients of perpendicular lines was introduced back in Chapter 5 on p.87.

Armed with the rule from the previous page, we can write down a step-by-step method for finding the equation of a tangent or normal to a curve...

To find the equation of the tangent or normal to a curve at a point:
- Differentiate the function.
- Find the gradient of the curve at that point.
- Use this to deduce the gradient, m, of the tangent or normal:

$$\text{gradient of the tangent} = \text{gradient of the curve}$$

$$\text{gradient of the normal} = -\frac{1}{\text{gradient of the curve}}$$

- Write the equation of the tangent or normal in the form $y = mx + c$.
- Work out the constant value c in the equation by using the coordinates of the point (which you know lies on the tangent/normal).

Tip: The tangent and normal are always straight lines, so their equations can be written $y = mx + c$. They can also be written in the form $y - y_1 = m(x - x_1)$ if you prefer.

Example 1

Find the equation of the tangent to the curve $y = (4 - x)(x + 2)$ at the point (2, 8), giving your answer in the form $ax + by + c = 0$, where a, b and c are integers.

- Write the curve in a form you can differentiate...

$$\begin{aligned} y &= (4 - x)(x + 2) \\ &= 4x + 8 - x^2 - 2x \\ &= 8 + 2x - x^2 \end{aligned}$$

...and differentiate it.

$$\begin{aligned} \frac{dy}{dx} &= 0 + 2 - 2x \\ &= 2 - 2x \end{aligned}$$

- Find the gradient of the curve at (2, 8).

$$x = 2 \Rightarrow \frac{dy}{dx} = 2 - (2 \times 2) = 2 - 4 = -2$$

So the gradient of the curve is -2 at (2, 8)

- Gradient of the tangent = gradient of the curve, so $m = -2$

- So the equation of the tangent is $y = -2x + c$.

- Use the point (2, 8) to work out the value of c:

$$x = 2,\, y = 8 \Rightarrow 8 = -4 + c \Rightarrow c = 12$$

So the tangent has equation $y = -2x + 12$.

Rearranging into the form $ax + by + c = 0$ gives:

$$2x + y - 12 = 0$$

Example 2

Find the equation of the normal to the curve $y = x(x - 3)(x + 2)$ at the point (2, –8), giving your answer in the form $y = mx + c$.

- Simplify and differentiate.

$$y = x(x - 3)(x + 2)$$
$$= x^3 - x^2 - 6x$$
$$\frac{dy}{dx} = 3x^2 - 2x - 6$$

Tip: Make sure you always check whether the question wants a normal or a tangent.

- Find the gradient of the curve at (2, –8).

$$x = 2 \Rightarrow \frac{dy}{dx} = 3(2^2) - 2(2) - 6 = 2$$

So the gradient of the curve is 2 at (2, –8)

- Gradient of the normal at (2, –8) is

$$m = -\frac{1}{\text{gradient of the curve at } (2, -8)} = -\frac{1}{2}$$

- So the equation of the normal is $y = -\frac{1}{2}x + c$.

- Use the point (2, –8) to work out the value of c.

$$x = 2, y = -8 \Rightarrow -8 = -1 + c \Rightarrow c = -7$$

So the normal has equation:

$$y = -\frac{1}{2}x - 7$$

Example 3

Find the equation of the normal to the curve $y = x^2(x + 1)$ at the point (2, 12), giving your answer in the form $ax + by + c = 0$, where a, b and c are integers.

- Simplify and differentiate.

$$y = x^2(x + 1) = x^3 + x^2$$
$$\frac{dy}{dx} = 3x^2 + 2x$$

- Find the gradient of the curve at (2, 12).

$$x = 2 \Rightarrow \frac{dy}{dx} = 3(2)^2 + 2(2)$$
$$= 12 + 4$$
$$= 16$$

So the gradient of the curve is 16 at (2, 12)

- Gradient of the normal line at (2, 12) is

$$m = -\frac{1}{\text{gradient of the curve at } (2, 12)} = -\frac{1}{16}$$

- Use $(y - y_1) = m(x - x_1)$ and the point (2, 12) to find the equation of the normal.

$$x = 2, y = 12 \Rightarrow y - 12 = -\frac{1}{16}(x - 2)$$

So the normal has equation $16y - 192 = -x + 2$.

Rearranging into the form $ax + by + c = 0$ gives:

$$x + 16y - 194 = 0$$

Tip: Rewriting the answer in the form the question asks for will get you easy marks.

Exercise 2.3

Q1 Find the equation of the tangent to each of these curves at the given point. Give your answer in the form $y = mx + c$.
  a) $y = 9x - 2x^2$, (1, 7)   b) $y = x^3 - 2x + 3$, (2, 7)
  c) $y = (x + 2)(2x - 3)$, (2, 4)   d) $y = x(x - 1)^2$, (−1, −4)
  e) $y = x^2(x + 3) - 10$, (2, 10)   f) $y = x(2x + 4)(x - 3)$, (−1, 8)

Q2 Find the normal to each of these curves at the given point, giving your answer in the form $ax + by + c = 0$, where a, b and c are integers.
  a) $y = 3x^2 - 4x + 2$, (2, 6)   b) $y = x^2(x + 4) - 5x$, (−1, 8)
  c) $y = x(x - 1)(x - 2)$, (3, 6)   d) $y = x(x - 3)(x + 4) - 10$, (−2, 10)
  e) $y = \dfrac{x^3 - 5x^2 - 14x}{x + 2}$, (5, −10)

Q3 Consider the curve with equation $y = f(x)$ where $f(x) = x^3 - 3x^2 + 3$.
  a) Find the coordinates of the point where $f'(x) = 9$ and $x > 0$.
  b) Find the equation of the tangent to the curve at this point, giving your answer in the form $y = mx + c$.
  c) Find the equation of the normal to the curve at this point, giving your answer in the form $ax + by + c = 0$, where a, b and c are integers.

Q4 a) Show that the curve $y = x^3 + x^2 + x + 5$ passes through the point (−2, −1).
  b) Find the equation of the tangent to the curve at this point, giving your answer in the form $ax + by + c = 0$, where a, b and c are integers.
  c) Find the equation of the normal to the curve at this point, giving your answer in the form $ax + by + c = 0$, where a, b and c are integers.

3. Using Differentiation

In this section you'll use differentiation to find the points on a graph where the gradient is zero — known as stationary points — and determine their nature by finding a second order derivative. You'll also see how to find where a graph is increasing or decreasing and, using this information, make accurate sketches of functions.

Learning Objectives:

- Be able to find the second derivative of functions.
- Be able to use differentiation to find all the stationary points on a curve.
- Be able to identify the nature of these stationary points.
- Be able to work out where a graph is increasing or decreasing.
- Be able to use this information to make accurate sketches of the graph of a function.

Finding second order derivatives

- If you differentiate y with respect to x, you get the derivative $\frac{dy}{dx}$.

- If you then differentiate $\frac{dy}{dx}$ with respect to x, you get the **second order derivative**, denoted $\frac{d^2y}{dx^2}$.

- The **second derivative** gives the **rate of change** of the **gradient** of the curve with respect to x.

- In function notation, the **second derivative** is written $f''(x)$.

Example 1

a) **For the function $f(x) = 2x^3 + 4x^2 + x$ find $f'(x)$ and $f''(x)$**

$$f(x) = 2x^3 + 4x^2 + x$$

$$f'(x) = 2(3x^2) + 4(2x) + 1 \quad \longleftarrow \boxed{\text{Differentiate for } f'(x).}$$
$$= 6x^2 + 8x + 1$$

$$f''(x) = 6(2x) + 8 \quad \longleftarrow \boxed{\begin{array}{l}\text{Differentiate again to get}\\ \text{the second derivative.}\end{array}}$$
$$= 12x + 8$$

b) **For the equation $y = (3x + 5)(2x - 1)$, find $\frac{dy}{dx}$ and $\frac{d^2x}{dy^2}$.**

$$y = (3x + 5)(2x - 1) \quad \longleftarrow \boxed{\text{Multiply the brackets...}}$$
$$= 6x^2 + 7x - 5$$

$$\frac{dy}{dx} = 6(2x) + 7 - 0 \quad \longleftarrow \boxed{\text{Differentiate for } \frac{dy}{dx}.}$$
$$= 12x + 7$$

$$\frac{d^2y}{dx^2} = 12 + 0 \quad \longleftarrow \boxed{\begin{array}{l}\text{Differentiate again to get}\\ \text{the second derivative.}\end{array}}$$
$$= 12$$

Until now, all the examples have been about differentiating functions of x to find gradients of curves. But **real life** examples often involve a function of t, time, and you'll need to differentiate to find the **rate of change** over time. The maths is **the same**, the **letters** are just different.

The next example looks at the **distance** a car has travelled as a function of **time**.

Example 2

A sports car pulls off from a junction and drives away, travelling x metres in t seconds. For the first 10 seconds, its journey can be described by the equation $x = 2t^2$.

a) Find the speed of the car after 8 seconds

Speed is the rate of change of distance with respect to time — it can be found by differentiating the expression for distance with respect to time.

So to work out the speed as a function of t, differentiate x to find $\dfrac{dx}{dt}$.

$$x = 2t^2$$

$$\frac{dx}{dt} = 4t$$

You've got speed as a function of t, so just put 8 seconds into the expression.

$$\text{When } t = 8, \frac{dx}{dt} = 32$$

So, the car is travelling at 32 ms^{-1} after 8 seconds.

b) Find the car's acceleration during this period.

Acceleration is the rate of change of speed with respect to time — it can be found by differentiating the expression for speed with respect to time.

The speed is $\dfrac{dx}{dt}$ so differentiate again to get the second derivative $\dfrac{d^2x}{dt^2}$.

$$\frac{dx}{dt} = 4t$$

$$\frac{d^2x}{dt^2} = 4$$

This means that the car's acceleration during this period is 4 ms^{-2}.

There are some more examples of real-life differentiation on pages 136-137.

Tip: Just like in all the other questions, $\dfrac{dx}{dt}$ is a gradient. If you were to draw a distance–time graph, it would just be the gradient of the graph as a function of t.

Tip: Careful with the units here — acceleration is measured in metres per second².

Q1 Find $\dfrac{dy}{dx}$ and $\dfrac{d^2y}{dx^2}$ for each of these functions:

a) $y = x^3$

b) $y = x^5$

c) $y = x^4$

d) $y = x$

e) $y = 3x^2$

f) $y = 5x^4$

g) $y = 2x$

h) $y = x^4 + 4x$

Q2 Find $f'(x)$ and $f''(x)$ for each of these functions:

a) $f(x) = x(3x^2 + 2)$

b) $f(x) = x(4x^2 - x)$

c) $f(x) = x(x^3 - x^2 + 7x)$

d) $f(x) = \dfrac{1}{x}(3x^4 - 2x^3)$

e) $f(x) = (x^2 - 3)(x - 4)$

f) $f(x) = \dfrac{4x^5 + 12x^3 - 40x}{4(x^2 + 5)}$

Q3 Find the value of the second derivative at the given value for x.

a) $f(x) = x^3 - x^2, \ x = 3$

b) $y = x^5 - x, \ x = 2$

c) $f(x) = 9x^2 + 3x, \ x = 1$

d) $y = (x^2 + x)(5 - x), \ x = -3$

e) $f(x) = x^2(x - 5)(x^2 + x), \ x = -1$

f) $y = \dfrac{x^5 + 4x^4 - 12x^3}{x + 6}, \ x = 5$

Q4 A particle moves along a path described by the equation $x = 3t^2 - 7t$, where t is the time in seconds and x is the distance in metres from its starting point.

a) Find the speed, $\dfrac{dx}{dt}$, of the particle as a function of t.

b) What is the speed of the particle in ms⁻¹ at:

    (i) $t = 2$ seconds   (ii) $t = 5$ seconds

c) Find the value of t when the speed is 17 ms⁻¹.

d) Find the acceleration $\dfrac{d^2x}{dt^2}$ of the particle as a function of t.

Q5 A particle moves along a path described by the equation $x = 2t^3 - 4t^2$, $t > 0$, where t is the time in seconds and x is the distance in metres from its starting point.

a) Find the speed of the particle after t seconds.

b) Find x and t when the speed is 30 ms⁻¹.

c) Find the acceleration of the particle after t seconds.

d) Find the acceleration at $t = 5$ seconds in ms⁻².

e) Find the speed when the acceleration is 16 ms⁻².

Q5 Hint: For part e), use the information given to work out the value of t first.

Stationary points

Stationary points occur when the **gradient** of a graph is **zero**.
There are three types of stationary point:

Maximum
When the gradient changes from positive to negative.

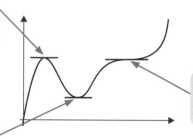

Point of inflection
When the graph briefly flattens out.

Minimum
When the gradient changes from negative to positive.

Tip: Some stationary points are called local maximum and minimum points because the function takes on bigger (or smaller) values in other parts of the graph.

Because stationary points occur when the gradient is zero, you can use **differentiation** to find them.
To find the stationary points of the graph of $y = f(x)$:

> **1.** Differentiate $f(x)$.
>
> **2.** Set $f'(x) = 0$.
>
> **3.** Solve $f'(x) = 0$ to find the x-values.
>
> **4.** Put the x-values back into the original equation to find the y-values.

Example 1

Find the stationary points of the curve $y = 2x^3 - 3x^2 - 12x + 5$.

- You need to find where $\dfrac{dy}{dx} = 0$, so start by **differentiating** the function:

$$y = 2x^3 - 3x^2 - 12x + 5 \quad \Rightarrow \quad \frac{dy}{dx} = 6x^2 - 6x - 12$$

- Then set the derivative **equal to zero** and solve for x:

$$6x^2 - 6x - 12 = 0$$

$$6x^2 - 6x - 12 = 0 \quad \Rightarrow \quad x^2 - x - 2 = 0$$
$$\Rightarrow \quad (x + 1)(x - 2) = 0$$
$$\Rightarrow \quad x = -1 \text{ or } x = 2$$

- Now you've found the **stationary points**. To find the coordinates of the stationary points, just put these x-values into the original equation.

  If $x = -1$, $y = 2(-1)^3 - 3(-1)^2 - 12(-1) + 5 = -2 - 3 + 12 + 5 = 12$

  If $x = 2$, $y = 2(2)^3 - 3(2)^2 - 12(2) + 5 = 16 - 12 - 24 + 5 = -15$

- This gives the coordinates $(-1, 12)$ and $(2, -15)$.

Tip: Don't forget this last step — once you've found x you need to also find y.

Example 2

Below is a sketch of the graph of $y = x^3(x^2 + x - 3)$. One stationary point occurs at $(-1.8, 9.1)$. Show that the other two occur when $x = 0$ and when $x = 1$, and find their coordinates.

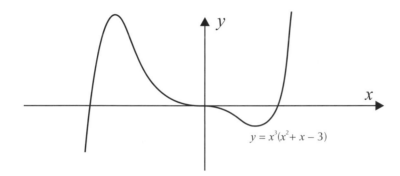

$y = x^3(x^2 + x - 3)$

- Start by **differentiating** the function. First, **multiply out** the brackets:
  $$y = x^3(x^2 + x - 3) = x^5 + x^4 - 3x^3$$

- Then you can just differentiate as normal:
  $$y = x^5 + x^4 - 3x^3 \quad \Rightarrow \quad \frac{dy}{dx} = 5x^4 + 4x^3 - 9x^2$$

- Stationary points occur when the **gradient** is **equal to zero**, so set $\frac{dy}{dx}$ equal to zero and solve for x:

  $5x^4 + 4x^3 - 9x^2 = 0 \Rightarrow x^2(5x^2 + 4x - 9) = 0$

  $\Rightarrow x^2(5x + 9)(x - 1) = 0$

  $\Rightarrow x = 0, x = -\dfrac{9}{5} = -1.8$ (given above) and $x = 1$.

  So the other two stationary points occur at $x = 0$ and $x = 1$.

- To find the **coordinates** of these points, just put the x-values into the original equation:

  $y = x^3(x^2 + x - 3) = 0^3(0^2 + 0 - 3) = 0(-3) = 0$

  $y = x^3(x^2 + x - 3) = 1^3(1^2 + 1 - 3) = 1(-1) = -1$

- So the coordinates of the stationary points are $(0, 0)$ and $(1, -1)$.

Q1 Without doing any calculations, say how many stationary points the graphs below have in the intervals shown.

a)

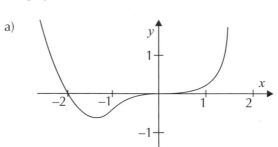

b)

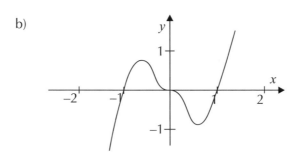

Q2 Find the x-coordinates of the stationary points of the curves with the following equations:

a) $y = x^2 + 3x + 2$ b) $y = (3 - x)(4 + 2x)$

Q3 Find the coordinates of the stationary points of the curves with the following equations:

a) $y = 2x^2 - 8x + 2$ b) $y = -x^2 + 6x - 4$

c) $y = 7 - 6x - 3x^2$ d) $y = (x - 12)(x + 2)$

Q4 Find the coordinates of the stationary points of the curves with the following equations:

a) $y = x^3 - 3x + 2$ b) $y = 4x^3 + 5$

Q5 Hint: If there are no stationary points, there are no values of x for which $f'(x) = 0$.

Q5 Show that the graph of the function given by $f(x) = x^5 + 3x + 2$ has no stationary points.

Q6 a) Differentiate $y = x^3 - 7x^2 - 5x + 2$

b) Hence find the coordinates of the stationary points of the curve with equation $y = x^3 - 7x^2 - 5x + 2$.

Q7 A graph is given by the function $f(x) = x^3 + kx$, where k is a constant. Given that the graph has no stationary points, find the range of possible values for k.

Maximum and minimum points

Once you've found where the stationary points are, you might be asked to decide if each one is a **maximum** or **minimum**. Maximum and minimum points are also know as **turning points**.

To decide whether a stationary point is a maximum or minimum, **differentiate again** to find $\frac{d^2y}{dx^2}$ or $f''(x)$ (see p.125).

Tip: That's what a question means when it asks you to "determine the nature of the turning points". (You won't be asked to do this for points of inflection.)

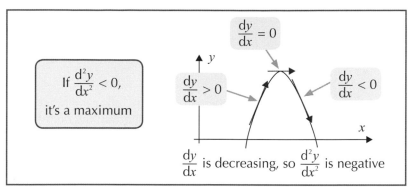

If $\frac{d^2y}{dx^2} < 0$, it's a maximum

$\frac{dy}{dx} = 0$

$\frac{dy}{dx} > 0$ $\frac{dy}{dx} < 0$

$\frac{dy}{dx}$ is decreasing, so $\frac{d^2y}{dx^2}$ is negative

If $\frac{d^2y}{dx^2} > 0$, it's a minimum

$\frac{dy}{dx} = 0$

$\frac{dy}{dx} < 0$ $\frac{dy}{dx} > 0$

$\frac{dy}{dx}$ is increasing, so $\frac{d^2y}{dx^2}$ is positive

Tip: If the second derivative is equal to zero, you can't tell what type of stationary point it is.

Example

Determine the nature of the stationary points in Example 1 on p.128 ($y = 2x^3 - 3x^2 - 12x + 5$).

- The first derivative has been found already: $\frac{dy}{dx} = 6x^2 - 6x - 12$.
  To determine the nature of the stationary points, **differentiate again**:

  $$\frac{dy}{dx} = 6x^2 - 6x - 12 \quad \Rightarrow \quad \frac{d^2y}{dx^2} = 12x - 6$$

- Then just put in the x-values of the coordinates of the **stationary points**.

- At $x = -1$, $\frac{d^2y}{dx^2} = -18$, which is **negative** — so (−1, 12) is a maximum.

- And at $x = 2$, $\frac{d^2y}{dx^2} = 18$, which is **positive** — so (2, −15) is a minimum.

- Since you know the **turning points** and the fact that it's a **cubic** with a positive coefficient of x^3, you can now **sketch** the graph (though the roots would be difficult to find accurately).

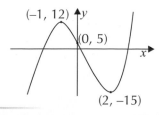

(−1, 12)
(0, 5)
(2, −15)

Tip: You found the coordinates of the stationary points for this function on p.129. They are (−1, 12) and (2, −15).

Tip: The y-intercept is just the value of y when $x = 0$.

Q1 The diagram below shows a sketch of the graph of $y = f(x)$. For each labelled turning point, say whether it is a maximum or minimum.

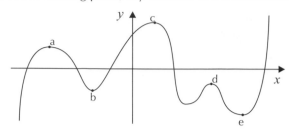

Q2 Find the stationary points on the graphs of the following functions and say whether they're maximum or minimum turning points:

a) $y = 5 - x^2$

b) $y = 2x^3 - 6x + 2$

c) $y = x^3 - 3x^2 - 24x + 15$

d) $y = x^4 + 4x^3 + 4x^2 - 10$

Q3 A function $y = f(x)$ is such that $f(1) = 3$, $f'(1) = 0$ and $f''(1) = 7$.

a) Give the coordinates of one of the turning points of $f(x)$.

b) Determine the nature of this turning point, explaining your answer.

Q4 Find the stationary points on the graphs of the following functions and say whether they're maximum or minimum turning points:

a) $f(x) = 8x^3 + 16x^2 + 8x + 1$

b) $f(x) = 2x^4 + x$

Q5 a) Given that $f(x) = x^3 - 3x^2 + 4$, find $f'(x)$ and $f''(x)$.

b) Hence find the coordinates of any stationary points on the graph $f(x)$ and say whether they're maximum or minimum turning points.

Q6 Walter makes different sized fishbowls. The volume of each bowl is given by $V = 4r^3 - 12r^2$, $r > 0$, where r is the radius of the bowl.

a) Find the value of r at which V has a stationary point.

b) Is this a minimum or maximum point?

Q6 Hint: This question's no different to the others in this exercise — just treat V as y and r as x, and carry on as normal.

Q7 The curve given by the function $f(x) = x^3 + ax^2 + bx + c$ has a stationary point with coordinates $(3, 10)$. If $f''(x) = 0$ at $(3, 10)$, find a, b and c.

Q8 a) Given that a curve with the equation $y = x^4 + kx^3 + x^2 + 17$ has only one stationary point, show that $k^2 < \frac{32}{9}$.

b) Find the coordinates of the stationary point and say whether it's a maximum or a minimum point.

Increasing and decreasing functions

As differentiation is about finding the gradients of curves, you can use it to find if a function is **increasing** or **decreasing** at a given point. This can help you to sketch the function and determine the nature of turning points.

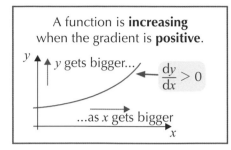

A function is **increasing** when the gradient is **positive**.

y gets bigger...
$\frac{dy}{dx} > 0$
...as x gets bigger

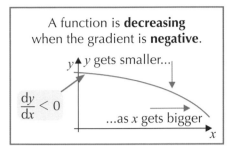

A function is **decreasing** when the gradient is **negative**.

y gets smaller...
$\frac{dy}{dx} < 0$
...as x gets bigger

You can also tell how **quickly** a function is increasing or decreasing by looking at the size of the gradient — the **bigger** the gradient (positive or negative), the **faster** the function is increasing or decreasing, so the **steeper** the curve.

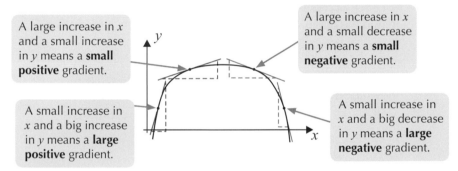

A large increase in x and a small increase in y means a **small positive** gradient.

A large increase in x and a small decrease in y means a **small negative** gradient.

A small increase in x and a big increase in y means a **large positive** gradient.

A small increase in x and a big decrease in y means a **large negative** gradient.

Example

Find the values of x for which the function $y = x^3 - 6x^2 + 9x + 3$, $x > 0$ is increasing.

- You want to know when y is increasing — so **differentiate**.

$$y = x^3 - 6x^2 + 9x + 3 \quad \Rightarrow \quad \frac{dy}{dx} = 3x^2 - 12x + 9$$

- It's an **increasing** function when the derivative is **greater** than zero, so write it down as an inequality and solve it.

$$\frac{dy}{dx} > 0 \quad \Rightarrow \quad 3x^2 - 12x + 9 > 0 \quad \Rightarrow \quad x^2 - 4x + 3 > 0 \quad \Rightarrow \quad (x-3)(x-1) > 0$$

- The coefficient of x^2 is **positive**, so the graph of this function would be **u-shaped**. It crosses the x-axis at $x = 1$ and $x = 3$, so $x^2 - 4x + 3 > 0$ when $x < 1$ or when $x > 3$ (sketch the graph if you're struggling to get your head round this).

- $x > 0$, so the function is increasing when $0 < x < 1$ or $x > 3$.

Tip: Often you'll be given a cubic equation, which will differentiate to a quadratic (which you should be able to factorise).

Tip: Have a look back at p.53 for more on solving quadratic inequalities.

- You could also look at the nature of the **stationary points** — this will tell you where the function goes from increasing to decreasing and vice versa.

$x = 1$ and $x = 3$ are the **stationary points** (as $\frac{dy}{dx} = 0$ at these points).

$$\frac{dy}{dx} = 3x^2 - 12x + 9 \quad \Rightarrow \quad \frac{d^2y}{dx^2} = 6x - 12$$

- When $x = 1$, $\frac{d^2y}{dx^2} = -6$, so it's a **maximum**, which means the function is increasing as it approaches $x = 1$ and starts decreasing after $x = 1$.
- When $x = 3$, $\frac{d^2y}{dx^2} = 6$, so it's a **minimum**, which means the function is decreasing as it approaches $x = 3$ and starts increasing after $x = 3$.

This fits in with what you know already — that the function is increasing when $0 < x < 1$ and $x > 3$.

Exercise 3.4

Q1 For each of these functions, calculate the first derivative and use this to find the range of values for which the function is increasing.
   a) $y = x^2 + 7x + 5$ b) $y = 5x^2 + 3x - 2$ c) $y = 2 - 9x^2$

Q2 For each of these functions, find f'(x) and find the range of values of x for which f(x) is decreasing.
   a) $f(x) = 16 - 3x - 2x^2$ b) $f(x) = (6 - 3x)(6 + 3x)$
   c) $f(x) = (1 - 2x)(7 - 3x)$

Q3 Calculate $\frac{dy}{dx}$ for each of these functions and state the range of values for which the function is increasing.
   a) $y = x^3 - 6x^2 - 15x + 25$ b) $y = x^3 + 6x^2 + 12x + 5$

Q4 Find the first derivative of each of the following functions and state the range of values for which the function is decreasing.
   a) $f(x) = x^3 - 3x^2 - 9x + 1$ b) $f(x) = x^3 - 4x^2 + 4x + 7$

Q5 Hint: An increasing function is one where f'(x) > 0 for all values of x.

Q5 Use differentiation to explain why $f(x) = x^3 + x$ is an increasing function for all values of x.

Q6 Is the function $f(x) = 3 - 3x - x^3$ an increasing or decreasing function? Explain your answer.

Q7 b) Hint: You might find it easier to find the nature of the stationary points instead of solving a cubic inequality.

Q7 Use differentiation to find the range of values of x for which each of these functions is decreasing:
   a) $y = 2x^4 + x$ b) $y = x^4 - 2x^3 - 5x^2 + 6$

Q8 The function $y = 5 - 3x - ax^5$ is a decreasing function for all values of x. Find the range of possible values for a.

Q8, 9 Hint: See which values of the variable satisfy the conditions of an increasing or decreasing function.

Q9 The function $y = x^k + x$, where k is a positive integer, is an increasing function for all values of x. Find all possible values of k.

Curve sketching

You saw how to sketch **quadratic graphs** in Chapter 2 (see pages 33-37) and how to sketch **cubic graphs** in Chapter 5 (pages 90-92). Now, you can use differentiation to find the stationary points of the curves — this will help you sketch a more **accurate** graph.

Tip: Remember — the highest power in a cubic equation is 3 (i.e. x^3) and the highest power in a quadratic is 2 (i.e. x^2). You won't have to sketch graphs of any higher powers in C1.

Example 1

Sketch the graph of $y = x^3 - 4x^2 + 4x$, showing clearly the coordinates of the stationary points.

- Start by finding where the curve **crosses the axes**.
  When $x = 0$, $y = 0$, so the curve goes through the origin.
  Find the other points where it meets the x-axis by solving the equation $f(x) = 0$:
  $$x^3 - 4x^2 + 4x = 0 \quad \Rightarrow \quad x(x^2 - 4x + 4) = 0 \quad \Rightarrow \quad x(x-2)(x-2) = 0$$
  $$\Rightarrow \boxed{x = 0 \text{ or } x = 2}$$

Tip: $x = 2$ is a double root so the curve only touches the x-axis here — see the example on page 91.

- Use differentiation to find the coordinates of the stationary points:
  $$y = x^3 - 4x^2 + 4x.$$
  $$\text{So } \frac{dy}{dx} = 3x^2 - 8x + 4.$$

  Setting this equal to zero and solving for x:
  $3x^2 - 8x + 4 = 0 \Rightarrow (3x - 2)(x - 2) = 0$. So $x = \frac{2}{3}$ and $x = 2$.
  At $x = \frac{2}{3}$, $y = (\frac{2}{3})^3 - 4(\frac{2}{3})^2 + 4(\frac{2}{3}) = \frac{32}{27}$.
  At $x = 2$, $y = (2)^3 - 4(2)^2 + 4(2) = 0$.

  So the coordinates of the stationary points are $\boxed{(\frac{2}{3}, \frac{32}{27}) \text{ and } (2, 0).}$

- Differentiate again to see if they're maximum or minimum points:
  $$\frac{d^2y}{dx^2} = 6x - 8.$$
  When $x = \frac{2}{3}$, $\frac{d^2y}{dx^2} = -4$ so it's a $\boxed{\text{maximum.}}$
  When $x = 2$, $\frac{d^2y}{dx^2} = 4$ so it's a $\boxed{\text{minimum.}}$

- So, the curve goes through the origin and touches the x-axis at $x = 2$.
  It has a local maximum at $(\frac{2}{3}, \frac{32}{27})$ and a local minimum at $(2, 0)$.
  Use this information to sketch the graph:

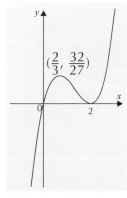

Tip: Remember from p.90-91 that if the curve has a positive coefficient of x^3, it'll go from bottom-left to top-right and have the characteristic cubic 'wiggle'.

Exercise 3.5

Q1 Sketch the graphs of the functions, showing clearly where they meet the coordinate axes and the coordinates of the stationary points:

   a) $y = (x + 1)(2x - 1)(x - 3)$

   b) $y = x^2(2x - 5)$

   c) $y = x(5 - x)^2$

   d) $y = -5x^2(3x - 2)$

Q1 Hint: It's OK to use a calculator if you need to — you won't get numbers as tricky as this in the exam.

4. Real-Life Problems

Learning Objective:

- Be able to describe a real-life situation in mathematical terms and use differentiation to find maximum and minimum solutions.

In real-life contexts you can use differentiation to find an optimum solution to a problem — e.g. finding the maximum size you can get out of a set amount of material, or finding the minimum material you need to use to make an object of given size.

Differentiation in real-life problems

Because differentiation can be used to find the maximum value of a function, it can be used in **real-life problems** to maximise a quantity subject to certain factors, e.g maximising the volume of a box that can be made with a set amount of cardboard.

To find the maximum value of something, all you need is an equation **in terms of only one variable** (e.g. x) — then just **differentiate as normal**.
Often there'll be too many variables in the question, so you've got to know how to manipulate the information to get rid of the unwanted variables.

Example 1

Ceara the farmer wants to build a rectangular sheep pen with length x m and width y m. She has 20 m of fencing in total, and wants the area inside the pen to be as large as possible. How long should each side of the pen be, and what will the area inside the pen be?

- Start by writing down an expression for the **area** of the pen:

$$\boxed{\text{Area} = \text{length} \times \text{width} = xy \text{ m}^2}$$

- This has **too many variables** for you to be able to work with, so you need to find an expression for y in terms of x. You know how much fencing is available, so find an expression for that in terms of x and y and rearrange it to make y the subject.

$$\text{Perimeter} = 20 \text{ m} = 2x + 2y \quad \Rightarrow \quad y = \frac{20 - 2x}{2} = 10 - x.$$

- Now you can substitute this into the expression you wrote down for the area and use **differentiation** to **maximise** it:

$$A = xy = x(10 - x) = 10x - x^2 \quad \Rightarrow \quad \frac{dA}{dx} = 10 - 2x$$

- Now just find when $\frac{dA}{dx} = 0$

$$\frac{dA}{dx} = 0 \quad \Rightarrow \quad 10 - 2x = 0, \quad \text{so} \quad x = 5 \quad \Rightarrow \quad y = 10 - x = 5$$

- To check that this is a maximum, **differentiate again**:

$$\frac{d^2A}{dx^2} = -2, \text{ which is negative, so this is a maximum.}$$

- So both x and y should be $\boxed{5}$ and the total area inside the pen will be $5 \times 5 = \boxed{25 \text{ m}^2}$.

Example 2

A jewellery box with a lid has dimensions $2x$ cm by x cm by y cm and a total surface area of 108 cm².

Show that the volume of the box can be expressed as: $V = 36x - \dfrac{4x^3}{3}$, and use calculus to find the maximum volume.

> **Tip:** 'Use calculus' here just means differentiate.

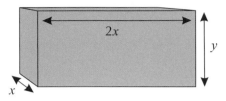

- You know the basic equation for volume:

    $V =$ length × width × height $= 2x \times x \times y = \boxed{2x^2y}$

- This has a y that you want to **get rid of** so look for a way of **replacing** y with an equation in x (like in Example 1). You can do this by finding an expression for the surface area of the box and rearranging:

    Surface area $= 2 \times [(2x \times x) + (2x \times y) + (x \times y)] = 108$

    $$\Rightarrow \quad 4x^2 + 6xy = 108$$

    $$\Rightarrow \quad y = \frac{108 - 4x^2}{6x} = \frac{18}{x} - \frac{2x}{3}$$

- And now you can substitute this into the expression for the volume of the box:

    $$V = 2x^2y = 2x^2\left(\frac{18}{x} - \frac{2x}{3}\right) = \boxed{36x - \frac{4x^3}{3}}$$

- Now just **differentiate** and find x at the **stationary point(s)**:

    $$V = 36x - \frac{4x^3}{3} \quad \Rightarrow \quad \frac{dV}{dx} = 36 - 4x^2$$

    When $\dfrac{dV}{dx} = 0$, $36 - 4x^2 = 0 \quad \Rightarrow \quad x^2 = \dfrac{36}{4} = 9 \quad \Rightarrow \quad x = \pm 3$

> **Tip:** x is a length so it can't have a negative value (−3).

- Check that $x = 3$ is actually a maximum, then just calculate V with $x = 3$:

    $\dfrac{d^2V}{dx^2} = -8x$. So when $x = 3$, $\dfrac{d^2V}{dx^2} = -24$ (so it's a maximum)

    $V = 36x - \dfrac{4x^3}{3}$. So when $x = 3$, $V = 36(3) - \dfrac{4(3)^3}{3} = \boxed{72 \text{ cm}^3}$

Differentiation isn't just limited to cuboids — it can be used on **any shape** as long as you can describe its (surface) area or volume with variables (i.e x, y).

Exercise 4.1

Q1 Hint: It might look like you're not given enough information here, but just call the length x and the width y and you're on your way.

Q1 A rectangular vegetable patch is enclosed by a wall on one side and fencing on three sides as shown in the diagram.

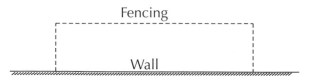

Use calculus to show that the maximum possible area that can be enclosed by 66 m of fencing is 544.5 m².

Q2 A ball is catapulted vertically with an initial speed of 30 m/s. After t seconds the height h of the ball, in m, is given by $h = 30t - 7.5t^2$.
Use calculus to find the maximum height the ball reaches.

Q3 A child makes a box by taking a piece of card 30 × 30 cm and cutting squares with side length x cm, as shown in the diagram. The sides are then folded up to make a box.

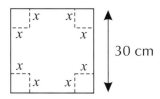

a) Write down a formula for the volume of the box V.

b) Find the maximum possible volume of the box.

Q4 Hint: It's OK to use a calculator here if you need to — you won't get numbers this hard in the exam.

Q4 The height of a roller coaster, h m, above ground level is given by the equation $h = \dfrac{1}{100}\left(\dfrac{x^4}{1200} - \dfrac{11}{90}x^3 + 4x^2\right)$ where x is the distance in metres along the track. The track is 97.5 m long and goes underground at some points. A ride photo of the roller coaster can only be taken when h is stationary.

a) Find $\dfrac{dh}{dx}$.

b) Find $\dfrac{d^2h}{dx^2}$.

The ride starts at $x = 0$.

c) Verify that this is a stationary point.

d) At which other distances along the track can ride photos be taken?

Q4 d) Hint: This is basically just asking you to find the other stationary points for h.

It is easier to take a photo when the ride is at a minimum point because the track is more accessible.

e) At what distance along the track should the ride photo be taken?

Review Exercise — Chapter 7

Q1 Differentiate the following functions from first principles:
   a) $y = x + 1$
   b) $y = 4x^2$
   c) $y = 3x$

Q2 Differentiate these functions with respect to x:
   a) $y = x^2 + 2$,
   b) $y = x^4 + x^2$,
   c) $y = x^2 - 3x + 12x^3$

Q3 What's the connection between the gradient of a curve at a point and the gradient of the tangent to the curve at the same point?

Q4 What's the connection between the gradient of a curve at a point and the gradient of the normal to the curve at the same point?

Q5 Find the gradients of these graphs at $x = 2$:
   a)
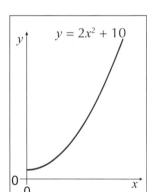
$y = 2x^2 + 10$
   b)
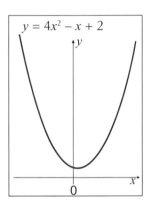
$y = 4x^2 - x + 2$
   c)
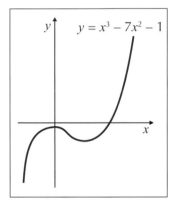
$y = x^3 - 7x^2 - 1$

Q6 Water is poured into a bowl. The volume (v) of water in the bowl (in ml) after t seconds is given by the function: $v = 3t^2 + 4$ with $0 \le t \le 10$.
   a) How much water is in the bowl initially?
   b) Find the rate at which water is being poured into the bowl when $t = 4$ seconds.

Q7 Find the equation of the tangent to the curve $y = x^3 + 4x^2 + 2x$ at $x = 1$.

Q8 Find the equations of the tangent and the normal to the curve $y = x^3 - 3x - 10$ at $x = 3$.

Q9 Consider the curve C given by the equation $y = x^2 - 6$ and the line L given by the equation $y = 3$.
   a) Find the coordinates of the points, A and B, where C and L intersect.
   b) Find the gradient of C at points A and B.
   c) Find the equations of the normals to C at A and B.

   The normals at points A and B meet the point D.
   d) Find the coordinates of the point D.

Q10 Consider the curve C given by the equation $y = x^3 - 2x^2 + 1$, $x > 0$,
and the line L given by the equation $y = 1$.
a) Write down the gradient of the line L for any x.
b) Find the point at which the curve C has the same gradient as the line L.
c) Hence give the equation of the tangent to C at this point.

Q11 Find the equations of the tangent and the normal to the curve $y = 1 + x^3$ at $x = 2$.

Q12 A particle moves along a path described by the equation $x = t^3 - 8t$, $t > 0$,
where t is the time in seconds and x is the distance from the starting position in metres.
a) Find the speed $\frac{dx}{dt}$ of the particle as a function of t.
b) Find x and t when the speed is 19 ms^{-1}.
c) Find the acceleration $\frac{d^2x}{dt^2}$ of the particle as a function of t.
d) Find the acceleration, in ms^{-2}, after 2 seconds.
e) Find the speed, in ms^{-1}, when the acceleration is 24 ms^{-2}.

Q13 Consider the curve with equation $y = f(x)$, where $f(x) = x^3 - 3x$.
a) Work out the gradient of this curve when $x = -1$.
b) Show that $2f''(x) - 3f'(x) + f(x) = x^3 + 9(1 + x - x^2)$.

Q14 Let $f(x) = x^4$. Find $f''(x) + 2f'(x) - 4f(x)$.

Q15 Find the stationary points of the graph of $y = x^3 - 6x^2 - 63x + 21$.

Q16 Find all the stationary points of the graph of $y = 2x^4 - x^2 + 4$ and determine their nature.

Q17 Find when the function $y = 6(x + 2)(x - 3)$ is increasing and decreasing.

Q18 Sketch the graph of $y = 3x^3 - 16x$, clearly showing the coordinates of any turning points.

Q19 Sketch the graph of $y = -3x^3 + 6x^2$, clearly showing the coordinates of any turning points.

Q15, 18-20 Hint: Use a calculator for these questions if you need to.

Q20 The height (h m) a firework can reach is related to the mass (m g) of fuel it carries as shown below:

$$h = \frac{m^2}{10} - \frac{m^3}{800}, \text{ for } 0 < m < 80$$

Find the mass of fuel required to achieve the maximum height and state what the maximum height is to 3 s.f.

1   The curve C is given by the equation $y = 2x^3 - 4x^2 - 4x + 12$.

 a)   Find $\dfrac{dy}{dx}$.

(2 marks)

 b)   Find the gradient of the tangent to the curve at the point where $x = 2$.

(1 mark)

 c)   Hence find an equation for the normal to the curve at this point.

(3 marks)

2   a)   Find $\dfrac{dy}{dx}$ for the curve $y = 4x^3 - 15x^2 + 12x + 6$.

(2 marks)

 b)   Hence, find the coordinates of the stationary points on the curve.

(5 marks)

 c)   Determine the nature of each stationary point.

(3 marks)

3   Ayesha is building a closed-back bookcase. She uses a total of 72 m² of wood (not including shelving) to make a bookcase that is x metres high, $\dfrac{x}{2}$ metres wide and d metres deep, as shown.

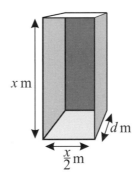

 a)   Show that the full capacity of the bookcase is given by: $V = 12x - \dfrac{x^3}{12}$.

(4 marks)

 b)   Find the value of x for which V is stationary. Leave your answer in surd form.

(4 marks)

 c)   Show that this is a maximum point and hence calculate the exact value of the maximum V.

(4 marks)

4   The curve C is given by $y = f(x)$, where $f(x) = 3x + 4 + x^4$, $x > 0$.

 a)   Find $f'(x)$.

(1 mark)

 b)   Given that $f'(x) = 111$, find x.

(2 marks)

5   The curve C is given by the equation $y = mx^3 - x^2 + 8x + 2$, for a constant m.

a)   Find $\dfrac{dy}{dx}$.

(2 marks)

The point P lies on C, and has the x-value 5.
The normal to C at P is parallel to the line given by the equation $y + 4x - 3 = 0$.

b)   Find the gradient of curve C at P.

(3 marks)

c)   (i)   Hence find the value of m,

(3 marks)

(ii)   and the y-value at P.

(2 marks)

6   The function $f(x) = \dfrac{1}{2}x^4 - 2x$ has a single stationary point.

a)   Find the coordinates of the stationary point.

(3 marks)

b)   Determine the nature of the stationary point.

(2 marks)

c)   State the range of values of x for which $f(x)$ is:

(i)   increasing,

(1 mark)

(ii)   decreasing.

(1 mark)

7   a)   Determine the coordinates of the stationary points for the curve
$y = x(x^2 + 4x - 3)$.

(4 marks)

b)   Find whether each of these points is a maximum or minimum.

(3 marks)

c)   Sketch the curve of y, showing where the curve crosses the axes.

(3 marks)

8   For $x \geq 0$ and $y \geq 0$, x and y satisfy the equation $2x - y = 6$.

a)   If $W = x^2 y^2$, show that $W = 4x^4 - 24x^3 + 36x^2$.

(2 marks)

b)   (i)   Show that $\dfrac{dW}{dx} = k(2x^3 - 9x^2 + 9x)$, and find the value of the integer k.

(3 marks)

(ii)   Find the value of $\dfrac{dW}{dx}$ when $x = 1$.

(1 mark)

c)   Find $\dfrac{d^2 W}{dx^2}$ and give its value when $x = 1$.

(2 marks)

1. Indefinite Integration

Integration is just the process of getting from $\dfrac{dy}{dx}$ back to y itself.

Indefinite integration

Integration is the '**opposite**' of differentiation. When you integrate something, you're trying to find a function that returns to **what you started with** when you differentiate it. This function is called an **integral**.

The integral of a **function** f(x) with respect to x is written:

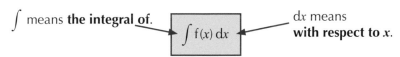

$\int$ means **the integral of**. $\int f(x)\,dx$ dx means **with respect to x**.

For example, 'the integral of $2x$ with respect to x' is written $\int 2x\,dx$. The answer could be **any function** which differentiates to give $2x$.

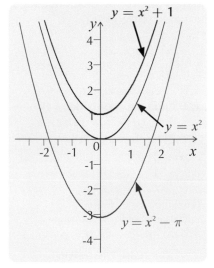

$y = x^2 + 1$

$y = x^2$

$y = x^2 - \pi$

From Chapter 7, we know that:

$$\frac{d}{dx}(x^2) = 2x$$

$$\frac{d}{dx}(x^2 + 1) = 2x$$

$$\frac{d}{dx}(x^2 - \pi) = 2x$$

If you differentiate any of these functions, you get $2x$ — they're **all possible integrals** because they all have the **same gradient**.

In fact, if you differentiate **any** function which is of the form $x^2 +$ '**a constant**' — you'll get $2x$.

So the answer to this integral is actually...

$$\int 2x\,dx = x^2 + C$$

C is a constant representing 'any number'— it's known as the **constant of integration**.

This is an example of **indefinite integration** — a good way to remember this is that C can take an **indefinite number** of values. There are **lots of answers** to an indefinite integral, so you need to add a **constant of integration** to show that it could be **any number**.

Learning Objectives:

- Be able to use the integral symbol $\int$.
- Be able to integrate powers of x.
- Be able to integrate more complicated functions containing powers of x.
- Be able to find the equation of a curve, given the gradient and a point on the curve.

Tip: Remember that differentiating a constant always gives zero.

Integrating x^n

The formula below tells you how to integrate **powers of x**.

$$\int x^n \, \mathrm{d}x = \frac{x^{n+1}}{n+1} + C$$

This just says:

To integrate a power of x: (i) **Increase the power** by one
                — then divide by it.

                and   (ii) Add a **constant**.

Example 1

Find $\int x^3 \, \mathrm{d}x$.

Increase the power to 4...

$$\int x^3 \, \mathrm{d}x = \frac{x^4}{4} + C$$

...divide by 4....

...and add a constant of integration.

Tip: It's easy to forget the constant of integration and lose easy marks. Make sure you get used to adding it on.

You can always check that you've got the right answer by differentiating it — you should end up with the thing you started with:

$$\frac{\mathrm{d}}{\mathrm{d}x}\left(\frac{x^4}{4} + C\right) = \frac{\mathrm{d}}{\mathrm{d}x}\left(\frac{x^4}{4}\right) + \frac{\mathrm{d}}{\mathrm{d}x}(C) = x^3 + 0 = x^3$$

If the power of x is multiplied by a **constant**, you can take it **outside** the integral like this:

$$\int ax^n \, \mathrm{d}x = a \int x^n \, \mathrm{d}x$$

Example 2

Find $\int 12x^5 \, \mathrm{d}x$.

Take the 12 outside the integral...

...increase the power by 1 to 6...

$$\int 12x^5 \, \mathrm{d}x = 12 \int x^5 \, \mathrm{d}x = 12\left(\frac{x^6}{6}\right) + C = 2x^6 + C$$

...divide by 6...

...and add a constant of integration.

Tip: You don't need to multiply the constant by 12 as it represents any number.

Check your answer is correct by differentiating:

$$\frac{\mathrm{d}}{\mathrm{d}x}(2x^6 + C) = \frac{\mathrm{d}}{\mathrm{d}x}(2x^6) + \frac{\mathrm{d}}{\mathrm{d}x}(C) = 12x^5 + 0 = 12x^5$$

Example 3

Find $\int 4\,dx$.

There's no x^n here, but $x^0 = 1$, so you can multiply by x^0 without changing anything.

$$\int 4\,dx = \int 4x^0\,dx$$

————Increase the power from 0 to 1.

$$= \frac{4x^1}{1} + C$$

————Divide by the power.

$$= 4x + C$$

Tip: The integral $\int n\,dx$ where n is any constant value, will always be $nx + C$.

Exercise 1.1

Q1 Find an expression for y when $\frac{dy}{dx}$ is the following:

a) x^7 b) $2x^3$ c) $8x$ d) $-5x^4$ e) x^6

f) $4x^4$ g) $-6x^5$ h) -12 i) x^0 j) 40

Q2 Find the following:

a) $\int x^2\,dx$ b) $\int 7x^4\,dx$ c) $\int \frac{x}{2}\,dx$

d) $\int 3x^3\,dx$ e) $\int 14x\,dx$ f) $\int -1.2x^2\,dx$

g) $\int -2x^4\,dx$ h) $\int -\frac{3}{2}x^2\,dx$ i) $\int -\frac{4}{3}x^3\,dx$

Integrating functions

Just like differentiating, if there are **lots of terms** in an expression, you can just integrate each bit **separately**, like this:

$$\int (f(x) + g(x))\,dx = \int f(x)\,dx + \int g(x)\,dx$$

Examples

Find $\int (3x^2 - 2x + 7)\,dx$.

Take the constants outside the integral.

$$\int (3x^2 - 2x + 7)\,dx = 3\int x^2\,dx - 2\int x\,dx + 7\int x^0\,dx$$

Integrate each term separately.

$$= \frac{3x^3}{3} - \frac{2x^2}{2} + \frac{7x^1}{1} + C$$

Just add one constant of integration.

$$= x^3 - x^2 + 7x + C$$

Tip: When you're doing lots of separate integrations, you only need one constant of integration for the whole expression — if each integral gives a constant, you can just add them up to get a new constant.

Find y if $\dfrac{dy}{dx} = \dfrac{1}{2}x^3 - 4x^2x^3$.

Integrate the
derivative of
y to get y.

$$y = \int \frac{dy}{dx}\,dx = \int \left(\tfrac{1}{2}x^3 - 4x^2x^3\right)dx$$
$$= \int \left(\tfrac{1}{2}x^3 - 4x^5\right)dx$$
$$= \tfrac{1}{2} \times \frac{x^4}{4} + (-4) \times \frac{x^6}{6} + C$$
$$= \frac{x^4}{8} - \frac{2}{3}x^6 + C$$

Find $\displaystyle\int 4(x-1)(x+2)\,dx$.   Split into separate terms.

Tip: Some expressions
will need simplifying
before you integrate
with the formula for
powers of x.

$$\int 4(x-1)(x+2)\,dx = \int 4(x^2 + x - 2)\,dx = \int (4x^2 + 4x - 8)\,dx$$

Do each of these
bits separately.

$$= \frac{4x^3}{3} + \frac{4x^2}{2} - 8x + C$$
$$= \frac{4x^3}{3} + 2x^2 - 8x + C$$

Exercise 1.2

Q1 Hint: Remember
f′(x) is just another way
of saying $\frac{dy}{dx}$.

When you integrate f′(x)
you get f(x) and when
you differentiate f(x) you
get f′(x).

Q1 Find f(x) when f′(x) is given by the following:

a) $5x + 3x^4$ b) $4x(x^2 - 1)$ c) $(x-3)^2$

d) $x\left(6x^2 + \tfrac{1}{4}x\right)$ e) $\left(x + \tfrac{1}{2}\right)^2$ f) $x(3x - 2)$

g) $6x^3 - x^5$ h) $-2 - 7x^2x^4$ i) $5x^3 - 3x + 7$

Q2 Find the following integrals:

a) $\displaystyle\int (0.8x - 3x^2)\,dx$ b) $\displaystyle\int (8x^3 - 2x + 5x^2)\,dx$

c) $\displaystyle\int ((x^2)^3 + x)\,dx$ d) $\displaystyle\int (x(7x^2 - 1 - 2x))\,dx$

e) $\displaystyle\int ((3x^2 - 5x)^2)\,dx$ f) $\displaystyle\int \left(\frac{2x^3 - x}{x}\right)dx$

g) $\displaystyle\int (10x^2 + x + 4)\,dx$ h) $\displaystyle\int ((5x - 3)^2)\,dx$

i) $\displaystyle\int (x(3 - x)^2)\,dx$ j) $\displaystyle\int ((x + 1)(x^2 - 2))\,dx$

Q3 Given that $\dfrac{dy}{dx} = 1.5x^2 - 4x$, find y.

Q4 Given that $f'(x) = 4x^3 + 5x^2$, find f(x).

Q5 Find $\displaystyle\int \left(x\left(\tfrac{3}{2}x^3 - x^2 + 1\right)\right)dx$.

Q6 Find: a) $\displaystyle\int \left(\frac{(x^2 + x)(x + 1)}{x}\right)dx$ b) $\displaystyle\int \left(x\left(x - \tfrac{x}{2}\right)^2\right)dx$.

Integrating to find equations of curves

As you saw in Chapter 7, **differentiating** the equation of a curve gives its **gradient**. **Integrating** the gradient of a curve does the **opposite** — it gives you the **equation** of the curve.

But integrating actually gives you **many** possible curves because of the **constant of integration**, C. C can take any value and each different value represents a different curve (all translations of each other in the y-direction).

So to find the equation of a **particular curve** by integration you need to know the coordinates of **one point** on it, which you can use to find C.

Example 1

The curve $y = f(x)$ goes through the point (2, 16) and $\dfrac{dy}{dx} = 2x^3$.
Find the equation of the curve.

You know the derivative $\dfrac{dy}{dx}$ and need to find y.

$$\frac{dy}{dx} = 2x^3$$

So integrating gives...

$$y = \int 2x^3 \, dx = \frac{2x^4}{4} + C = \boxed{\frac{x^4}{2} + C}$$

Check this is correct by differentiating it and making sure you get what you started with.

$$y = \frac{x^4}{2} + C$$
$$\frac{dy}{dx} = \frac{1}{2}(4x^3) + 0$$
$$\frac{dy}{dx} = 2x^3$$

So this function's got the correct derivative — but you've not finished yet. You now need to find C — and you do this by using the fact that it goes through the point (2, 16).

$$y = \frac{x^4}{2} + C$$

Putting $x = 2$ and $y = 16$ in the above equation gives...

$$16 = \frac{2^4}{2} + C$$
$$\Rightarrow 16 - 2^3 + C$$
$$\Rightarrow \boxed{C = 8}$$

So the solution you need is:

$$\boxed{y = \frac{x^4}{2} + 8}$$

Example 2

The curve $y = f(x)$ goes through the point (2, 8) and $f'(x) = 6x(x - 1)$. Find $f(x)$.

You know $f'(x)$ and need to find the function $f(x)$.

$$f'(x) = 6x(x - 1) = 6x^2 - 6x$$

So integrate...

$$f(x) = \int (6x^2 - 6x)\, dx$$

$$\Rightarrow f(x) = \frac{6x^3}{3} - \frac{6x^2}{2} + C$$

$$\Rightarrow f(x) = 2x^3 - 3x^2 + C$$

Check this is correct by differentiating...

$$f(x) = 2x^3 - 3x^2 + C$$
$$f'(x) = 2(3x^2) - 3(2x^1)$$
$$f'(x) = 6x^2 - 6x$$

You now need to find C using the point (2, 8).

Put $x = 2$ and $y = 8$ into $f(x) = 2x^3 - 3x^2 + C$.

$$8 = (2 \times 2^3) - (3 \times 2^2) + C$$
$$\Rightarrow 8 = 16 - 12 + C$$
$$\Rightarrow C = 4$$

Tip: It may seem odd to substitute the value of y into an equation without any y's, but remember that y is just the same as $f(x)$, so put the value for y wherever you see $f(x)$.

So the answer is: $f(x) = 2x^3 - 3x^2 + 4$

It's a cubic equation — and the graph looks like this...

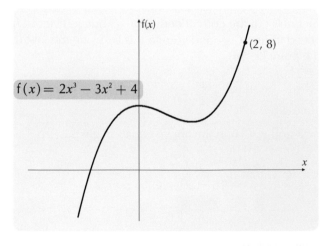

Exercise 1.3

Q1 For each of the following, the curve $y = f(x)$ passes through the given point. Find $f(x)$.

a) $f'(x) = 4x^3$, $(0, 5)$

b) $f'(x) = 3x^2 - 4x + 3$, $(1, -3)$

c) $f'(x) = 6x(x + 2)$, $(-1, 1)$

d) $f'(x) = 5x^2 + 2x$, $(2, 5)$

e) $f'(x) = 3x^2(x - 4)$, $(2, -10)$

f) $f'(x) = (3x + 1)(x - 1)$, $(3, -3)$

g) $f'(x) = x(x + 3x^2)$, $(-1, 0)$

h) $f'(x) = \dfrac{9x^3 + 2x^2}{x}$, $(-1, 2)$

Q2 A curve that passes through the point $(2, -3)$ has derivative
$$\frac{dy}{dx} = (x - 2)(3x - 4)$$
Find the equation of the curve.

Q3 A curve $y = f(x)$ that passes through the point $(4, 9)$ has gradient function
$$f'(x) = 3x^2 + 2x$$
Find the equation of the curve.

> **Q3 Hint:** The gradient function is just the function which tells you the gradient — i.e. the derivative.

Q4 The gradient function of a curve is given by
$$\frac{dy}{dx} = 3x + x^2$$
Find the equation of the curve if it passes through the point $(1, 7)$.

Q5 Consider $\dfrac{dy}{dt} = (t - 3)^2$.
Given that $y = 9$ when $t = 4$, find y as a function of t.

Q6 The curve $y = f(x)$ goes through the point $\left(1, \frac{1}{3}\right)$ and $f'(x) = x(5x - 1)$. Find $f(x)$.

Q7 The curve $y = f(x)$ has derivative $f'(x) = x^2 + \frac{x}{2} + 3$ and passes through the point $(1, -1)$. Find the equation of the curve.

Q8 The gradient function of a curve is given by $\dfrac{dy}{dx} = \dfrac{x^2 - 6x}{x} + 2$.
Find the equation of the curve if it passes through the point $(3, -1)$.

2. Definite Integration

Learning Objectives:

- Be able to calculate definite integrals.
- Be able to find the area between a curve and the x-axis using definite integration.
- Be able to use integration to calculate the area between a line and a curve or the area between two curves.

Once you know how to integrate, you can use it to find areas under curves — this is known as definite integration.

Definite integrals

Definite integrals have **limits** (little numbers) next to the integral sign. The limits just tell you the **range of x-values** to integrate the function between.

> The definite integral of **f(x)** with respect to x between the limits $x = a$ and $x = b$ is written:
>
> The upper limit goes here.
>
> $$\int_a^b f(x)\,dx$$
>
> The lower limit goes here.

Finding a definite integral isn't really any harder than an indefinite one — there's just an **extra stage** you have to do.

- Integrate the function as normal but **don't** add a **constant of integration**.
- Once you've integrated the function, work out the **value** of the definite integral by **putting in the limits**:

Tip: You might be asked to 'evaluate' a definite integral — this just means 'find the value'.

Tip: The proper way to write out definite integrals is to use square brackets with the limits to the right as shown.

> If you know that the integral of f(x) is $\int f(x)\,dx = g(x) + C$ then:
>
> $$\int_a^b f(x)\,dx = [g(x)]_a^b = g(b) - g(a)$$
>
> **Subtract** the value of g at the **lower** limit from the value of g at the **upper** limit.

Example

Evaluate $\displaystyle\int_1^3 (x^2 + 2)\,dx$**.**

- Find the integral in the normal way — but put the integrated function in **square brackets** and rewrite the **limits** on the right-hand side.

$$\int_1^3 (x^2 + 2)\,dx = \left[\frac{x^3}{3} + 2x\right]_1^3$$

Notice that there's no constant of integration.

- Put in the limits:

Put the upper limit into the integral... ...then subtract the value of the integral at the lower limit.

$$\left[\frac{x^3}{3} + 2x\right]_1^3 = \left(\frac{3^3}{3} + 6\right) - \left(\frac{1^3}{3} + 2\right)$$

$$= 15 - \frac{7}{3} = \frac{38}{3}$$

Tip: A definite integral always comes out as a number.

The area under a curve

The value of a **definite integral** represents the **area** between the curve of the function you're integrating and the x-axis, between the two limits.

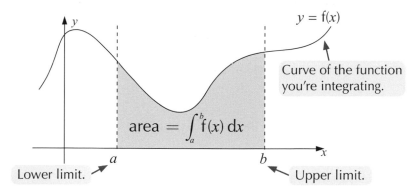

area $= \int_a^b f(x)\,dx$

Lower limit.

Upper limit.

Curve of the function you're integrating.

$y = f(x)$

Example

Find the area between the graph of $y = x^2$, the x-axis and the lines $x = -1$ and $x = 2$.

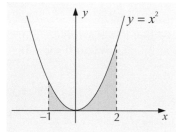

You just need to integrate the function $f(x) = x^2$ between -1 and 2 with respect to x.

The limits of integration are -1 and 2.

$f(x) = x^2$

Put in the limits

$$\int_{-1}^2 x^2\,dx = \left[\frac{x^3}{3}\right]_{-1}^2 = \left(\frac{2^3}{3}\right) - \left(\frac{(-1)^3}{3}\right) = \frac{8}{3} + \frac{1}{3} = \frac{9}{3} = 3$$

So the area is 3.

If you integrate part of a curve that lies **below** the x-axis, it'll give a **negative** value.

If you need to find an area like this, you'll need to make your answer **positive** at the end as you can't have **negative** area.

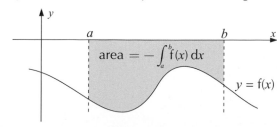

area $= -\int_a^b f(x)\,dx$

$y = f(x)$

Tip: It's important to note that you're actually finding the area between the curve and the **x-axis**, not the area under the curve (the area below a curve that lies under the x-axis will be infinite).

Examples

a) Find the area between the graph of $y = x^3$ and the x-axis between $x = 0$ and $x = 2$.

- Just integrate the function between these limits:

$$\int_0^2 x^3 = \left[\frac{x^4}{4}\right]_0^2 = \frac{1}{4}[x^4]_0^2 = \frac{1}{4}(2^4 - 0^4) = \frac{16}{4} = \boxed{4}$$

Tip: Sometimes it's easier to take a common factor outside the square brackets — here, I've taken out ¼.

b) Find the area between the graph of $y = x^3$ and the x-axis between $x = -2$ and $x = 0$.

- Again, just integrate the function between these limits:

$$\int_{-2}^0 x^3 = \left[\frac{x^4}{4}\right]_{-2}^0 = \frac{1}{4}[x^4]_{-2}^0 = \frac{1}{4}(0^4 - (-2)^4) = -\frac{16}{4} = -4$$

This gives a negative answer, and area can't be negative — the area is just the positive value of this integral, so the area is $\boxed{4}$.

- You might have noticed that the answers to a) and b) are the same — if you have a look at the graph you'll see why:

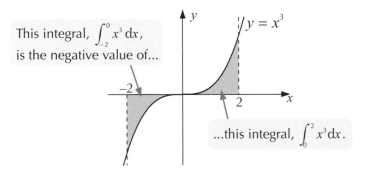

This integral, $\int_{-2}^0 x^3\,dx$, is the negative value of...

...this integral, $\int_0^2 x^3\,dx$.

- If you wanted to work out the total area between $x = -2$ and $x = 2$, you'd have to work out the positive and negative areas separately (as above) and then **add** them together.

Tip: You don't need to worry about this too much — in C1, you'll only be given curves that are completely above or completely below the x-axis.

- So the total area of the shaded region of the graph above is:

$$\text{Area} = 4 + 4 = \boxed{8}$$

- Notice that you can't just integrate between −2 and 2, as the positive and negative areas would cancel out and you'd be left with an area of 0 — but you can see from the graph that the area isn't 0.

$$\int_{-2}^2 x^3\,dx = \left[\frac{x^4}{4}\right]_{-2}^2 = \left(\frac{2^4}{4}\right) - \left(\frac{(-2)^4}{4}\right) = \frac{16}{4} - \frac{16}{4} = \boxed{0}$$

Q1 Find the value of the following:

a) $\displaystyle\int_1^3 3x^2 \, dx$

b) $\displaystyle\int_{-2}^0 (4x^3 + 2x) \, dx$

c) $\displaystyle\int_0^2 (x^3 + x) \, dx$

d) $\displaystyle\int_{-5}^{-2} (x + 1)^2 \, dx$

Q1 Hint: Don't let minus signs catch you out. Remember you're subtracting the whole bracket so if there's a minus sign in the bracket, the two negatives make a positive.

Q2 Given that $\displaystyle\int_0^a x^3 \, dx = 4$, find a, where $a > 0$.

Q3 Calculate the shaded area in the following diagrams:

a)
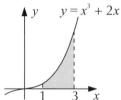

b)
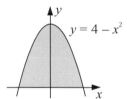

Q4 Find the area enclosed by the curve with equation $y = (x - 1)(3x + 9)$, the x-axis and the lines $x = -2$ and $x = 1$ (shown below).

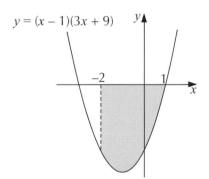

Q5 Find the area between the graph of $y = x^2 + x$, the x-axis and the lines $x = 1$ and $x = 3$.

Q5-6 Hint: Think about whether y is positive or negative in the given intervals.

Q6 Find the area enclosed by the graph of $y = 5x^3$, the x-axis and the lines $x = -2$ and $x = -1$.

Finding the area between curves and lines

You've seen how to find the area between a curve and the x-axis using integration, but you can also use integration to find the area between a **curve** and a **line** (or even **two curves**).

You'll either have to **add** or **subtract** integrals to find the area you're after — it's always best to **draw a diagram** showing the area you're interested in.

Example 1

Find the area enclosed by the curve $y = x^2$, the line $y = 2 - x$ and the x-axis.

- Draw a diagram of the curve and the line.

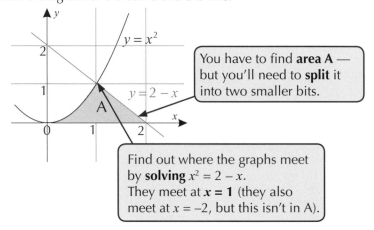

You have to find **area A** — but you'll need to **split** it into two smaller bits.

Find out where the graphs meet by **solving** $x^2 = 2 - x$. They meet at $x = 1$ (they also meet at $x = -2$, but this isn't in A).

Tip: You need to find the x-coordinate of the point of intersection between the line and the curve so that you know the limits to integrate between.

- The area A is the area under the **red** curve between 0 and 1 **added to** the area under the **blue** line between 1 and 2.

A_1 is the area under the curve $y = x^2$ between $x = 0$ and $x = 1$, so integrate between these limits to find the area:

$$A_1 = \int_0^1 x^2 \, dx = \left[\frac{x^3}{3}\right]_0^1 = \frac{1}{3} - 0 = \frac{1}{3}$$

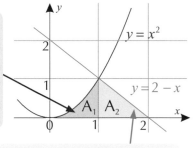

A_2 is the area under the line $y = 2 - x$ between $x = 1$ and $x = 2$, so integrate between these limits to find the area:

$$A_2 = \int_1^2 (2 - x) \, dx = \left[2x - \frac{x^2}{2}\right]_1^2$$
$$= \left(2(2) - \frac{2^2}{2}\right) - \left(2(1) - \frac{1^2}{2}\right)$$
$$= 2 - \frac{3}{2} = \frac{1}{2}$$

Tip: A_2 is just a triangle with base 1 and height 1, so you could also calculate its area using the formula for the area of a triangle.

- **Add** the areas together to find the area A:

$$A = A_1 + A_2 = \frac{1}{3} + \frac{1}{2} = \boxed{\frac{5}{6}}$$

Sometimes you'll need to find the area **enclosed** by the graphs of two functions — this usually means **subtracting** one area from another. Here is an example with two curves:

Example 2

Find the area enclosed by the curves $y = x^2 + 1$ and $y = 9 - x^2$.

- Draw a diagram of the two curves.

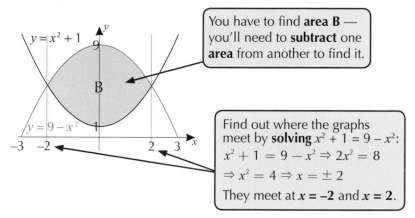

You have to find **area B** — you'll need to **subtract** one **area** from another to find it.

Find out where the graphs meet by **solving** $x^2 + 1 = 9 - x^2$:
$x^2 + 1 = 9 - x^2 \Rightarrow 2x^2 = 8$
$\Rightarrow x^2 = 4 \Rightarrow x = \pm 2$
They meet at $x = -2$ and $x = 2$.

- The area B is the area under the **blue** curve between $x = -2$ and $x = 2$ **minus** the area under the **red** curve between $x = -2$ and $x = 2$.

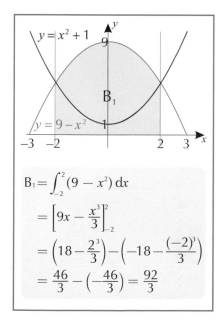

$$B_1 = \int_{-2}^{2}(9 - x^2)\,dx$$
$$= \left[9x - \frac{x^3}{3}\right]_{-2}^{2}$$
$$= \left(18 - \frac{2^3}{3}\right) - \left(-18 - \frac{(-2)^3}{3}\right)$$
$$= \frac{46}{3} - \left(-\frac{46}{3}\right) = \frac{92}{3}$$

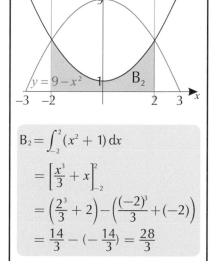

$$B_2 = \int_{-2}^{2}(x^2 + 1)\,dx$$
$$= \left[\frac{x^3}{3} + x\right]_{-2}^{2}$$
$$= \left(\frac{2^3}{3} + 2\right) - \left(\frac{(-2)^3}{3} + (-2)\right)$$
$$= \frac{14}{3} - \left(-\frac{14}{3}\right) = \frac{28}{3}$$

Tip: Instead of integrating each bit separately and then subtracting, you could try 'subtracting the curves' and then integrating.

Just subtract one curve from the other and then integrate the resulting expression over the limits.

So B can be expressed as $\int_{-2}^{2}(9 - x^2) - (x^2 + 1)\,dx$
Make sure you always subtract the lower curve from the upper curve — if you do it the wrong way round, you'll get a negative answer.

- **Subtract** B_2 from B_1 to find the area B:

$$B = B_1 - B_2 = \frac{92}{3} - \frac{28}{3} = \boxed{\frac{64}{3}}$$

Q1   Find the shaded area in the following diagrams:

a)

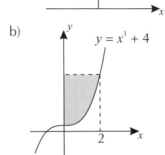

$y = 3x^2 + 4$
$y = 16$

b)

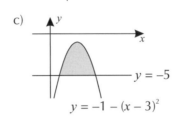

$y = x^3 + 4$

2

c)

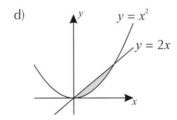

$y = -5$

$y = -1 - (x - 3)^2$

d)

$y = x^2$

$y = 2x$

Q2   Find the area enclosed by the curve $y = x^2 + 4$ and the line $y = x + 4$.

Q3   The area enclosed by the graphs of $y = x^2$ and $y = ax$ is 36, where a is a constant and $a > 0$. Find a.

Q4   Find the area enclosed by the curves $y = x^2$ and $y = 2 - x^4$.

Q5   Find the area enclosed by the curve $y = 4 - x^2$, the line $y = 4 - x$ and the x-axis.

Q6   Find the area enclosed by the curve $y = x^2 + x + 1$, the line $y = 4 - x$ and the x-axis for $x \geq 0$.

Review Exercise — Chapter 8

Q1 Find y in terms of x:

$$\frac{dy}{dx} = \frac{5}{7}x^4 + \frac{2}{3}x + \frac{1}{4}$$

Q2 Work out the equation of the curve that has derivative $\frac{dy}{dx} = 6x - 7$ and goes through the point $(1, 0)$.

Q3 The gradient function of a curve is given by
$$\frac{dy}{dx} = 2(3x - 6.5)$$
The curve passes through the point $(1, 2)$.
a) Find the equation of the curve.
b) Sketch the curve, stating the coordinates of the points where the curve crosses the axes.

Q4 A curve $y = f(x)$ that passes through the origin has derivative
$$\frac{dy}{dx} = 6x^2 + 6x - 5$$
a) Find the equation of the curve.
b) Factorise and hence sketch the curve, showing the points where the curve cuts the axes.

Q5 The curve C with equation $y = f(x)$ has derivative
$$f'(x) = 6x^2 - 12 + 2x$$
and passes through the point P with coordinates $(-2, 5)$.
Find the equation of the curve C.

Q6 Evaluate the following definite integrals:
a) $\displaystyle\int_0^1 (4x^3 + 3x^2 + 2x + 1)\,dx$ b) $\displaystyle\int_1^2 (12x^5 + 10x^4)\,dx$ c) $\displaystyle\int_0^1 (4x^7 - 3)\,dx$

Q7 a) Evaluate $\displaystyle\int_{-3}^3 (9 - x^2)\,dx$

b) Sketch the area represented by this integral.

Q8 Find area A in the diagrams below:
a)

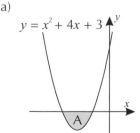

$y = x^2 + 4x + 3$

b)

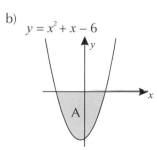

$y = x^2 + x - 6$

Q9 Use integration to find the shaded area, A, in each of these graphs:

a)

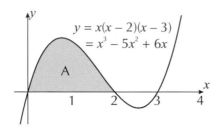

$y = x(x - 2)(x - 3)$
$= x^3 - 5x^2 + 6x$

A

b)

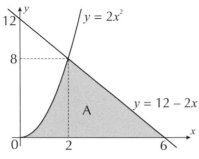

$y = 2x^2$

$y = 12 - 2x$

A

c)

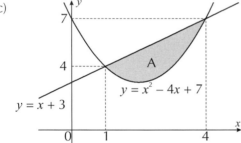

$y = x^2 - 4x + 7$

$y = x + 3$

A

Q10 Use integration to find the shaded area between the curves $y = 3 - 2x - x^2$ and $y = x^3 - 4x$, as shown below.

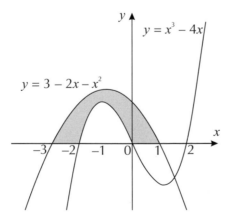

$y = x^3 - 4x$

$y = 3 - 2x - x^2$

1   a)   Show that $(5 + 2\sqrt{x})(5 - 2\sqrt{x})$ can be written in the form $a - bx$, stating the values of the constants a and b.

(2 marks)

    b)   Find $\int (5 + 2\sqrt{x})(5 - 2\sqrt{x})\,dx$.

(3 marks)

2   Find the value of $\int_{1}^{2} (2x - 6x^2 + x^3)\,dx$.

(5 marks)

3   The curve $y = (x - 2)^2(x + 1)$ is sketched on the diagram below:

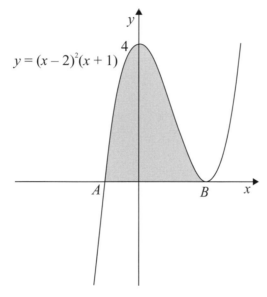

Calculate the shaded area under the curve between point A, where it intersects the x-axis, and point B, where it touches the x-axis.

(8 marks)

4   Curve C has equation $y = f(x)$, $x \neq 0$, where the derivative is given by $f'(x) = x^3 - 2x^2$.

The point $P\,(1, 2)$ lies on C.

    a)   Find the equation for the tangent to C at the point P, giving your answer in the form $y = mx + c$, where m and c are integers.

(3 marks)

    b)   Find $f(x)$.

(4 marks)

5    $f'(x) = (x - 1)(3x - 1)$ where $x > 0$.

   a)   The curve C is given by $y = f(x)$ and goes through point P (3, 10). Find $f(x)$.

   (6 marks)

   b)   The equation for the normal to C at the point P can be written
        in the form $y = \dfrac{a - x}{b}$ where a and b are integers.
        Find the values of a and b.

   (4 marks)

6   The curve C passes through the point P with coordinates (4, 1) and has derivative
     $$f'(x) = 2x - 6x^2 + \frac{x^3}{2}.$$

   a)   Find $f(x)$, simplifying your answer.

   (6 marks)

   b)   Find the equation of the tangent to C at P,
        giving your answer in the form $y = mx + c$.

   (4 marks)

7   The diagram below shows the curve $y = (x + 1)(x - 5)$.
     Points J (–1, 0) and K (4, –5) lie on the curve.

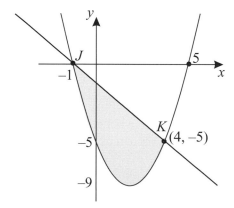

   a)   Find the equation of the straight line joining J and K in the form $y = mx + c$.

   (2 marks)

   b)   Calculate $\displaystyle\int_{-1}^{4} (x + 1)(x - 5)\,dx$.

   (5 marks)

   c)   Find the area of the shaded region.

   (4 marks)

Answers

Chapter 1: Algebra
1. Algebraic Expressions
Exercise 1.1 — Expanding brackets

Q1   **a)** $5(x + 4) = 5x + (5 \times 4) = 5x + 20$

  b) $a(4 - 2b) = 4a + (a \times -2b) = 4a - 2ab$

  c) $-2(x^2 + y) = -2x^2 - 2y$

  d) $pq(r - q) = pqr - pqq = pqr - pq^2$

  e) $6mn(m + 1) = 6mnm + 6mn = 6m^2n + 6mn$

  f) $7z^2(2 + z) = 14z^2 + 7z^2z = 14z^2 + 7z^3$

  g) $3xy(3 - x^2 - xy)$
$$= (3xy \times 3) + (3xy \times -x^2) + (3xy \times -xy)$$
$$= 9xy - 3x^3y - 3x^2y^2$$

  h) $-4ht(t^2 - 2ht - 3h^3)$
$$= -4ht \times t^2 + (-4ht \times -2ht) + (-4ht \times -3h^3)$$
$$= -4ht^3 + 8h^2t^2 + 12h^4t$$

  i) $7xy(x^2 + z^2) = (7xy \times x^2) + (7xy \times z^2)$
$$= 7x^3y + 7xyz^2$$

  j) $4(x + 2) + 3(x - 5) = 4x + 8 + 3x - 15$
$$= 7x - 7$$

  k) $p(3p^2 - 2q) + (q + 4p^3)$
$$= (p \times 3p^2) + (p \times -2q) + q + 4p^3$$
$$= 3p^3 - 2pq + q + 4p^3 = 7p^3 - 2pq + q$$
  Don't forget to simplify your answer if possible.

Q2   **a)** $(x + 5)(x - 3) = x^2 - 3x + 5x - 15$
$$= x^2 + 2x - 15$$

  b) $(2z + 3)(3z - 2) = 6z^2 - 4z + 9z - 6$
$$= 6z^2 + 5z - 6$$

  c) $(u + 8)^2 = (u + 8)(u + 8)$
$$= u^2 + 8u + 8u + 64$$
$$= u^2 + 16u + 64$$

  d) $(ab + cd)(ac + bd)$
$$= abac + abbd + cdac + cdbd$$
$$= a^2bc + ab^2d + ac^2d + bcd^2$$

  e) $(10 + f)(2f^2 - 3g)$
$$= 20f^2 - 30g + 2f^3 - 3fg$$

  f) $(7 + q)(7 - q) = 49 - 7q + 7q - q^2$
$$= 49 - q^2$$

  g) $(2 - 3w)^2 = (2 - 3w)(2 - 3w)$
$$= 2^2 - 6w - 6w + 9w^2$$
$$= 4 - 12w + 9w^2$$

  h) $(4rs^2 + 3)^2 = (4rs^2 + 3)(4rs^2 + 3)$
$$= 16r^2s^4 + 12rs^2 + 12rs^2 + 9$$
$$= 16r^2s^4 + 24rs^2 + 9$$

  i) $(5k^2l - 2kn)^2 = (5k^2l - 2kn)(5k^2l - 2kn)$
$$= 25k^4l^2 - 10k^3nl - 10k^3nl + 4k^2n^2$$
$$= 25k^4l^2 - 20k^3ln + 4k^2n^2$$

  In parts c), g), h) and i), you could get straight to the answer by using $(a + b)^2 = a^2 + 2ab + b^2$.

Q3   **a)** $(l + 5)(l^2 + 2l + 3)$
$$= l(l^2 + 2l + 3) + 5(l^2 + 2l + 3)$$
$$= l^3 + 2l^2 + 3l + 5l^2 + 10l + 15$$
$$= l^3 + 7l^2 + 13l + 15$$

  b) $(2 + q)(3 - q + 4q^2)$
$$= 2(3 - q + 4q^2) + q(3 - q + 4q^2)$$
$$= 6 - 2q + 8q^2 + 3q - q^2 + 4q^3$$
$$= 6 + q + 7q^2 + 4q^3$$

  c) $(m + 1)(m + 2)(m - 4)$
$$= (m^2 + 2m + m + 2)(m - 4)$$
$$= (m^2 + 3m + 2)(m - 4)$$
$$= m^2(m - 4) + 3m(m - 4) + 2(m - 4)$$
$$= m^3 - 4m^2 + 3m^2 - 12m + 2m - 8$$
$$= m^3 - m^2 - 10m - 8$$

  d) $(r + s)^3 = (r + s)(r + s)(r + s)$
$$= (r^2 + rs + sr + s^2)(r + s)$$
$$= (r^2 + 2rs + s^2)(r + s)$$
$$= r^2(r + s) + 2rs(r + s) + s^2(r + s)$$
$$= r^3 + r^2s + 2r^2s + 2rs^2 + rs^2 + s^3$$
$$= r^3 + 3r^2s + 3rs^2 + s^3$$

  e) $(4 + x + y)(1 - x - y)$
$$= 4(1 - x - y) + x(1 - x - y) + y(1 - x - y)$$
$$= 4 - 4x - 4y + x - x^2 - xy + y - xy - y^2$$
$$= 4 - 3x - 3y - 2xy - x^2 - y^2$$

  f) $(2c^2 - cd + d)(2d - c - 5c^2)$
$$= 2c^2(2d - c - 5c^2) - cd(2d - c - 5c^2)$$
$$\qquad\qquad + d(2d - c - 5c^2)$$
$$= 4c^2d - 2c^3 - 10c^4 - 2cd^2 + c^2d + 5c^3d$$
$$\qquad\qquad + 2d^2 - dc - 5c^2d$$
$$= -10c^4 - 2c^3 + 5c^3d - 2cd^2 - cd + 2d^2$$

Exercise 1.2 — Factorising

Q1   **a)** $9k + 15l = (3 \times 3k) + (3 \times 5l) = 3(3k + 5l)$

  b) $u^2 - uv = u(u - v)$

  c) $10w + 15 = (5 \times 2w) + (5 \times 3) = 5(2w + 3)$

  d) $2x^2y - 12xy^2 = (2xy \times x) - (2xy \times 6y)$
$$= 2xy(x - 6y)$$

  e) $f^2g^2 - fg = (fg \times fg) - (fg \times 1)$
$$= fg(fg - 1)$$

f) $3u^2v^2 + 5u^4v^4 + 12u^2v$

$= (u^2v \times 3v) + (u^2v \times 5u^2v^3) + (u^2v \times 12)$

$= u^2v(3v + 5u^2v^3 + 12)$

g) $p^3 + 3pq^3 + 2p$

$= (p \times p^2) + (p \times 3q^3) + (p \times 2)$

$= p(p^2 + 3q^3 + 2)$

h) $abcde - bcdef - cdefg$

$= (cde \times ab) - (cde \times bf) - (cde \times fg)$

$= cde(ab - bf - fg)$

i) $11xy^2 - 11x^2y - 11x^2y^2$

$= (11xy \times y) - (11xy \times x) - (11xy \times xy)$

$= 11xy(y - x - xy)$

j) $mnp^2 + 7m^2np^3 = (mnp^2 \times 1) + (mnp^2 \times 7mp)$

$= mnp^2(1 + 7mp)$

Q2 a) $x^2 - y^2 = (x + y)(x - y)$
This is just using the formula for the 'difference of two squares'.

b) $9a^2 - 4b^2 = (3a)^2 - (2b)^2 = (3a + 2b)(3a - 2b)$

c) $25x^2 - 49z^2 = (5x)^2 - (7z)^2 = (5x + 7z)(5x - 7z)$

d) $a^2c - 16b^2c = c(a^2 - 16b^2)$
$= c(a^2 - (4b)^2) = c(a + 4b)(a - 4b)$

Q3 a) $(4 - z)^2(2 - z) + p(2 - z)$
$= (2 - z)[(4 - z)^2 + p]$

b) $(r - d)^3 + 5(r - d)^2 = (r - d)^2[(r - d) + 5]$
$= (r - d)^2(r - d + 5)$

c) $(b + c)^5(a + b) - (b + c)^5$
$= (b + c)^5[(a + b) - 1]$
$= (b + c)^5(a + b - 1)$

d) $l^2m(a - 2x) + rp^2(2x - a)$
$= l^2m(a - 2x) + rp^2(-(a - 2x))$
$= l^2m(a - 2x) - rp^2(a - 2x)$
$= (a - 2x)(l^2m - rp^2)$

You might have factorised this slightly differently and ended up with $(2x - a)(rp^2 - l^2m)$ instead.

Q4 a) $(p + q)^2 + 2q(p + q) = (p + q)[(p + q) + 2q]$
$= (p + q)(p + 3q)$

b) $2(2x - y)^2 - 6x(2x - y)$
$= 2(2x - y)[(2x - y) - 3x]$
$= -2(2x - y)(x + y)$

c) $(r + 6s)^2 - (r + 6s)(r - s)$
$= (r + 6s)[(r + 6s) - (r - s)]$
$= (r + 6s)(7s) = 7s(r + 6s)$

d) $(l + w + h)^2 - l(l + w + h)$
$= (l + w + h)[(l + w + h) - l]$
$= (l + w + h)(w + h)$

Q5 a) $(m + 5)(m^2 - 5m + 25)$
$= m(m^2 - 5m + 25) + 5(m^2 - 5m + 25)$
$= m^3 - 5m^2 + 25m + 5m^2 - 25m + 125$
$= m^3 + 125$

b) $(p - 2q)(p^2 + 2pq + 4q^2)$
$= p(p^2 + 2pq + 4q^2) - 2q(p^2 + 2pq + 4q^2)$
$= p^3 + 2p^2q + 4pq^2 - 2p^2q - 4pq^2 - 8q^3$
$= p^3 - 8q^3$

Parts a) and b) were likely to need the brackets expanding because the quadratic in the second bracket won't factorise.

c) $(u - v)(u + v) - (u + v)^2$
$= (u + v)[(u - v) - (u + v)]$
$= (u + v)(-2v) = -2v(u + v)$

d) $(c + d)^3 - c(c + d)^2 - d(c + d)^2$
$= (c + d)^2[(c + d) - c - d]$
$= (c + d)^2(0) = 0$

Exercise 1.3 — Algebraic fractions

Q1 a) The common denominator is 3×4:

$\frac{x}{3} + \frac{x}{4} = \frac{4x}{12} + \frac{3x}{12} = \frac{7x}{12}$

b) The common denominator is t^2:

$\frac{2}{t} + \frac{13}{t^2} = \frac{2t}{t^2} + \frac{13}{t^2} = \frac{2t + 13}{t^2}$

c) The common denominator is $2 \times p \times 5 \times q = 10pq$:

$\frac{1}{2p} - \frac{1}{5q} = \frac{5q}{10pq} - \frac{2p}{10pq} = \frac{5q - 2p}{10pq}$

d) The common denominator is $a \times b \times c$:

$\frac{ab}{c} + \frac{bc}{a} + \frac{ca}{b} = \frac{abab}{abc} + \frac{bcbc}{abc} + \frac{caca}{abc}$

$= \frac{a^2b^2 + b^2c^2 + c^2a^2}{abc}$

e) The common denominator is mn:

$\frac{2}{mn} - \frac{3m}{n} + \frac{n^2}{m} = \frac{2}{mn} - \frac{3m^2}{mn} + \frac{n^3}{mn}$

$= \frac{2 - 3m^2 + n^3}{mn}$

f) The common denominator is $a^3 \times b^3 = a^3b^3$:

$\frac{2}{ab^3} - \frac{9}{a^3b} = \frac{2a^2}{a^3b^3} - \frac{9b^2}{a^3b^3} = \frac{2a^2 - 9b^2}{a^3b^3}$

Q2 a) The common denominator is $(y - 1)(y - 2)$:

$\frac{5}{y - 1} + \frac{3}{y - 2}$

$= \frac{5(y - 2)}{(y - 1)(y - 2)} + \frac{3(y - 1)}{(y - 1)(y - 2)}$

$= \frac{5(y - 2) + 3(y - 1)}{(y - 1)(y - 2)}$

$= \frac{5y - 10 + 3y - 3}{(y - 1)(y - 2)}$

$= \frac{8y - 13}{(y - 1)(y - 2)}$

b) The common denominator is $(r-5)(r+3)$:

$$\frac{7}{r-5} - \frac{4}{r+3} = \frac{7(r+3)}{(r-5)(r+3)} - \frac{4(r-5)}{(r-5)(r+3)}$$
$$= \frac{7(r+3) - 4(r-5)}{(r-5)(r+3)}$$
$$= \frac{7r + 21 - 4r + 20}{(r-5)(r+3)}$$
$$= \frac{3r + 41}{(r-5)(r+3)}$$

c) The common denominator is $p(p-3)$:

$$\frac{8}{p} - \frac{1}{p-3} = \frac{8(p-3)}{p(p-3)} - \frac{p}{p(p-3)}$$
$$= \frac{8p - 24 - p}{p(p-3)} = \frac{7p - 24}{p(p-3)}$$

d) The common denominator is $2(w-2)(w-7)$:

$$\frac{w}{2(w-2)} + \frac{3w}{w-7}$$
$$= \frac{w(w-7)}{2(w-2)(w-7)} + \frac{3w \times 2(w-2)}{2(w-2)(w-7)}$$
$$= \frac{w^2 - 7w}{2(w-2)(w-7)} + \frac{6w(w-2)}{2(w-2)(w-7)}$$
$$= \frac{w^2 - 7w + 6w(w-2)}{2(w-2)(w-7)}$$
$$= \frac{w^2 - 7w + 6w^2 - 12w}{2(w-2)(w-7)}$$
$$= \frac{7w^2 - 19w}{2(w-2)(w-7)} = \frac{w(7w-19)}{2(w-2)(w-7)}$$

e) The common denominator is $(z+2)(z+4)$:

$$\frac{z+1}{z+2} - \frac{z+3}{z+4}$$
$$= \frac{(z+1)(z+4)}{(z+2)(z+4)} - \frac{(z+2)(z+3)}{(z+2)(z+4)}$$
$$= \frac{(z+1)(z+4) - (z+2)(z+3)}{(z+2)(z+4)}$$
$$= \frac{(z^2 + 5z + 4) - (z^2 + 5z + 6)}{(z+2)(z+4)}$$
$$= \frac{-2}{(z+2)(z+4)}$$

f) The common denominator is $(q+1)(q-2)$:

$$\frac{1}{q+1} + \frac{3}{q-2}$$
$$= \frac{(q-2)}{(q+1)(q-2)} + \frac{3(q+1)}{(q+1)(q-2)}$$
$$= \frac{(q-2) + 3(q+1)}{(q+1)(q-2)}$$
$$= \frac{q - 2 + 3q + 3}{(q+1)(q-2)}$$
$$= \frac{4q + 1}{(q+1)(q-2)}$$

Q3 **a)** $\dfrac{2x+10}{6} = \dfrac{2(x+5)}{6} = \dfrac{x+5}{3}$

b) $\dfrac{6a - 12b - 15c}{3} = \dfrac{3(2a - 4b - 5c)}{3}$
$$= 2a - 4b - 5c$$

c) $\dfrac{np^2 - 2n^2p}{np} = \dfrac{np(p - 2n)}{np} = p - 2n$

d) $\dfrac{4st + 6s^2t + 9s^3t}{2t} = \dfrac{st(4 + 6s + 9s^2)}{2t}$
$$= \dfrac{s(4 + 6s + 9s^2)}{2}$$

e) $\dfrac{10yz^3 - 40y^3z^3 + 60y^2z^3}{10z^2} = \dfrac{10yz^3(1 - 4y^2 + 6y)}{10z^2}$
$$= yz(1 - 4y^2 + 6y)$$

f) $\dfrac{12cd - 6c^2d + 3c^3d^2}{12c^2de} = \dfrac{3cd(4 - 2c + c^2d)}{12c^2de}$
$$= \dfrac{4 - 2c + c^2d}{4ce}$$

2. Surds

Exercise 2.1 — The laws of surds

Q1 **a)** $\sqrt{8} = \sqrt{4 \times 2} = \sqrt{4}\sqrt{2} = 2\sqrt{2}$

b) $\sqrt{24} = \sqrt{4 \times 6} = \sqrt{4}\sqrt{6} = 2\sqrt{6}$

c) $\sqrt{50} = \sqrt{25 \times 2} = \sqrt{25}\sqrt{2} = 5\sqrt{2}$

d) $\sqrt{63} = \sqrt{9 \times 7} = \sqrt{9}\sqrt{7} = 3\sqrt{7}$

e) $\sqrt{72} = \sqrt{36 \times 2} = \sqrt{36}\sqrt{2} = 6\sqrt{2}$

f) $\sqrt{\dfrac{5}{4}} = \dfrac{\sqrt{5}}{\sqrt{4}} = \dfrac{\sqrt{5}}{2}$

g) $\sqrt{\dfrac{7}{100}} = \dfrac{\sqrt{7}}{\sqrt{100}} = \dfrac{\sqrt{7}}{10}$

h) $\sqrt{\dfrac{11}{9}} = \dfrac{\sqrt{11}}{\sqrt{9}} = \dfrac{\sqrt{11}}{3}$

Q2 **a)** $2\sqrt{3} \times 4\sqrt{3} = 2 \times 4 \times \sqrt{3} \times \sqrt{3}$
$$= 8\sqrt{3}\sqrt{3} = 8 \times 3 = 24$$

b) $\sqrt{5} \times 3\sqrt{5} = 3\sqrt{5}\sqrt{5} = 3 \times 5 = 15$

c) $(\sqrt{7})^2 = \sqrt{7}\sqrt{7} = 7$

d) $2\sqrt{2} \times 3\sqrt{5} = 2 \times 3 \times \sqrt{2} \times \sqrt{5}$
$$= 6\sqrt{2}\sqrt{5} = 6\sqrt{10}$$

e) $(2\sqrt{11})^2 = (2\sqrt{11})(2\sqrt{11}) = 4\sqrt{11}\sqrt{11}$
$$= 4 \times 11 = 44$$

f) $5\sqrt{8} \times 2\sqrt{2} = 5\sqrt{4 \times 2} \times 2\sqrt{2}$
$$= 5 \times 2\sqrt{2} \times 2\sqrt{2}$$
$$= 5 \times 4 \times \sqrt{2} \times \sqrt{2}$$
$$= 20 \times 2 = 40$$

g) $4\sqrt{3} \times 2\sqrt{27} = 4 \times 2 \times \sqrt{3}\sqrt{27}$
$$= 8\sqrt{3 \times 27} = 8\sqrt{81}$$
$$= 8 \times 9 = 72$$

h) $2\sqrt{6} \times 5\sqrt{24} = 2 \times 5 \times \sqrt{6} \times \sqrt{24}$
$$= 10\sqrt{6 \times 24} = 10\sqrt{144}$$
$$= 10 \times 12 = 120$$

i) $\dfrac{\sqrt{10}}{6} \times \dfrac{12}{\sqrt{5}} = \dfrac{12\sqrt{10}}{6\sqrt{5}} = \dfrac{12}{6} \times \dfrac{\sqrt{10}}{\sqrt{5}}$
$$= 2 \times \sqrt{\dfrac{10}{5}} = 2\sqrt{2}$$

j) $\dfrac{\sqrt{12}}{3} \times \dfrac{2}{\sqrt{27}} = \dfrac{2\sqrt{12}}{3\sqrt{27}} = \dfrac{2}{3} \times \dfrac{\sqrt{12}}{\sqrt{27}}$

$\qquad = \dfrac{2}{3} \times \dfrac{\sqrt{4 \times 3}}{\sqrt{9 \times 3}} = \dfrac{2}{3} \times \dfrac{\sqrt{4}\sqrt{3}}{\sqrt{9}\sqrt{3}}$

$\qquad = \dfrac{2}{3} \times \dfrac{2\sqrt{3}}{3\sqrt{3}} = \dfrac{2}{3} \times \dfrac{2}{3} = \dfrac{4}{9}$

Q3 a) $\sqrt{20} + \sqrt{5} = \sqrt{4 \times 5} + \sqrt{5} = \sqrt{4}\sqrt{5} + \sqrt{5}$

$\qquad = 2\sqrt{5} + \sqrt{5} = 3\sqrt{5}$

b) $\sqrt{32} - \sqrt{8} = \sqrt{16 \times 2} - \sqrt{4 \times 2}$

$\qquad = \sqrt{16}\sqrt{2} - \sqrt{4}\sqrt{2}$

$\qquad = 4\sqrt{2} - 2\sqrt{2} = 2\sqrt{2}$

c) $\sqrt{27} + 4\sqrt{3} = \sqrt{9 \times 3} + 4\sqrt{3} = \sqrt{9}\sqrt{3} + 4\sqrt{3}$

$\qquad = 3\sqrt{3} + 4\sqrt{3} = 7\sqrt{3}$

d) $2\sqrt{8} - 3\sqrt{2} = 2\sqrt{4 \times 2} - 3\sqrt{2}$

$\qquad = 2\sqrt{4}\sqrt{2} - 3\sqrt{2}$

$\qquad = 4\sqrt{2} - 3\sqrt{2} = \sqrt{2}$

e) $3\sqrt{10} + \sqrt{250} = 3\sqrt{10} + \sqrt{25 \times 10}$

$\qquad = 3\sqrt{10} + \sqrt{25}\sqrt{10}$

$\qquad = 3\sqrt{10} + 5\sqrt{10}$

$\qquad = 8\sqrt{10}$

f) $4\sqrt{27} + 2\sqrt{48} + 5\sqrt{108}$

$\qquad = 4\sqrt{9 \times 3} + 2\sqrt{16 \times 3} + 5\sqrt{36 \times 3}$

$\qquad = 4\sqrt{9}\sqrt{3} + 2\sqrt{16}\sqrt{3} + 5\sqrt{36}\sqrt{3}$

$\qquad = 12\sqrt{3} + 8\sqrt{3} + 30\sqrt{3} = 50\sqrt{3}$

Q4 a) $(1 + \sqrt{2})(2 + \sqrt{2}) = 2 + \sqrt{2} + 2\sqrt{2} + \sqrt{2}\sqrt{2}$

$\qquad\qquad = 2 + 3\sqrt{2} + 2 = 4 + 3\sqrt{2}$

b) $(3 + 4\sqrt{3})(2 - \sqrt{3})$

$\qquad = 6 - 3\sqrt{3} + 8\sqrt{3} - 4\sqrt{3}\sqrt{3}$

$\qquad = 6 + 5\sqrt{3} - 12 = 5\sqrt{3} - 6$

c) By the difference of two squares rule:

$(\sqrt{11} + 2)(\sqrt{11} - 2) = (\sqrt{11})^2 - 2^2$

$\qquad\qquad = 11 - 4 = 7$

d) By the difference of two squares rule:

$(9 - 2\sqrt{5})(9 + 2\sqrt{5}) = 9^2 - (2\sqrt{5})^2$

$\qquad\qquad = 81 - 20 = 61$

e) $(\sqrt{3} + 2)^2 = (\sqrt{3} + 2)(\sqrt{3} + 2)$

$\qquad = \sqrt{3}\sqrt{3} + 2\sqrt{3} + 2\sqrt{3} + 4$

$\qquad = 3 + 4\sqrt{3} + 4 = 7 + 4\sqrt{3}$

f) $(3\sqrt{5} - 4)^2 = (3\sqrt{5} - 4)(3\sqrt{5} - 4)$

$\qquad = (3\sqrt{5})^2 - 12\sqrt{5} - 12\sqrt{5} + 16$

$\qquad = 45 - 24\sqrt{5} + 16$

$\qquad = 61 - 24\sqrt{5}$

You could have used the rule $(a + b)^2 = a^2 + 2ab + b^2$ for parts e and f.

Q5 You may want to draw the triangle:

Using Pythagoras:

$(\sqrt{2})^2 + (BC)^2 = (5\sqrt{2})^2$

So, $2 + (BC)^2 = 50 \Rightarrow (BC)^2 = 48$

$\Rightarrow BC = \sqrt{48} = \sqrt{16 \times 3} = 4\sqrt{3}$

Exercise 2.2 — Rationalising the denominator

Q1 a) $\dfrac{6}{\sqrt{3}} = \dfrac{6\sqrt{3}}{\sqrt{3}\sqrt{3}} = \dfrac{6\sqrt{3}}{3} = 2\sqrt{3}$

b) $\dfrac{21}{\sqrt{7}} = \dfrac{21\sqrt{7}}{\sqrt{7}\sqrt{7}} = \dfrac{21\sqrt{7}}{7} = 3\sqrt{7}$

c) $\dfrac{30}{\sqrt{5}} = \dfrac{30\sqrt{5}}{\sqrt{5}\sqrt{5}} = \dfrac{30\sqrt{5}}{5} = 6\sqrt{5}$

d) $\sqrt{45} + \dfrac{15}{\sqrt{5}} = \sqrt{45} + \dfrac{15\sqrt{5}}{\sqrt{5}\sqrt{5}}$

$\qquad = \sqrt{45} + \dfrac{15\sqrt{5}}{5}$

$\qquad = \sqrt{9 \times 5} + 3\sqrt{5}$

$\qquad = \sqrt{9}\sqrt{5} + 3\sqrt{5}$

$\qquad = 3\sqrt{5} + 3\sqrt{5} = 6\sqrt{5}$

e) $\dfrac{\sqrt{54}}{3} - \dfrac{12}{\sqrt{6}} = \dfrac{\sqrt{9 \times 6}}{3} - \dfrac{12\sqrt{6}}{\sqrt{6}\sqrt{6}}$

$\qquad = \dfrac{\sqrt{9}\sqrt{6}}{3} - \dfrac{12\sqrt{6}}{6}$

$\qquad = \dfrac{3\sqrt{6}}{3} - \dfrac{12\sqrt{6}}{6}$

$\qquad = \sqrt{6} - 2\sqrt{6} = -\sqrt{6}$

f) $\dfrac{\sqrt{300}}{5} + \dfrac{30}{\sqrt{12}} = \dfrac{\sqrt{100 \times 3}}{5} + \dfrac{30\sqrt{12}}{\sqrt{12}\sqrt{12}}$

$\qquad = \dfrac{\sqrt{100}\sqrt{3}}{5} + \dfrac{30\sqrt{4 \times 3}}{12}$

$\qquad = \dfrac{10\sqrt{3}}{5} + \dfrac{30\sqrt{4}\sqrt{3}}{12}$

$\qquad = 2\sqrt{3} + \dfrac{60\sqrt{3}}{12}$

$\qquad = 2\sqrt{3} + 5\sqrt{3} = 7\sqrt{3}$

Q2 a) $\dfrac{4}{1 + \sqrt{3}} = \dfrac{4(1 - \sqrt{3})}{(1 + \sqrt{3})(1 - \sqrt{3})}$

$\qquad = \dfrac{4 - 4\sqrt{3}}{1 - 3} = \dfrac{4 - 4\sqrt{3}}{-2} = -2 + 2\sqrt{3}$

The denominator was simplified by using the difference of two squares rule. It will be used in almost every question in the rest of this exercise, so watch out for it and make sure you understand what's going on.

b) $\dfrac{11}{4 - \sqrt{5}} = \dfrac{11(4 + \sqrt{5})}{(4 - \sqrt{5})(4 + \sqrt{5})} = \dfrac{44 + 11\sqrt{5}}{16 - 5}$

$\qquad = \dfrac{44 + 11\sqrt{5}}{11} = 4 + \sqrt{5}$

c) $\dfrac{8}{\sqrt{7}+3} = \dfrac{8(\sqrt{7}-3)}{(\sqrt{7}+3)(\sqrt{7}-3)} = \dfrac{8\sqrt{7}-24}{7-9}$

$= \dfrac{8\sqrt{7}-24}{-2} = \dfrac{24-8\sqrt{7}}{2} = 12-4\sqrt{7}$

d) $\dfrac{8}{-1+\sqrt{5}} = \dfrac{8(-1-\sqrt{5})}{(-1+\sqrt{5})(-1-\sqrt{5})}$

$= \dfrac{-8-8\sqrt{5}}{1-5} = \dfrac{-8-8\sqrt{5}}{-4}$

$= 2+2\sqrt{5}$

e) $\dfrac{1}{\sqrt{26}-5} = \dfrac{\sqrt{26}+5}{(\sqrt{26}-5)(\sqrt{26}+5)} = \dfrac{\sqrt{26}+5}{26-25}$

$= \dfrac{\sqrt{26}+5}{1} = 5+\sqrt{26}$

f) $\dfrac{18}{\sqrt{10}-4} = \dfrac{18(\sqrt{10}+4)}{(\sqrt{10}-4)(\sqrt{10}+4)} = \dfrac{18\sqrt{10}+72}{10-16}$

$= \dfrac{18\sqrt{10}+72}{-6} = -12-3\sqrt{10}$

Q3 a) $\dfrac{\sqrt{2}+1}{\sqrt{2}-1} = \dfrac{(\sqrt{2}+1)(\sqrt{2}+1)}{(\sqrt{2}-1)(\sqrt{2}+1)}$

$= \dfrac{2+\sqrt{2}+\sqrt{2}+1}{2-1}$

$= \dfrac{2\sqrt{2}+3}{1} = 3+2\sqrt{2}$

b) $\dfrac{\sqrt{5}+3}{\sqrt{5}-2} = \dfrac{(\sqrt{5}+3)(\sqrt{5}+2)}{(\sqrt{5}-2)(\sqrt{5}+2)}$

$= \dfrac{5+2\sqrt{5}+3\sqrt{5}+6}{5-4}$

$= \dfrac{11+5\sqrt{5}}{1} = 11+5\sqrt{5}$

c) $\dfrac{3-\sqrt{3}}{4+\sqrt{3}} = \dfrac{(3-\sqrt{3})(4-\sqrt{3})}{(4+\sqrt{3})(4-\sqrt{3})}$

$= \dfrac{12-3\sqrt{3}-4\sqrt{3}+3}{16-3}$

$= \dfrac{15-7\sqrt{3}}{13} = \dfrac{15}{13}-\dfrac{7}{13}\sqrt{3}$

d) $\dfrac{3\sqrt{5}-1}{2\sqrt{5}-3} = \dfrac{(3\sqrt{5}-1)(2\sqrt{5}+3)}{(2\sqrt{5}-3)(2\sqrt{5}+3)}$

$= \dfrac{(2\sqrt{5})(3\sqrt{5})+9\sqrt{5}-2\sqrt{5}-3}{(2\sqrt{5})^2-9}$

$= \dfrac{27+7\sqrt{5}}{(2\sqrt{5})^2-9} = \dfrac{27+7\sqrt{5}}{11}$

$= \dfrac{27}{11}+\dfrac{7}{11}\sqrt{5}$

e) $\dfrac{\sqrt{2}+\sqrt{3}}{3\sqrt{2}-\sqrt{3}} = \dfrac{(\sqrt{2}+\sqrt{3})(3\sqrt{2}+\sqrt{3})}{(3\sqrt{2}-\sqrt{3})(3\sqrt{2}+\sqrt{3})}$

$= \dfrac{3\sqrt{2}\sqrt{2}+\sqrt{2}\sqrt{3}+3\sqrt{3}\sqrt{2}+3}{(3\sqrt{2})^2-(\sqrt{3})^2}$

$= \dfrac{6+\sqrt{2}\sqrt{3}+3\sqrt{3}\sqrt{2}+3}{18-3}$

$= \dfrac{9+4\sqrt{3}\sqrt{2}}{15} = \dfrac{9}{15}+\dfrac{4}{15}\sqrt{2}\sqrt{3}$

$= \dfrac{3}{5}+\dfrac{4}{15}\sqrt{6}$

f) $\dfrac{2\sqrt{7}-\sqrt{5}}{\sqrt{7}+2\sqrt{5}} = \dfrac{(2\sqrt{7}-\sqrt{5})(\sqrt{7}-2\sqrt{5})}{(\sqrt{7}+2\sqrt{5})(\sqrt{7}-2\sqrt{5})}$

$= \dfrac{2\sqrt{7}\sqrt{7}-4\sqrt{7}\sqrt{5}-\sqrt{5}\sqrt{7}+10}{7-(2\sqrt{5})^2}$

$= \dfrac{14-4\sqrt{7}\sqrt{5}-\sqrt{5}\sqrt{7}+10}{7-20}$

$= \dfrac{24-5\sqrt{35}}{-13} = -\dfrac{24}{13}+\dfrac{5}{13}\sqrt{35}$

Q4 $8 = (\sqrt{5}-1)x$

$\Rightarrow x = \dfrac{8}{(\sqrt{5}-1)} = \dfrac{8(\sqrt{5}+1)}{(\sqrt{5}-1)(\sqrt{5}+1)}$

$= \dfrac{8\sqrt{5}+8}{5-1} = \dfrac{8\sqrt{5}+8}{4} = 2+2\sqrt{5}$

Q5 $5+\sqrt{7} = (3-\sqrt{7})y$

$\Rightarrow y = \dfrac{5+\sqrt{7}}{3-\sqrt{7}} = \dfrac{(5+\sqrt{7})(3+\sqrt{7})}{(3-\sqrt{7})(3+\sqrt{7})}$

$= \dfrac{15+5\sqrt{7}+3\sqrt{7}+7}{9-7}$

$= \dfrac{22+8\sqrt{7}}{2} = 11+4\sqrt{7}$

Q6 The area of a rectangle is given by
area(A) = length(l) × width(w) so:

$(2+\sqrt{2}) = l \times (3\sqrt{2}-4)$

$\Rightarrow l = \dfrac{(2+\sqrt{2})}{(3\sqrt{2}-4)} = \dfrac{(2+\sqrt{2})(3\sqrt{2}+4)}{(3\sqrt{2}-4)(3\sqrt{2}+4)}$

$= \dfrac{6\sqrt{2}+8+6+4\sqrt{2}}{(3\sqrt{2})^2-16}$

$= \dfrac{14+10\sqrt{2}}{18-16} = \dfrac{14+10\sqrt{2}}{2}$

$= (7+5\sqrt{2})\,\text{cm}$

Don't forget the units here.

Review Exercise — Chapter 1

Q1 A, C and D are identities because the left-hand side is identical to the right-hand side in each case — you can rearrange one side to get the other. B is not an identity because the left-hand side is only equal to the right-hand side for certain values of x and y, not all values.

Q2 a) $a^2 - b^2$ by the difference of two squares.

b) $a^2 + ab + ab + b^2 = a^2 + 2ab + b^2$

c) $35xy + 125y^2 + 175xy - 100y^2 = 25y^2 + 210xy$

d) $x(3x + y + 7) + 3y(3x + y + 7) + 2(3x + y + 7)$
$= 3x^2 + 10xy + 3y^2 + 13x + 23y + 14$

Q3 a) $xy(2x + a + 2y)$

b) $a^2x(1 + b^2x)$

c) $8(2y + xy + 7x)$

d) $(x - 2)(x - 3)$

Q4 a) The common denominator is 5 × 12 = 60:

$\dfrac{2x \times 20}{60} + \dfrac{y \times 5}{60} + \dfrac{x \times 12}{60} = \dfrac{52x + 5y}{60}$

b) The common denominator is x^2y^2:

$$\frac{5 \times x}{x^2y^2} - \frac{2 \times y}{x^2y^2} = \frac{5x - 2y}{x^2y^2}$$

c) The common denominator is
$x(x - y)(x + y) = x(x^2 - y^2)$ so :

$$\frac{1 \times (x^2 - y^2)}{x(x^2 - y^2)} + \frac{x \times x(x - y)}{x(x^2 - y^2)} + \frac{y \times x(x + y)}{x(x^2 - y^2)}$$

$$= \frac{x^3 + x^2 - y^2 + xy^2}{x(x - y)(x + y)}$$

Q5 a) $\dfrac{2a \times 2}{2b} - \dfrac{a}{2b} = \dfrac{4a}{2b} - \dfrac{a}{2b} = \dfrac{3a}{2b}$

b) $\dfrac{2p(p - q)}{(p + q)(p - q)} + \dfrac{2q(p + q)}{(p + q)(p - q)}$

$$= \frac{2(p^2 + q^2)}{(p + q)(p - q)}$$

Q6 a) $x^2 = 5 \Rightarrow x = \pm\sqrt{5}$

b) $(x + 2)^2 = 3 \Rightarrow x = -2 \pm \sqrt{3}$

Q7 a) $\sqrt{4 \times 7} = 2\sqrt{7}$ **b)** $\dfrac{\sqrt{5}}{\sqrt{36}} = \dfrac{\sqrt{5}}{6}$

c) $\sqrt{9 \times 2} = 3\sqrt{2}$ **d)** $\dfrac{\sqrt{9}}{\sqrt{16}} = \dfrac{3}{4}$

Q8 a) $\dfrac{8}{\sqrt{2}} = \dfrac{8}{\sqrt{2}} \times \dfrac{\sqrt{2}}{\sqrt{2}} = \dfrac{8\sqrt{2}}{2} = 4\sqrt{2}$

b) $\dfrac{\sqrt{2}}{2} = \dfrac{\sqrt{2}}{(\sqrt{2})^2} = \dfrac{1}{\sqrt{2}}$

Q9 $(6\sqrt{3} + 2\sqrt{7})(6\sqrt{3} + 2\sqrt{7})$

$$= (6\sqrt{3})^2 + 2(2\sqrt{7})(6\sqrt{3}) + (2\sqrt{7})^2$$

$$= 108 + 24\sqrt{7}\sqrt{3} + 28$$

$$= 136 + 24\sqrt{21}$$

Q10 $\dfrac{2(3 - \sqrt{7})}{(3 + \sqrt{7})(3 - \sqrt{7})} = \dfrac{6 - 2\sqrt{7}}{9 - 7} = 3 - \sqrt{7}$

Exam-Style Questions — Chapter 1

Q1 a) $(5\sqrt{3})^2 = (5^2)(\sqrt{3})^2 = 25 \cdot 3$

$$= 75 \;\; \textit{[1 mark]}$$

b) $(5 + \sqrt{6})(2 - \sqrt{6})$

$$= 10 - 5\sqrt{6} + 2\sqrt{6} - 6 \;\; \textit{[1 mark]}$$

$$= 4 - 3\sqrt{6} \;\;\;\; \textit{[1 mark]}$$

Q2 Multiply top and bottom by $3 + \sqrt{5}$ to 'rationalise the denominator':

$$\frac{5 + \sqrt{5}}{3 - \sqrt{5}} = \frac{(5 + \sqrt{5})(3 + \sqrt{5})}{(3 - \sqrt{5})(3 + \sqrt{5})} \;\; \textit{[1 mark]}$$

$$= \frac{15 + 5\sqrt{5} + 3\sqrt{5} + 5}{9 - 5} \;\; \textit{[1 mark]}$$

$$= \frac{20 + 8\sqrt{5}}{4} \;\; \textit{[1 mark]}$$

$$= 5 + 2\sqrt{5} \;\; \textit{[1 mark]}$$

Q3 $\sqrt{18} - 2\sqrt{8} + \dfrac{4}{\sqrt{2}}$

$$= \sqrt{9 \times 2} - 2\sqrt{4 \times 2} + \frac{4\sqrt{2}}{\sqrt{2} \times \sqrt{2}}$$

$$= 3\sqrt{2} - 4\sqrt{2} + 2\sqrt{2}$$

$$= \sqrt{2}$$

[4 marks available — 1 mark each for correctly simplifying each initial term, 1 mark for correct final answer]

Q4 $\dfrac{4\sqrt{32}}{\sqrt{2}} - 2\sqrt{3} + \dfrac{4\sqrt{5}}{\sqrt{20}} + \sqrt{12}$

$$= \frac{4\sqrt{16 \times 2}}{\sqrt{2}} - 2\sqrt{3} + \frac{4\sqrt{5}}{\sqrt{4 \times 5}} + \sqrt{4 \times 3}$$

$$= \frac{4\sqrt{16}\sqrt{2}}{\sqrt{2}} - 2\sqrt{3} + \frac{4\sqrt{5}}{\sqrt{4}\sqrt{5}} + \sqrt{4}\sqrt{3}$$

$$= 16 - 2\sqrt{3} + 2 + 2\sqrt{3}$$

$$= 18$$

[4 marks available — 1 mark each for simplifying each of the three initial terms that can be simplified, 1 mark for correct final answer]

Q5 Find the common denominator:

$$\frac{4}{3x^2} - \frac{2}{7x} = \frac{4 \times 7}{3x^2 \times 7} - \frac{2 \times 3x}{7x \times 3x}$$

$$= \frac{28}{21x^2} - \frac{6x}{21x^2} \;\; \textit{[1 mark]}$$

$$= \frac{28 - 6x}{21x^2}$$

$$= \frac{2(14 - 3x)}{21x^2} = \;\; \textit{[1 mark]}$$

Q6 a) $(3x + 4)(4x(3x + 4) + 1)$ *[1 mark]*

$$= (3x + 4)(12x^2 + 16x + 1) \;\; \textit{[1 mark]}$$

b) $4x(3x + 4)^2 = 4x(3x + 4)(3x + 4)$

$$= 4x(9x^2 + 12x + 12x + 16)$$

$$= 4x(9x^2 + 24x + 16) \;\; \textit{[1 mark]}$$

$$= 36x^3 + 96x^2 + 64x \;\; \textit{[1 mark]}$$

Q7 $2x^4 - 32x^2 = 2x^2(x^2 - 16)$

$$= 2x^2(x + 4)(x - 4)$$

[3 marks available in total — 1 mark for each correct factor]

Chapter 2: Quadratics

1. Quadratic Equations

Exercise 1.1 — Factorising a quadratic

Q1 **a)** $x^2 - 6x + 5 = (x - 5)(x - 1)$

b) $x^2 - 3x - 18 = (x - 6)(x + 3)$

c) $x^2 + 22x + 121 = (x + 11)(x + 11) = (x + 11)^2$

d) $x^2 - 12x = x(x - 12)$

Note that if every term contains an x, you can just take a factor of x out of the bracket.

e) $y^2 - 13y + 42 = (y - 6)(y - 7)$

f) $x^2 + 51x + 144 = (x + 48)(x + 3)$

g) $x^2 - 121 = (x + 11)(x - 11)$

If there is no 'b' term, see if the expression is a 'difference of two squares' (chances are it will be).

h) $x^2 + 2\sqrt{3}x + 3 = (x + \sqrt{3})(x + \sqrt{3}) = (x + \sqrt{3})^2$

Q2 **a)** $x^2 - 2x - 8 = 0$
$\Rightarrow (x - 4)(x + 2) = 0$
$\Rightarrow x - 4 = 0$ or $x + 2 = 0$
$\Rightarrow x = 4$ or $x = -2$

b) $2x^2 + 2x - 40 = 0$
$2(x^2 + x - 20) = 0$

This is an example of a question where you can simplify the equation before factorising. You can divide through by 2.

$x^2 + x - 20 = 0$
$\Rightarrow (x + 5)(x - 4) = 0$
$\Rightarrow x + 5 = 0$ or $x - 4 = 0$
$\Rightarrow x = -5$ or $x = 4$

c) $p^2 + 21p + 38 = 0$
$\Rightarrow (p + 19)(p + 2) = 0$
$\Rightarrow p + 19 = 0$ or $p + 2 = 0$
$\Rightarrow p = -19$ or $p = -2$

d) $x^2 - 15x + 54 = 0$
$\Rightarrow (x - 9)(x - 6) = 0$
$\Rightarrow x - 9 = 0$ or $x - 6 = 0$
$\Rightarrow x = 9$ or $x = 6$

e) $x^2 + 18x = -65$
$\Rightarrow x^2 + 18x + 65 = 0$
$\Rightarrow (x + 5)(x + 13) = 0$
$\Rightarrow x + 5 = 0$ or $x + 13 = 0$
$\Rightarrow x = -5$ or $x = -13$

f) $x^2 - x = 42$
$\Rightarrow x^2 - x - 42 = 0$
$\Rightarrow (x - 7)(x + 6) = 0$
$\Rightarrow x - 7 = 0$ or $x + 6 = 0$
$\Rightarrow x = 7$ or $x = -6$

g) $x^2 + 1100x + 100\,000 = 0$
$\Rightarrow (x + 100)(x + 1000) = 0$
$\Rightarrow x + 100 = 0$ or $x + 1000 = 0$
$\Rightarrow x = -100$ or $x = -1000$

h) $3x^2 - 3x - 6 = 0$
$\Rightarrow 3(x^2 - x - 2) = 0$
$\Rightarrow x^2 - x - 2 = 0$
$\Rightarrow (x - 2)(x + 1) = 0$
$\Rightarrow x - 2 = 0$ or $x + 1 = 0$
$\Rightarrow x = 2$ or $x = -1$

Q3 **a)** $4x^2 - 4x - 3 = (2x + 1)(2x - 3)$

b) $2x^2 + 23x + 11 = (2x + 1)(x + 11)$

c) $7x^2 - 19x - 6 = (7x + 2)(x - 3)$

d) $-x^2 - 5x + 36 = (-x + 4)(x + 9)$

e) $2x^2 - 2 = 2(x^2 - 1)$
$\qquad = 2(x + 1)(x - 1)$

f) $6x^2 + 11x + 4 = (3x + 4)(2x + 1)$

Q4 **a)** $-5x^2 - 22x + 15 = 0$
$\Rightarrow 5x^2 + 22x - 15 = 0$
$\Rightarrow (5x - 3)(x + 5) = 0$
$\Rightarrow 5x - 3 = 0$ or $x + 5 = 0$
$\Rightarrow x = \frac{3}{5}$ or $x = -5$

If you want to get rid of the minus sign in front of the x^2 just multiply through by -1, the right hand side will remain 0 and the left hand side will change signs.

b) $32x^2 + 60x + 13 = 0$
$\Rightarrow (4x + 1)(8x + 13) = 0$
$\Rightarrow 4x + 1 = 0$ or $8x + 13 = 0$
$\Rightarrow x = -\frac{1}{4}$ or $x = -\frac{13}{8}$

c) $5a^2 + 12a = 9$
$\Rightarrow 5a^2 + 12a - 9 = 0$
$\Rightarrow (5a - 3)(a + 3) = 0$
$\Rightarrow 5a - 3 = 0$ or $a + 3 = 0$
$\Rightarrow a = \frac{3}{5}$ or $a = -3$

d) $8x^2 + 22x + 15 = 0$
$\Rightarrow (4x + 5)(2x + 3) = 0$
$\Rightarrow 4x + 5 = 0$ or $2x + 3 = 0$
$\Rightarrow x = -\frac{5}{4}$ or $x = -\frac{3}{2}$

Q5 $(x-1)(x-2) = 37 - x$

$\Rightarrow x^2 - 3x + 2 = 37 - x$

$\Rightarrow x^2 - 2x - 35 = 0$

$\Rightarrow (x-7)(x+5) = 0$

$\Rightarrow x - 7 = 0 \text{ or } x + 5 = 0$

$\Rightarrow x = 7 \text{ or } x = -5$

Q6 The function f(x) meets the x-axis when f(x) = 0 so set the expression for f(x) equal to 0.

$-x^2 + 7x + 30 = 0$

$\Rightarrow x^2 - 7x - 30 = 0$

$\Rightarrow (x-10)(x+3) = 0$

$\Rightarrow x - 10 = 0 \text{ or } x + 3 = 0$

$\Rightarrow x = 10 \text{ or } x = -3$

So the graph of f(x) meets the x-axis when $x = 10$ and $x = -3$.

Q7 *This question looks harder because it has y's in it as well as x's — just treat the y as a constant. You'll need two numbers which multiply to give $8y^2$ and add or subtract to give 6y.*

4y and 2y multiply to $8y^2$ and add to give 6y so these are the numbers you need.

$x^2 + 6xy + 8y^2 = (x + 4y)(x + 2y)$

Exercise 1.2 — The quadratic formula

Q1 **a)** $x^2 - 4x = -2$

$\Rightarrow x^2 - 4x + 2 = 0$

$a = 1, b = -4, c = 2$

$x = \dfrac{-b \pm \sqrt{b^2 - 4ac}}{2a}$

$= \dfrac{-(-4) \pm \sqrt{(-4)^2 - 4 \times 1 \times 2}}{2 \times 1}$

$= \dfrac{4 \pm \sqrt{16 - 8}}{2}$

$= \dfrac{4 \pm \sqrt{8}}{2}$

$= \dfrac{4 \pm 2\sqrt{2}}{2}$

$= 2 \pm \sqrt{2}$

b) $x^2 - 2x - 44 = 0$

$a = 1, b = -2, c = -44$

$x = \dfrac{-b \pm \sqrt{b^2 - 4ac}}{2a}$

$= \dfrac{-(-2) \pm \sqrt{(-2)^2 - 4 \times 1 \times (-44)}}{2 \times 1}$

$= \dfrac{2 \pm \sqrt{4 + (4 \times 1 \times 44)}}{2}$

$= \dfrac{2 \pm \sqrt{180}}{2}$

$= \dfrac{2 \pm \sqrt{36 \times 5}}{2}$

$= \dfrac{2 \pm 6\sqrt{5}}{2}$

$= 1 \pm 3\sqrt{5}$

c) $x^2 - 14x + 42 = 0$

$a = 1, b = -14, c = 42$

$x = \dfrac{-b \pm \sqrt{b^2 - 4ac}}{2a}$

$= \dfrac{-(-14) \pm \sqrt{(-14)^2 - 4 \times 1 \times 42}}{2 \times 1}$

$= \dfrac{14 \pm \sqrt{196 - 168}}{2}$

$= \dfrac{14 \pm \sqrt{28}}{2}$

$= \dfrac{14 \pm \sqrt{4 \times 7}}{2}$

$= \dfrac{14 \pm 2\sqrt{7}}{2}$

$= 7 \pm \sqrt{7}$

d) $4x^2 + 4x - 1 = 0$

$a = 4, b = 4, c = -1$

$x = \dfrac{-b \pm \sqrt{b^2 - 4ac}}{2a}$

$= \dfrac{-4 \pm \sqrt{(4)^2 - 4 \times 4 \times (-1)}}{2 \times 4}$

$= \dfrac{-4 \pm \sqrt{16 + 16}}{8}$

$= \dfrac{-4 \pm \sqrt{32}}{8}$

$= \dfrac{-4 \pm \sqrt{32}}{8}$

$= \dfrac{-4 \pm 4\sqrt{2}}{8}$

$= -\dfrac{1}{2} \pm \dfrac{1}{2}\sqrt{2}$

e) $x^2 - \dfrac{5}{6}x + \dfrac{1}{6} = 0$

$6x^2 - 5x + 1 = 0$

$a = 6, b = -5, c = 1$

$x = \dfrac{-b \pm \sqrt{b^2 - 4ac}}{2a}$

$= \dfrac{-(-5) \pm \sqrt{(-5)^2 - 4 \times 6 \times 1}}{2 \times 6}$

$= \dfrac{5 \pm \sqrt{25 - 24}}{12}$

$= \dfrac{5 \pm 1}{12}$

$= \dfrac{1}{2} \text{ or } \dfrac{1}{3}$

Removing the fractions right at the start here saves you lots of fraction headaches in the working. This one wasn't actually too hard to factorise — you'd get (3x − 1)(2x − 1).

f) $x^2 - x - \dfrac{35}{2} = 0$

$a = 1, \; b = -1, \; c = -\dfrac{35}{2}$

$x = \dfrac{-b \pm \sqrt{b^2 - 4ac}}{2a}$

$= \dfrac{-(-1) \pm \sqrt{(-1)^2 - 4 \times 1 \times \left(-\frac{35}{2}\right)}}{2 \times 1}$

$= \dfrac{1 \pm \sqrt{1 + \left(4 \times 1 \times \frac{35}{2}\right)}}{2}$

$= \dfrac{1 \pm \sqrt{1 + 70}}{2}$

$= \dfrac{1 \pm \sqrt{71}}{2}$

Q2 a) $(x - 2 + \sqrt{5})(x - 2 - \sqrt{5})$

$\qquad = x(x - 2 - \sqrt{5})$
$\qquad \quad -2(x - 2 - \sqrt{5})$
$\qquad \quad + \sqrt{5}(x - 2 - \sqrt{5})$

$\qquad = x^2 - 2x - \sqrt{5}x$
$\qquad \quad - 2x + 4 + 2\sqrt{5}$
$\qquad \quad + \sqrt{5}x - 2\sqrt{5} - 5$

$\qquad = x^2 - 4x - 1$

Use the method for multiplying out
long brackets from Chapter 1.

b) $x^2 - 4x - 1 = 0$

$a = 1, \; b = -4, \; c = -1$

$x = \dfrac{-b \pm \sqrt{b^2 - 4ac}}{2a}$

$= \dfrac{-(-4) \pm \sqrt{(-4)^2 - 4 \times 1 \times (-1)}}{2 \times 1}$

$= \dfrac{4 \pm \sqrt{16 + 4}}{2}$

$= \dfrac{4 \pm \sqrt{20}}{2}$

$= \dfrac{4 \pm 2\sqrt{5}}{2}$

$= 2 \pm \sqrt{5}$

c) The roots produced by the quadratic formula in part b) are the same as the numbers subtracted from x in the expression from a) — this is because it's just the factorised version of the same quadratic. If you put the factorised version equal to zero and solved the equation, you'd get the same roots.

Q3 $x^2 + 8x + 13 = 0$

$a = 1, \; b = 8, \; c = 13$

$x = \dfrac{-b \pm \sqrt{b^2 - 4ac}}{2a}$

$= \dfrac{-8 \pm \sqrt{8^2 - 4 \times 1 \times 13}}{2 \times 1}$

$= \dfrac{-8 \pm \sqrt{64 - 52}}{2}$

$= \dfrac{-8 \pm \sqrt{12}}{2}$

$= \dfrac{-8 \pm 2\sqrt{3}}{2}$

$= -4 \pm \sqrt{3}$

So A = -4 and B = 3.

Q4 a) $x^2 + x + \dfrac{1}{4} = 0$

$a = 1, \; b = 1, \; c = \dfrac{1}{4}$

$x = \dfrac{-b \pm \sqrt{b^2 - 4ac}}{2a}$

$= \dfrac{-1 \pm \sqrt{1^2 - 4 \times 1 \times \frac{1}{4}}}{2 \times 1}$

$= \dfrac{-1 \pm \sqrt{1 - 1}}{2}$

$= \dfrac{-1 \pm 0}{2}$

$= -\dfrac{1}{2}$

b) $25x^2 - 30x + 7 = 0$

$a = 25, \; b = -30, \; c = 7$

$x = \dfrac{-b \pm \sqrt{b^2 - 4ac}}{2a}$

$= \dfrac{-(-30) \pm \sqrt{(-30)^2 - 4 \times 25 \times 7}}{2 \times 25}$

$= \dfrac{30 \pm \sqrt{900 - 700}}{2 \times 25}$

$= \dfrac{30 \pm \sqrt{200}}{50}$

$= \dfrac{30 \pm 10\sqrt{2}}{50}$

$= \dfrac{30}{50} \pm \dfrac{10}{50}\sqrt{2}$

$= \dfrac{3}{5} \pm \dfrac{1}{5}\sqrt{2}$

c) $60x - 5 = -100x^2 - 3$

$\Rightarrow 100x^2 + 60x - 2 = 0 \Rightarrow 50x^2 + 30x - 1 = 0$

$a = 50, \ b = 30, \ c = -1$

$x = \dfrac{-b \pm \sqrt{b^2 - 4ac}}{2a}$

$= \dfrac{-30 \pm \sqrt{30^2 - 4 \times 50 \times (-1)}}{2 \times 50}$

$= \dfrac{-30 \pm \sqrt{900 + 200}}{100}$

$= \dfrac{-30 \pm \sqrt{1100}}{100}$

$= \dfrac{-30 \pm \sqrt{11 \times 100}}{100}$

$= \dfrac{-30 \pm \sqrt{100}\sqrt{11}}{100}$

$= \dfrac{-30 \pm 10\sqrt{11}}{100}$

$= -\dfrac{3}{10} \pm \dfrac{1}{10}\sqrt{11}$

d) $2x(x - 4) = 7 - 3x$

$\Rightarrow 2x^2 - 8x = 7 - 3x$

$\Rightarrow 2x^2 - 5x - 7 = 0$

$a = 2, \ b = -5, \ c = -7$

$x = \dfrac{-b \pm \sqrt{b^2 - 4ac}}{2a}$

$= \dfrac{-(-5) \pm \sqrt{(-5)^2 - 4 \times 2 \times (-7)}}{2 \times 2}$

$= \dfrac{5 \pm \sqrt{25 + 56}}{4}$

$= \dfrac{5 \pm \sqrt{81}}{4}$

$= \dfrac{5 \pm 9}{4}$

$= \dfrac{5 + 9}{4}$ or $\dfrac{5 - 9}{4}$

$= \dfrac{14}{4}$ or $\dfrac{-4}{4}$

$= \dfrac{7}{2}$ or -1

Exercise 1.3 — Completing the square

Q1 a) Take the square root of both sides to get:

$x + 4 = \pm\sqrt{25} \Rightarrow x = -4 \pm \sqrt{25} = -4 \pm 5$

So $x = 1$ or -9

b) Take the square root of both sides to get:

$5x - 3 = \pm\sqrt{21} \Rightarrow 5x = 3 \pm \sqrt{21} \Rightarrow x = \dfrac{3}{5} \pm \dfrac{\sqrt{21}}{5}$

Q2 a) $x^2 + 6x + 8 = (x + 3)^2 - 9 + 8 = (x + 3)^2 - 1$

b) $x^2 + 8x - 10 = (x + 4)^2 - 16 - 10 = (x + 4)^2 - 26$

c) $x^2 - 3x - 10 = \left(x - \dfrac{3}{2}\right)^2 - \dfrac{9}{4} - 10$

$= \left(x - \dfrac{3}{2}\right)^2 - \dfrac{9}{4} - \dfrac{40}{4} = \left(x - \dfrac{3}{2}\right)^2 - \dfrac{49}{4}$

d) $-x^2 + 20x + 15 = -(x - 10)^2 + 100 + 15$

$= -(x - 10)^2 + 115$

e) $x^2 - 2mx + n = (x - m)^2 - m^2 + n$

$= (x - m)^2 + (-m^2 + n)$

f) $3x^2 - 12x + 7 = 3(x - 2)^2 - 12 + 7 = 3(x - 2)^2 - 5$

Q3 a) First complete the square of the expression:

$x^2 - 6x - 16 = (x - 3)^2 - 9 - 16 = (x - 3)^2 - 25$

Now set the completed square equal to zero:

$(x - 3)^2 - 25 = 0 \Rightarrow (x - 3)^2 = 25$

$\Rightarrow x - 3 = \pm\sqrt{25} \Rightarrow x = 3 \pm \sqrt{25} = 3 \pm 5$

$\Rightarrow x = 8$ or -2

b) Write the equation in standard quadratic form:

$p^2 - 10p = 200 \Rightarrow p^2 - 10p - 200 = 0$

Then complete the square of the expression:

$p^2 - 10p - 200 = (p - 5)^2 - 25 - 200$

$= (p - 5)^2 - 225$

Now set the completed square equal to zero:

$(p - 5)^2 - 225 = 0 \Rightarrow (p - 5)^2 = 225$

$\Rightarrow p - 5 = \pm\sqrt{225} \Rightarrow x = 5 \pm \sqrt{225} = 5 \pm 15$

$\Rightarrow p = 20$ or -10

c) First complete the square of the expression:

$x^2 + 2x + k = (x + 1)^2 - 1 + k = (x + 1)^2 + (k - 1)$

Now set the completed square equal to zero:

$(x + 1)^2 + (k - 1) = 0 \Rightarrow (x + 1)^2 = 1 - k$

$\Rightarrow x + 1 = \pm\sqrt{1 - k} \Rightarrow x = -1 \pm \sqrt{1 - k}$

d) Write the equation in standard quadratic form:

$9x^2 + 18x = 16 \Rightarrow 9x^2 + 18x - 16 = 0$

Then complete the square of the expression:

$9x^2 + 18x - 16 = 9(x + 1)^2 - 9 - 16$

$= 9(x + 1)^2 - 25$

Now set the completed square equal to zero:

$9(x + 1)^2 - 25 = 0 \Rightarrow 9(x + 1)^2 = 25$

$\Rightarrow (x + 1)^2 = \dfrac{25}{9}$

$\Rightarrow x + 1 = \pm\sqrt{\dfrac{25}{9}} \Rightarrow x = -1 \pm \sqrt{\dfrac{25}{9}}$

$\Rightarrow x = -1 \pm \dfrac{5}{3}$

So $x = \dfrac{2}{3}$ or $-\dfrac{8}{3}$

e) First complete the square of the expression:

$x^2 + 4x - 8 = (x + 2)^2 - 4 - 8 = (x + 2)^2 - 12$

Now set the completed square equal to zero:

$(x + 2)^2 - 12 = 0 \Rightarrow (x + 2)^2 = 12$

$\Rightarrow x + 2 = \pm\sqrt{12} \Rightarrow x = -2 \pm \sqrt{12}$

So $x = -2 \pm 2\sqrt{3}$

f) First complete the square of the expression:

$2x^2 - 12x + 9 = 2(x - 3)^2 - 18 + 9$

$= 2(x - 3)^2 - 9$

Now set the completed square equal to zero:

$2(x - 3)^2 - 9 = 0 \Rightarrow 2(x - 3)^2 = 9$

$\Rightarrow (x - 3)^2 = \dfrac{9}{2} \Rightarrow x - 3 = \pm\sqrt{\dfrac{9}{2}}$

$\Rightarrow x = 3 \pm \sqrt{\dfrac{9}{2}} \Rightarrow x = 3 \pm \dfrac{3}{\sqrt{2}} = 3 \pm \dfrac{3\sqrt{2}}{2}$

g) First divide through by 2:
$$x^2 - 6x - 27 = (x-3)^2 - 9 - 27$$
$$= (x-3)^2 - 36$$
Now set the completed square equal to zero:
$$(x-3)^2 - 36 = 0 \Rightarrow (x-3)^2 = 36$$
$$\Rightarrow x - 3 = \pm 6 \Rightarrow x = 3 \pm 6$$
So $x = 9$ or -3

h) First complete the square of the expression:
$$5x^2 - 3x + \frac{2}{5} = 5\left(x - \frac{3}{10}\right)^2 - \frac{9}{20} + \frac{2}{5}$$
$$= 5\left(x - \frac{3}{10}\right)^2 + \frac{-9 + 8}{20}$$
$$= 5\left(x - \frac{3}{10}\right)^2 - \frac{1}{20}$$
Now set the completed square equal to zero:
$$5\left(x - \frac{3}{10}\right)^2 - \frac{1}{20} = 0 \Rightarrow 5\left(x - \frac{3}{10}\right)^2 = \frac{1}{20}$$
$$\Rightarrow \left(x - \frac{3}{10}\right)^2 = \frac{1}{100} \Rightarrow x - \frac{3}{10} = \pm\sqrt{\frac{1}{100}}$$
$$\Rightarrow x - \frac{3}{10} = \pm\frac{1}{10} \Rightarrow x = \frac{3}{10} \pm \frac{1}{10}$$
So $x = \frac{2}{5}$ or $\frac{1}{5}$

Q4 First complete the square of the expression:
$$ax^2 + bx + c = a\left(x + \frac{b}{2a}\right)^2 - \frac{b^2}{4a} + c$$
Now set the completed square equal to zero and rearrange to find the roots:
$$a\left(x + \frac{b}{2a}\right)^2 - \frac{b^2}{4a} + c = 0$$
$$\Rightarrow \left(x + \frac{b}{2a}\right)^2 = \frac{b^2}{4a^2} - \frac{c}{a}$$
$$\Rightarrow \left(x + \frac{b}{2a}\right)^2 = \frac{b^2 - 4ac}{4a^2}$$
$$\Rightarrow x + \frac{b}{2a} = \pm\sqrt{\frac{b^2 - 4ac}{4a^2}}$$
$$\Rightarrow x = -\frac{b}{2a} \pm \frac{\sqrt{b^2 - 4ac}}{2a}$$
$$\Rightarrow x = \frac{-b \pm \sqrt{b^2 - 4ac}}{2a}$$

This last question was quite tricky, but if you got there you should have noticed something quite special — you've just proved the quadratic formula... wow.

2. Quadratic Functions and Roots

Exercise 2.1
— The roots of a quadratic function

Q1 a) 2 distinct real roots.

b) 2 equal roots / 1 real root.

c) No real roots.

d) 2 distinct real roots.

Q2 Completing the square:
$$f(x) = x^2 + 6x + 10 = (x+3)^2 - 9 + 10 = (x+3)^2 + 1$$
The smallest the $(x+3)^2$ bit can be is 0, and 1 is positive which means that $f(x)$ is always positive and the smallest it can be is 1. So $f(x)$ has no real roots.

Q3 $f(x) = -\left(x + \frac{7}{2}\right)^2 + \frac{25}{4} = 0$ when $\left(x + \frac{7}{2}\right)^2 = \frac{25}{4}$.
This can be solved by taking the square root (since the RHS is positive) — so it has real roots.

Exercise 2.2 — Using the discriminant

Q1 a) $a = 1$, $b = 8$, $c = 15$.
So $b^2 - 4ac = 8^2 - 4 \times 1 \times 15 = 64 - 60 = 4$.

b) $a = 1$, $b = 2\sqrt{3}$, $c = 3$.
So $b^2 - 4ac = (2\sqrt{3})^2 - 4 \times 1 \times 3 = 12 - 12 = 0$.

c) Write in standard form:
$(2x + 1)(5x - 3) = 10x^2 - x - 3$
so $a = 10$, $b = -1$ and $c = -3$.
$b^2 - 4ac = (-1)^2 - 4 \times 10 \times -3 = 1 + 120 = 121$

d) $a = -3$, $b = -\frac{11}{5}$, $c = -\frac{2}{5}$.
So $b^2 - 4ac = \left(-\frac{11}{5}\right)^2 - 4 \times (-3) \times \left(-\frac{2}{5}\right)$
$$= \frac{121}{25} - \frac{24}{5} = \frac{121}{25} - \frac{120}{25} = \frac{1}{25}$$

e) $a = 9$, $b = 20$, $c = 0$.
So $b^2 - 4ac = 20^2 - 4 \times 9 \times 0 = 400 - 0 = 400$.

f) $a = \frac{19}{16}$, $b = 0$, $c = -4$.
So $b^2 - 4ac = 0^2 - 4 \times \frac{19}{16} \times (-4) = 0 + 19 = 19$.

Q2 Find the discriminant of the equation by first writing it in standard form: $15x^2 + bx = 2 \Rightarrow 15x^2 + bx - 2 = 0$

$a = 15$, $b = b$, $c = -2$.

So $b^2 - 4ac = b^2 - 4 \times 15 \times (-2) = b^2 + 120$.
Now you know that the discriminant is 169 so let
$b^2 + 120 = 169 \Rightarrow b^2 = 49 \Rightarrow b = \pm 7$.

Q3 First find the discriminant: $a = a$, $b = 7$, $c = \frac{1}{4}$.
So $b^2 - 4ac = 7^2 - 4 \times a \times \frac{1}{4} = 49 - a$.
The equation has one real root which means its discriminant must be 0. So $49 - a = 0 \Rightarrow a = 49$.

Q4 a) $a = 13$, $b = 8$, $c = 2$
so $b^2 - 4ac = 8^2 - 4 \times 13 \times 2 = 64 - 104 = -40$.
The discriminant is negative so the equation has no real roots.

b) $a = \frac{1}{3}$, $b = \frac{5}{2}$, $c = 3$
so $b^2 - 4ac = \left(\frac{5}{2}\right)^2 - 4 \times \frac{1}{3} \times 3 = \frac{25}{4} - 4$
$$= \frac{25}{4} - \frac{16}{4} = \frac{9}{4}$$
The discriminant is positive so the equation has two distinct real roots.

Q5 $a = 1$, $b = -12$, $c = 27 + p$.
So $b^2 - 4ac = (-12)^2 - 4 \times 1 \times (27 + p)$
$= 144 - (108 + 4p) = 36 - 4p$.

If the equation has two distinct real roots, the discriminant must be positive so $36 - 4p > 0$
$\Rightarrow 36 > 4p \Rightarrow p < 9$.

Q6 $a = 10$, $b = -10$, $c = \dfrac{q}{2}$.

So $b^2 - 4ac = (-10)^2 - 4 \times 10 \times \dfrac{q}{2} = 100 - 20q$

If the equation has two distinct real roots, the discriminant must be positive so $100 - 20q > 0$
$\Rightarrow 100 > 20q \Rightarrow q < 5$.

Q7 $a = 2$, $b = 10p + 1$, $c = 5$.

So $b^2 - 4ac = (10p + 1)^2 - 4 \times 2 \times 5$
$\qquad\qquad = (100p^2 + 20p + 1) - 40$
$\qquad\qquad = 100p^2 + 20p - 39$.

If the equation has no real roots, the discriminant must be negative so $100p^2 + 20p - 39 < 0$
$\Rightarrow 100p^2 + 20p < 39 \Rightarrow 20p(5p + 1) < 39$
$\Rightarrow p(5p + 1) < \dfrac{39}{20}$.

Q8   First find the discriminant of the equation.
$a = -2$, $b = -2$, $c = k$.
So $b^2 - 4ac = (-2)^2 - 4 \times (-2) \times k = 4 + 8k$.

   a)   If the equation has two distinct real roots, the discriminant must be positive so $4 + 8k > 0$
$\Rightarrow 8k > -4 \Rightarrow k > -\dfrac{1}{2}$.

   b)   If the equation has one real root, the discriminant must be zero so $4 + 8k = 0 \Rightarrow k = -\dfrac{1}{2}$.

   c)   If the equation has no real roots, the discriminant must be negative so $4 + 8k < 0 \Rightarrow k < -\dfrac{1}{2}$.

Q9   **a)**   First work out the discriminant:

$a = 1$, $b = k + 5$, $c = \dfrac{k^2}{4}$

So $b^2 - 4ac = (k + 5)^2 - 4 \times 1 \times \dfrac{k^2}{4}$
$\qquad\qquad = (k^2 + 10k + 25) - k^2$
$\qquad\qquad = 10k + 25$

The equation has no real roots so the discriminant is negative so $10k + 25 < 0$.

   b)   To find the range of values of k, solve the inequality in part a).

$10k + 25 < 0 \Rightarrow 10k < -25 \Rightarrow k < -\dfrac{25}{10}$

So $k < -\dfrac{5}{2}$

Q10 a) $a = k - \dfrac{6}{5}$, $b = \sqrt{k}$, $c = \dfrac{5}{4}$

$b^2 - 4ac = (\sqrt{k})^2 - 4 \times \left(k - \dfrac{6}{5}\right) \times \dfrac{5}{4}$
$\qquad\qquad = k - 5\left(k - \dfrac{6}{5}\right)$
$\qquad\qquad = k - 5k + 6$
$\qquad\qquad = -4k + 6$

   b)   **(i)**   For one real root, discriminant = 0:
$-4k + 6 = 0 \Rightarrow k = \dfrac{6}{4} = \dfrac{3}{2}$.

      (ii)   For no real roots, discriminant is negative:
$-4k + 6 < 0$ so $k > \dfrac{3}{2}$.

      (iii)   For two distinct real roots, discriminant is positive:
$-4k + 6 > 0$ so $k < \dfrac{3}{2}$.

3. Quadratic Graphs

Exercise 3.1

— Sketching a quadratic graph

Q1   **a) & b)**

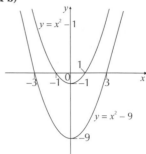

Q2   **a)** $f(x) = x^2 - 10x + 9 = (x - 9)(x - 1)$

    b) & c)

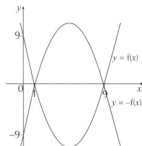

To sketch $y = -f(x)$, multiply $f(x)$ by -1 and sketch the graph of the resulting equation (it's $-x^2 + 10x - 9$). The graph is actually reflected in the x-axis — you'll learn more about this in C2.

Q3   **a)** $y = -x^2 + 2x + 1$

    (i)   The x^2 coefficient is -1 so it is n-shaped.

    (ii)   Letting $x = 0$, $y = 1$ is the y-intercept.

    (iii)   Calculate the discriminant to work out the number of roots: $a = -1$, $b = 2$, $c = 1$.
$b^2 - 4ac = 2^2 - 4 \times (-1) \times 1 = 4 + 4 = 8$
The discriminant is positive so there are 2 distinct real roots.

    (iv)   To find the x-intercepts — find the roots:
$y = -x^2 + 2x + 1 = -(x - 1)^2 + 2$ by completing the square. Setting this equal to zero:
$-(x - 1)^2 + 2 = 0$ so $(x - 1)^2 = 2$
so $x - 1 = \pm\sqrt{2} \Rightarrow x = 1 \pm \sqrt{2}$.

    (v)   The vertex is a maximum since the graph's n-shaped. The maximum can be found by looking at the completed square
$y = -(x - 1)^2 + 2$. The highest value $-(x - 1)^2$ can take is 0, so the maximum is at $y = 2$ and $x = 1$ (to make the bracket 0).

(vi)

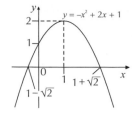

b) $y = x^2 - 7x + 15$

(i) The x^2 coefficient is 1 so the graph's u-shaped.

(ii) Letting $x = 0$, $y = 15$ is the y-intercept.

(iii) Calculate the discriminant to work out the number of roots: $a = 1$, $b = -7$, $c = 15$.
$b^2 - 4ac = (-7)^2 - 4 \times 1 \times 15 = 49 - 60 = -11$
The discriminant is negative so there are no real roots.

(iv) There are no real roots so the graph does not intersect the x-axis.

(v) The vertex is a minimum since the graph's u-shaped. The minimum can be found by completing the square.
$y = x^2 - 7x + 15 = (x - \frac{7}{2})^2 + \frac{11}{4}$
The lowest value $(x - \frac{7}{2})^2$ can take is zero — so the minimum is at $y = \frac{11}{4}$ and so $x = \frac{7}{2}$ (to make the bracket 0).

(vi)

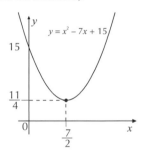

c) $y = 2x^2 + 4x - 9$

(i) The x^2 coefficient is 2 so it is u-shaped.

(ii) Letting $x = 0$, $y = -9$ is the y-intercept.

(iii) Calculate the discriminant to work out the number of roots: $a = 2$, $b = 4$, $c = -9$.
$b^2 - 4ac = 4^2 - 4 \times 2 \times (-9) = 16 + 72 = 88$
The discriminant is positive so there are 2 distinct real roots.

(iv) To find the x-intercepts, find the roots:
$2x^2 + 4x - 9 = 0$
Completing the square gives:
$2(x + 1)^2 - 2 - 9 = 0$
$2(x + 1)^2 - 11 = 0$
Solving:
$(x + 1)^2 = \frac{11}{2}$
$x = -1 \pm \sqrt{\frac{11}{2}}$

(v) The vertex is a minimum since the graph is u-shaped. The minimum occurs when the square is 0, so it's $(-1, -11)$

(vi)

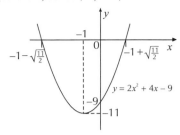

Q4 a) The minimum point is shown on the graph as $(-4, 2)$. The coordinates of the vertex of the graph of the function $f(x) = p(x + q)^2 + r$ are $(-q, r)$. In this case $p = 1$ and from the minimum on the graph you can see $-q = -4$, so $q = 4$ and $r = 2$. So you can write the function $f(x) = (x + 4)^2 + 2$.

b) $g(x) = (x + 4)^2$ is in the form $p(x + q)^2 + r$ with $p = 1$ so the graph is u-shaped and the minimum is at $(-q, r) = (-4, 0)$.

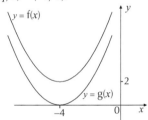

c) $f(x)$ does not have any real roots as its graph does not touch the x-axis.

Q5 a) $x^2 - 6x + 5 = (x - 3)^2 - 9 + 5 = (x - 3)^2 - 4$

b) $x^2 - 6x + 5 = 0 \Rightarrow (x - 3)^2 - 4 = 0 \Rightarrow (x - 3)^2 = 4$
$\Rightarrow x - 3 = \pm \sqrt{4} \Rightarrow x = 3 \pm \sqrt{4} = 3 \pm 2 = 5$ or 1

c) The graph is u-shaped. The function has roots $x = 1$ and 5 so these are the x-intercepts. Putting $x = 0$ into the original equation gives $y = 5$, so this is the y-intercept. Completing the square gives the minimum as $(3, -4)$. Putting all this together gives the following graph:

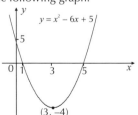

Q6 a) $f(x) = x^2 - 2x + 1 = (x - 1)^2$ so the function has one root (i.e. two equal roots) at $x = 1$. Letting $x = 0$ gives $f(x) = 1$ so the y-intercept is at 1. The graph is u-shaped.

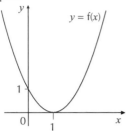

b) $f(x) = x^2 + x - 1 = (x + \frac{1}{2})^2 - \frac{5}{4}$ and solving $f(x) = 0$ gives $x = -\frac{1}{2} \pm \frac{\sqrt{5}}{2}$ as the x-intercepts. Letting $x = 0$ we get $f(x) = -1$ so this is the y-intercept. The graph is u-shaped.

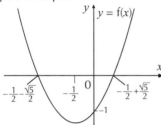

c) $f(x) = x^2 - 8x + 18 = (x - 4)^2 + 2$. Solving $f(x) = 0$ gives $x = 4 \pm \sqrt{-2}$ so there are no x-intercepts as you cannot take the square root of –2.
You could have worked out the discriminant to see that there were no real roots to save you trying to solve the equation.

Letting $x = 0$ gives $f(x) = 18$. The graph is u-shaped but it could be one of two graphs which are u-shaped with a y-intercept of 18. To find out which, work out the vertex. It has a minimum as it is u-shaped and from completing the square, the minimum is at (4, 2).

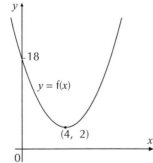

d) $f(x) = -x^2 + 3$ so setting $f(x) = 0$ gives $x = \pm\sqrt{3}$ as the x-intercepts. Letting $x = 0$ gives $f(x) = 3$ so 3 is the y-intercept. The graph is n-shaped.

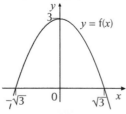

Q7 a) The roots of the quadratic function are the values of x where the graph crosses the x-axis. So the roots are $x = -2$ and $x = 1$.

b) One root of the equation is $x = -2$ which means $x + 2$ will be a factor. The other root $x = 1$ means that $x - 1$ will be a factor. So the quadratic function should be of the form $y = a(x + 2)(x - 1)$ for some value of a. But you know the equation has the form $y = -x^2 + px + q$. So a should be –1 to produce the term $-x^2$. So $y = -(x + 2)(x - 1)$ which gives $y = -x^2 - x + 2$, so $p = -1$ and $q = 2$.
The trickiest part of this question is realising you might also need a number factor, a, to form the factorised quadratic. Without it, you'd have got the wrong answer of $x^2 + x - 2$.

Review Exercise — Chapter 2

Q1 a) $(x + 1)^2$ **b)** $(x - 10)(x - 3)$
c) $(x + 2)(x - 2)$ **d)** $(3 - x)(x + 1)$
e) $(2x + 1)(x - 4)$ **f)** $(5x - 3)(x + 2)$

Q2 a) $(x - 2)(x - 1) = 0$, so $x = 2$ or 1
b) $(x + 4)(x - 3) = 0$, so $x = -4$ or 3
c) $(2 - x)(x + 1) = 0$, so $x = 2$ or –1
d) $(x + 4)(x - 4) = 0$, so $x = \pm4$
e) $(3x + 2)(x - 7) = 0$, so $x = -\frac{2}{3}$ or 7
f) $(2x + 1)(2x - 1) = 0$, so $x = \pm\frac{1}{2}$
g) $(2x - 3)(x - 1) = 0$, so $x = \frac{3}{2}$ or 1

Q3 a) $(x - 2)^2 - 7$; minimum value = –7 at $x = 2$, and the graph crosses the x-axis at $x = 2 \pm \sqrt{7}$.
b) $\frac{21}{4} - (x + \frac{3}{2})^2$; maximum value = $\frac{21}{4}$ at $x = -\frac{3}{2}$, and the graph crosses the x-axis at $-\frac{3}{2} \pm \frac{\sqrt{21}}{2}$.
c) $2(x - 1)^2 + 9$; minimum value = 9 at $x = 1$, and the graph doesn't cross the x-axis.
d) $4(x - \frac{7}{2})^2 - 1$; minimum value = –1 at $x = \frac{7}{2}$, and the graph crosses the x-axis at $x = \frac{7}{2} \pm \frac{1}{2}$, i.e. $x = 4$ or $x = 3$.

Q4 a) $b^2 - 4ac = 16$, so 2 distinct real roots. Factorising gives: $(x + 1)(x - 3) = 0$

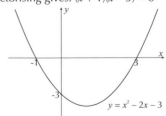

b) $b^2 - 4ac = 0$, so 2 equal roots (or 1 root).
Factorising gives: $(x - 3)^2 = 0$

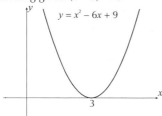

c) $b^2 - 4ac = -8$, so no real roots.
Completing the square gives:
$2(x + 1)^2 + 1 = 0$, so vertex at $(-1, 1)$.

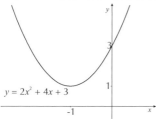

Q5 a) Using the quadratic formula with $a = 3$, $b = -7$ and $c = 3$:

$$x = \frac{-(-7) \pm \sqrt{(-7)^2 - (4 \times 3 \times 3)}}{(2 \times 3)}$$

$$= \frac{7 \pm \sqrt{49 - 36}}{6} = \frac{7 \pm \sqrt{13}}{6}$$

so $x = \dfrac{7 + \sqrt{13}}{6}$, $x = \dfrac{7 - \sqrt{13}}{6}$.

b) First divide through by 2 to get:
$x^2 - 3x - 1 = 0$
Now using the quadratic formula
with $a = 1$, $b = -3$ and $c = -1$:

$$x = \frac{-(-3) \pm \sqrt{(-3)^2 - (4 \times 1 \times -1)}}{(2 \times 1)}$$

$$= \frac{3 \pm \sqrt{9 + 4}}{2} = \frac{3 \pm \sqrt{13}}{2}$$

so $x = \dfrac{3 + \sqrt{13}}{2}$, $x = \dfrac{3 - \sqrt{13}}{2}$.

c) Using the quadratic formula
with $a = 1$, $b = 4$ and $c = -6$:

$$x = \frac{-(4) \pm \sqrt{(4)^2 - (4 \times 1 \times -6)}}{(2 \times 1)}$$

$$= \frac{-4 \pm \sqrt{16 + 24}}{2}$$

$$= \frac{-4 \pm \sqrt{40}}{2}$$

$$= \frac{-4 \pm 2\sqrt{10}}{2}$$

$$= -2 \pm \sqrt{10}$$

so $x = -2 + \sqrt{10}$, $x = -2 - \sqrt{10}$.

Q6 $k^2 - (4 \times 1 \times 4) > 0$, so $k^2 > 16$ and so $k > 4$ or $k < -4$.

Exam-Style Questions — Chapter 2

Q1 For equal roots, $b^2 - 4ac = 0$ *[1 mark]*
$a = 1$, $b = 2k$ and $c = 4k$

so $(2k)^2 - (4 \times 1 \times 4k) = 0$ *[1 mark]*
$$4k^2 - 16k = 0$$
$$4k(k - 4) = 0 \quad \text{[1 mark]}$$

so $k = 4$ (as k is non-zero).   *[1 mark]*

Q2 For distinct real roots, $b^2 - 4ac > 0$ *[1 mark]*
$a = p$, $b = 2p + 3$ and $c = p$, so:

$$(2p + 3)^2 - (4 \times p \times p) > 0 \quad \text{[1 mark]}$$
$$4p^2 + 12p + 9 - 4p^2 > 0$$
$$12p + 9 > 0 \quad \text{[1 mark]}$$
$$p > -\frac{3}{4} \quad \text{[1 mark]}$$

Q3 Expanding the brackets on the RHS gives the
quadratic $mx^2 + 4mx + 4m + p$. Equating the
coefficients of x^2 gives $m = 5$ *[1 mark]*. Equating the
coefficients of x gives $n = 4m$, so $n = 20$ *[1 mark]*.
Equating the constant terms gives
$14 = 4m + p \Rightarrow p = -6$ *[1 mark]*.

Q4 a) Completing the square gives:
$(x - 6)^2 - 36 + 15$
$(x - 6)^2 - 21$
[1 mark for the square, 1 mark for '−21']

b) (i) The minimum occurs when the expression
in brackets is equal to 0, which means the
minimum is the value of b, which from (a)
above is −21 *[1 mark]*.

(ii) From above, the minimum occurs when the
expression in brackets is equal to 0, i.e. when
$x = 6$ *[1 mark]*.

*Part (b) is easy once you've completed the square — you
can just take your values straight from there.*

Q5 a) Put $a = 1$, $b = -14$ and $c = 25$ into the quadratic
formula:

$$x = \frac{-(-14) \pm \sqrt{(-14)^2 - (4 \times 1 \times 25)}}{(2 \times 1)}$$

$$= \frac{14 \pm \sqrt{196 - 100}}{2}$$

$$= \frac{14 \pm \sqrt{96}}{2}$$

$$= \frac{14 \pm 4\sqrt{6}}{2}$$

$$= 7 \pm 2\sqrt{6}$$

so $x = 7 + 2\sqrt{6}$, $x = 7 - 2\sqrt{6}$
***[3 marks available — 1 mark for putting correct
values of a, b and c into the quadratic formula,
1 mark each for final x-value.]***

b)

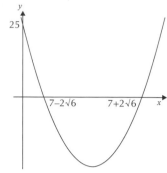

[3 marks available — 1 mark for drawing u-shaped curve, 1 mark for using answers from a) as x-axis intercepts and 1 mark for correct y-axis intercept (0, 25).]

c) As the graph is u-shaped, the function is < 0 when x is between the two intercepts,
$\Rightarrow 7 - 2\sqrt{6} \leq x \leq 7 + 2\sqrt{6}$ **[1 mark]**.
Quadratic inequalities like this are covered in detail in Chapter 3 — have a look if you want more info.

Q6 a) (i) First, rewrite the quadratic as:
$-x^2 + 10x - 27$
And complete the square ($a = -1$):
$-(x - 5)^2 + 25 - 27 = -(x - 5)^2 - 2$
Rewrite the square in the form given in the question:
$-(-(5 - x))^2 - 2 = -(5 - x)^2 - 2$
[1 mark for m = 5, 1 mark for n = –2]
The last couple of steps are using the fact that $(-a)^2 = a^2$ to show that $(m - n)^2 = (n - m)^2$...

(ii) $(5 - x)^2 \geq 0$ for all values of x, so $-(5 - x)^2 \leq 0$.
Therefore: $(5 - x)^2 - 2 < 0$ for all x,
i.e. the function is always negative. **[1 mark]**

b) (i) The y-coordinate is the maximum value, which is –2 **[1 mark]**, and this occurs when the expression in the brackets = 0.
The x-value that makes the expression in the brackets 0 is 5 **[1 mark]**, so the coordinates of the maximum point are (5, –2).

(ii)

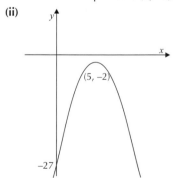

[2 marks available — 1 mark for drawing n-shaped curve that sits below the x-axis with the maximum roughly where shown (even if its position is not labelled), 1 mark for correct y-axis intercept (0, –27).]

Chapter 3: Simultaneous Equations and Inequalities

1. Simultaneous Equations
Exercise 1.1 — Simultaneous equations — both linear

Q1 a) (1) $2x - 3y = 3$
(2) $x + 3y = 6$
(1) + (2) $3x = 9 \Rightarrow x = 3$
$x = 3$ in (2) $3 + 3y = 6 \Rightarrow 3y = 3 \Rightarrow y = 1$
So the solution is $x = 3$, $y = 1$

b) (1) $3x + 2y = 7$
(2) $7x - y = -12$
(2) × 2 $14x - 2y = -24$ (3)
(1) + (3) $17x = -17 \Rightarrow x = -1$
$x = -1$ in (1) $-3 + 2y = 7$
$\Rightarrow 2y = 10 \Rightarrow y = 5$
So the solution is $x = -1$, $y = 5$

c) (1) $4x + 3y = -4$
(2) $6x - 4y = 11$
(1) × 3 $12x + 9y = -12$ (3)
(2) × 2 $12x - 8y = 22$ (4)
(3) − (4) $17y = -34 \Rightarrow y = -2$
$y = -2$ in (2) $6x + 8 = 11 \Rightarrow 6x = 3 \Rightarrow x = \frac{1}{2}$
So the solution is $x = \frac{1}{2}$, $y = -2$

d) (1) $7x - 6y = 4$
(2) $11x + 9y = -6$
(1) × 3 $21x - 18y = 12$ (3)
(2) × 2 $22x + 18y = -12$ (4)
(3) + (4) $43x = 0 \Rightarrow x = 0$
$x = 0$ in (2) $0 + 9y = -6 \Rightarrow y = -\frac{6}{9} = -\frac{2}{3}$
So the solution is $x = 0$, $y = -\frac{2}{3}$

e) Rearrange (1) $6x + 2y = 8$
Rearrange (2) $4x + 3y = -3$
(1) × 2 $12x + 4y = 16$ (3)
(2) × 3 $12x + 9y = -9$ (4)
(3) − (4) $-5y = 25 \Rightarrow y = -5$
$y = -5$ in (2) $4x - 15 = -3$
               $\Rightarrow 4x = 12 \Rightarrow x = 3$
So the solution is $x = 3$, $y = -5$

f) Rearrange (1) $2x + 18y = 21$
Rearrange (2) $-3x - 14y = 14$
(1) × 3 $6x + 54y = 63$ (3)
(2) × 2 $-6x - 28y = 28$ (4)
(3) + (4) $26y = 91 \Rightarrow y = \frac{7}{2}$
$y = \frac{7}{2}$ in (1) $2x + 63 = 21$
               $\Rightarrow 2x = -42 \Rightarrow x = -21$
So the solution is $x = -21$, $y = \frac{7}{2}$

g) (1) $\qquad 2x + 16y = 10$

Rearrange (2) $\quad 3x + 64y = 5$

(1) $\times 4 \qquad 8x + 64y = 40 \qquad$ (3)

(2) $-$ (3) $\qquad -5x = -35 \Rightarrow x = 7$

$x = 7$ in (1) $\quad 14 + 16y = 10$

$\qquad\qquad\qquad \Rightarrow 16y = -4 \Rightarrow y = -\frac{1}{4}$

So the solution is $x = 7$, $y = -\frac{1}{4}$

Q2 a) Rearrange the equations into the form $ax + by = c$ and multiply though to get rid of any fractions:

$y = 2x - 3 \Rightarrow 2x - y = 3$ and

$y = \frac{1}{2}x + 3 \Rightarrow x - 2y = -6$. Then solve as before:

(1) $\qquad\qquad 2x - y = 3$

(2) $\qquad\qquad x - 2y = -6$

(2) $\times 2 \qquad 2x - 4y = -12 \qquad$ (3)

(1) $-$ (3) $\qquad 3y = 15 \Rightarrow y = 5$

$y = 5$ in (1) $\quad 2x - 5 = 3 \Rightarrow 2x = 8 \Rightarrow x = 4$

So they intersect at (4, 5)

b) Rearrange the equations as in part a) to get

$2x + 3y = 21$ and $x - 2y = -21$.

(1) $\qquad\qquad 2x + 3y = 21$

(2) $\qquad\qquad x - 2y = -21$

(2) $\times 2 \qquad 2x - 4y = -42 \qquad$ (3)

(1) $-$ (3) $\qquad 7y = 63 \Rightarrow y = 9$

$y = 9$ in (1) $\quad 2x + 27 = 21$

$\qquad\qquad \Rightarrow 2x = -6 \Rightarrow x = -3$

So they intersect at (–3, 9)

c) Rearrange (1) $\qquad x + 2y = -5$

Rearrange (2) $\qquad 3x - 5y = 7$

(1) $\times 3 \qquad\qquad 3x + 6y = -15 \qquad$ (3)

(2) $-$ (3) $\qquad -11y = 22 \Rightarrow y = -2$

$y = -2$ in (1) $\quad x - 4 = -5 \Rightarrow x = -1$

So they intersect at (–1, –2)

d) (1) $\qquad 2x - 3y = 7$

(2) $\qquad 5x - \frac{15}{2}y = 9$

(1) $\times 5 \qquad 10x - 15y = 35 \qquad$ (3)

(2) $\times 2 \qquad 10x - 15y = 18 \qquad$ (4)

(3) $-$ (4) $\quad 0 = 17$

This is not possible — so these lines do not intersect.

The lines are actually parallel.

e) Rearrange (1) $8x + 3y = 10$

Rearrange (2) $6x + 9y = 3$

(1) $\times 3 \qquad\quad 24x + 9y = 30 \qquad$ (3)

(2) $-$ (3) $\qquad 18x - -27 \Rightarrow x = \frac{3}{2}$

$x = \frac{3}{2}$ in (2) $\quad 9 + 9y = 3$

$\qquad\qquad\qquad \Rightarrow 9y = -6 \Rightarrow y = -\frac{2}{3}$

So they intersect at $(\frac{3}{2}, -\frac{2}{3})$

f) (1) $\qquad\qquad 7x - 5y = 15$

Rearrange (2) $\qquad 2x - 3y = 9$

(1) $\times 2 \qquad\qquad 14x - 10y = 30 \qquad$ (3)

(2) $\times 7 \qquad\qquad 14x - 21y = 63 \qquad$ (4)

(3) $-$ (4) $\qquad\qquad 11y = -33 \Rightarrow y = -3$

$y = -3$ in (2) $\quad 2x + 9 = 9$

$\qquad\qquad\qquad \Rightarrow 2x = 0 \Rightarrow x = 0$

So they intersect at (0, –3)

Exercise 1.2 — Simultaneous equations — if one is quadratic

Q1 a) (1) $\qquad\qquad y = 4x + 3$

(2) $\qquad\qquad 2y - 3x = 1$

Sub (1) in (2) $\quad 2(4x + 3) - 3x = 1$

$\Rightarrow 8x + 6 - 3x = 1 \Rightarrow 5x = -5 \Rightarrow x = -1$

$x = -1$ in (1) $\quad y = 4 \times -1 + 3 = -1$

So the solution is $x = -1$, $y = -1$

b) (1) $\qquad\qquad 5x + 2y = 16$

Rearrange (2) $\qquad x = 2y - 4$

Sub (2) in (1) $\qquad 5(2y - 4) + 2y = 16$

$\Rightarrow 12y - 20 = 16 \Rightarrow 12y = 36 \Rightarrow y = 3$

$y = 3$ in (2) $\quad x = 2 \times 3 - 4 = 2$

So the solution is $x = 2$, $y = 3$

Q2 a) (1) $\qquad\qquad y = 2x + 5$

(2) $\qquad\qquad y = x^2 - x + 1$

Sub (1) in (2) $\quad 2x + 5 = x^2 - x + 1$

$\Rightarrow 0 = x^2 - 3x - 4 \Rightarrow (x - 4)(x + 1) = 0$

$\Rightarrow x = 4$ or $x = -1$

When $x = 4$, $y = 8 + 5 = 13$, and

when $x = -1$, $y = -2 + 5 = 3$

So $x = 4$, $y = 13 \quad$ or $\quad x = -1$, $y = 3$

b) (1) $\qquad\qquad y = 2x^2 - 3$

(2) $\qquad\qquad y = 3x + 2$

Sub (2) in (1) $\quad 3x + 2 = 2x^2 - 3$

$\Rightarrow 2x^2 - 3x - 5 = 0 \Rightarrow (2x - 5)(x + 1) = 0$

$\Rightarrow x = \frac{5}{2}$ or $x = -1$

When $x = \frac{5}{2}$, $y = \frac{15}{2} + 2 = \frac{19}{2}$, and

when $x = -1$, $y = -3 + 2 = -1$

So $x = \frac{5}{2}$, $y = \frac{19}{2} \quad$ or $\quad x = -1$, $y = -1$

c) (1) $\qquad\qquad 2x^2 - xy = 6$

Rearrange (2) $\qquad y = 3x - 7$

Sub (2) in (1) $\qquad 2x^2 - x(3x - 7) = 6$

$\Rightarrow 2x^2 - 3x^2 + 7x - 6 = 0$

$\Rightarrow -x^2 + 7x - 6 = 0 \Rightarrow x^2 - 7x + 6 = 0$

$\Rightarrow (x - 6)(x - 1) = 0$

$\Rightarrow x = 6$ or $x = 1$

When $x = 6$, $y = 18 - 7 = 11$, and

when $x = 1$, $y = 3 - 7 = -4$

So $x = 6$, $y = 11 \quad$ or $\quad x = 1$, $y = -4$

d) (1) $\qquad xy = 6$

Rearrange (2) $\quad 2y + 4 = x$

Sub (2) in (1) $\qquad y(2y + 4) = 6 \Rightarrow 2y^2 + 4y = 6$

$\Rightarrow 2y^2 + 4y - 6 = 0$

$\Rightarrow y^2 + 2y - 3 = 0 \Rightarrow (y + 3)(y - 1) = 0$

$\Rightarrow y = -3$ or $y = 1$

When $y = -3$, $x = -6 + 4 = -2$, and
when $y = 1$, $x = 2 + 4 = 6$

So $x = -2, y = -3 \quad$ or $\quad x = 6, y = 1$

e) (1) $\qquad y = x^2 - 2x - 3$

Rearrange (2) $\quad y = -x - 8$

Sub (2) in (1) $\qquad -x - 8 = x^2 - 2x - 3$

$\Rightarrow 0 = x^2 - x + 5$

$b^2 - 4ac = 1 - 20 = -19 < 0 \Rightarrow$ no real roots
So there are no solutions for the simultaneous equations.

f) (1) $\qquad y = 2x^2 - 3x + 5$

Rearrange (2) $\quad 5x - 3 = y$

Sub (2) in (1) $\qquad 5x - 3 = 2x^2 - 3x + 5$

$\Rightarrow 0 = 2x^2 - 8x + 8$

$\Rightarrow x^2 - 4x + 4 = 0$

$\Rightarrow (x - 2)^2 = 0 \Rightarrow x = 2$

When $x = 2$, $y = 10 - 3 = 7$, so $x = 2$, $y = 7$
There is only one solution here.

g) (1) $\qquad 2x^2 + 3y^2 = 77$

Rearrange (2) $\quad x = -3y + 14$

Sub (2) in (1) $\qquad 2(-3y + 14)^2 + 3y^2 = 77$

$\Rightarrow 2(9y^2 - 84y + 196) + 3y^2 = 77$

$\Rightarrow 21y^2 - 168y + 315 = 0 \Rightarrow y^2 - 8y + 15 = 0$

$\Rightarrow (y - 3)(y - 5) = 0 \Rightarrow y = 3$ or $y = 5$

When $y = 3$, $x = -9 + 14 = 5$, and
when $y = 5$, $x = -15 + 14 = -1$

So $x = 5, y = 3 \quad$ or $\quad x = -1, y = 5$

Q3 a) (1) $\qquad y = \frac{1}{2}x^2 + 4x - 8$

(2) $\qquad y = \frac{3}{2}x + 4$

Sub (2) in (1) $\quad \frac{3}{2}x + 4 = \frac{1}{2}x^2 + 4x - 8$

$\Rightarrow 3x + 8 = x^2 + 8x - 16$

$\Rightarrow 0 = x^2 + 5x - 24 \Rightarrow (x + 8)(x - 3) = 0$

$\Rightarrow x = -8$ or $x = 3$

When $x = -8$, $y = -12 + 4 = -8$, and
when $x = 3$, $y = \frac{9}{2} + 4 = \frac{17}{2}$

So they intersect at $(-8, -8)$ and $(3, \frac{17}{2})$

b) (1) $\qquad y = 2x^2 + x - 6$

Rearrange (2) $\quad 5x + 10 = y$

Sub (2) in (1) $\qquad 5x + 10 = 2x^2 + x - 6$

$\Rightarrow 0 = 2x^2 - 4x - 16 \Rightarrow x^2 - 2x - 8 = 0$

$\Rightarrow (x - 4)(x + 2) = 0 \Rightarrow x = 4$ or $x = -2$

When $x = 4$, $y = 20 + 10 = 30$, and
when $x = -2$, $y = -10 + 10 = 0$

So they intersect at $(4, 30)$ and $(-2, 0)$

c) (1) $\qquad x^2 + y^2 = 50$

Rearrange (2) $\quad x = -2y + 5$

Sub (2) in (1) $\qquad (-2y + 5)^2 + y^2 = 50$

$\Rightarrow 4y^2 - 20y + 25 + y^2 - 50 = 0$

$\Rightarrow 5y^2 - 20y - 25 = 0 \Rightarrow y^2 - 4y - 5 = 0$

$\Rightarrow (y - 5)(y + 1) = 0 \Rightarrow y = 5$ or $y = -1$

When $y = 5$, $x = -10 + 5 = -5$, and
when $y = -1$, $x = 2 + 5 = 7$

So they intersect at $(-5, 5)$ and $(7, -1)$

d) (1) $\qquad 2x^2 - y + 3x + 1 = 0$

Rearrange (2) $\quad y = x + 5$

Sub (2) in (1) $\qquad 2x^2 - (x + 5) + 3x + 1 = 0$

$\Rightarrow 2x^2 + 2x - 4 = 0 \Rightarrow x^2 + x - 2 = 0$

$\Rightarrow (x + 2)(x - 1) = 0 \Rightarrow x = -2$ or $x = 1$

When $x = -2$, $y = -2 + 5 = 3$, and
when $x = 1$, $y = 1 + 5 = 6$

So they intersect at $(-2, 3)$ and $(1, 6)$

Q4 a) (1) $\qquad x^2 + y^2 = 10$

Rearrange (2) $\quad x = 3y - 10$

Sub (2) in (1) $\qquad (3y - 10)^2 + y^2 = 10$

$\Rightarrow 9y^2 - 60y + 100 + y^2 - 10 = 0$

$\Rightarrow 10y^2 - 60y + 90 = 0 \Rightarrow y^2 - 6y + 9 = 0$

$\Rightarrow (y - 3)^2 = 0 \Rightarrow y = 3$

When $y = 3$, $x = 9 - 10 = -1$
So $x = -1, y = 3$.

b) $x^2 + y^2 = 10$ is a circle and $x - 3y + 10 = 0$ is a straight line. Part a) tells us that they intersect at a single point, so the line must actually be a tangent to the circle at the point $(-1, 3)$.

Q5 a) (1) $\qquad y = x^2 + 6x - 7$

(2) $\qquad y = 2x - 3$

Sub (2) in (1) $\quad 2x - 3 = x^2 + 6x - 7$

$\Rightarrow x^2 + 4x - 4 = 0$

So $b^2 - 4ac = 16 + 16 = 32 > 0$
So they will intersect at two points.

b) (1) $\qquad 3x^2 + 4y^2 = 7$

Rearrange (2) $\quad x = -\frac{4}{3}y + \frac{7}{3}$

Sub (2) in (1) $\qquad 3(-\frac{4}{3}y + \frac{7}{3})^2 + 4y^2 = 7$

$\Rightarrow 3(\frac{16}{9}y^2 - \frac{56}{9}y + \frac{49}{9}) + 4y^2 = 7$

$\Rightarrow \frac{16}{3}y^2 - \frac{56}{3}y + \frac{49}{3} + 4y^2 - 7 = 0$

$\Rightarrow 16y^2 - 56y + 49 + 12y^2 - 21 = 0$

$\Rightarrow 28y^2 - 56y + 28 = 0$

$\Rightarrow y^2 - 2y + 1 = 0$

Now $b^2 - 4ac = 4 - 4 = 0$

So they will intersect only once — (2) is a tangent to (1).

c) (1) $\qquad xy + 2x - y = 8$

Rearrange (2) $\quad x = -y + 1$

Sub (2) in (1) $\quad (-y + 1)y + 2(-y + 1) - y = 8$

$\Rightarrow -y^2 + y - 2y + 2 - y = 8$

$\Rightarrow -y^2 - 2y - 6 = 0$

$\Rightarrow y^2 + 2y + 6 = 0$

So $b^2 - 4ac = 4 - 24 = -20 < 0$

So the graphs will not intersect.

2. Inequalities
Exercise 2.1 — Linear inequalities

Q1 **a)** $2x - 1 < x + 4 \Rightarrow x < 5$

b) $4 - 3x \geq 10 - 5x \Rightarrow 2x \geq 6 \Rightarrow x \geq 3$

c) $5x + 7 > 3x + 1 \Rightarrow 2x > -6 \Rightarrow x > -3$

d) $3 - 2x \leq 5x - 4 \Rightarrow -7x \leq -7 \Rightarrow x \geq 1$

e) $9 - x \geq 7x + 5 \Rightarrow -8x \geq -4 \Rightarrow x \leq \dfrac{1}{2}$

Q2 **a)** $2(x + 3) > 3(x + 2)$

$\Rightarrow 2x + 6 > 3x + 6 \Rightarrow -x > 0 \Rightarrow x < 0$

b) $5(1 + 3x) \leq 7$

$\Rightarrow 5 + 15x \leq 7 \Rightarrow 15x \leq 2 \Rightarrow x \leq \dfrac{2}{15}$

Q3 **a)** $\dfrac{6 - 5x}{2} < \dfrac{4 - 8x}{3} \Rightarrow 3(6 - 5x) < 2(4 - 8x)$

$\Rightarrow 18 - 15x < 8 - 16x \Rightarrow x < -10$

b) $\dfrac{3x - 1}{4} \geq 2x \Rightarrow 3x - 1 \geq 8x \Rightarrow x \leq -\dfrac{1}{5}$

c) $\dfrac{x - 2}{2} - \dfrac{2x + 3}{3} < 7$

$\Rightarrow 3(x - 2) - 2(2x + 3) < 42$

$\Rightarrow 3x - 6 - 4x - 6 < 42 \Rightarrow -x < 54$

$\Rightarrow x > -54$

Q4 **a)** $-5 < 2x - 3 < 15$

$\Rightarrow -2 < 2x < 18 \Rightarrow -1 < x < 9$

b) $-5 \leq 4 - 3x < 19$

$\Rightarrow -9 \leq -3x < 15 \Rightarrow 3 \geq x > -5$

$\Rightarrow -5 < x \leq 3$

Make sure you rearrange your final answer so that the lower value is on the left.

Q5 **a)** $2x \geq 3 - x \Rightarrow 3x \geq 3 \Rightarrow x \geq 1$

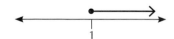

b) $5x - 1 < 3x + 5 \Rightarrow 2x < 6 \Rightarrow x < 3$

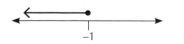

c) $2x + 1 \geq 3x + 2 \Rightarrow -x \geq 1 \Rightarrow x \leq -1$

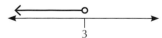

d) $3x - 1 \leq 5x - 7 \Rightarrow -2x \leq -6 \Rightarrow x \geq 3$

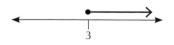

e) $9 - x \leq 3 - 4x \Rightarrow 3x \leq -6 \Rightarrow x \leq -2$

$\qquad -2$

f) $\dfrac{2(x - 3)}{3} + 1 < \dfrac{2x - 1}{2}$

$\Rightarrow 4(x - 3) + 6 < 3(2x - 1)$

$\Rightarrow 4x - 12 + 6 < 6x - 3 \Rightarrow -2x < 3 \Rightarrow x > -\dfrac{3}{2}$

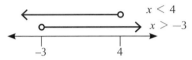

$\qquad -\dfrac{3}{2}$

Q6 **a)** $7 \leq 3x - 2 < 16 \Rightarrow 9 \leq 3x \leq 18 \Rightarrow 3 \leq x < 6$

b)

$\qquad 3 \qquad\qquad 6$

Q7 $4 - 2x < 10 \Rightarrow -2x < 6 \Rightarrow x > -3$

and $3x - 1 < x + 7 \Rightarrow 2x < 8 \Rightarrow x < 4$

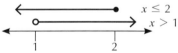

The solutions overlap between –3 and 4, so:
$-3 < x < 4$

Q8 **a)** $2x \geq 3x - 5 \Rightarrow -x \geq -5 \Rightarrow x \leq 5$

and $3x - 2 \geq x - 6 \Rightarrow 2x \geq -4 \Rightarrow x \geq -2$

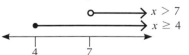

Solution: $-2 \leq x \leq 5$

b) $5x + 1 \leq 11 \Rightarrow 5x \leq 10 \Rightarrow x \leq 2$

and $2x - 3 < 5x - 6 \Rightarrow -3x < -3 \Rightarrow x > 1$

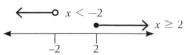

Solution: $1 < x \leq 2$

c) $2x - 1 \leq 3x - 5 \Rightarrow -x \leq -4 \Rightarrow x \geq 4$

and $5x - 6 > x + 22 \Rightarrow 4x > 28 \Rightarrow x > 7$

$\qquad\qquad\qquad\qquad x > 7$
$\qquad\qquad\qquad\qquad x \geq 4$

$\qquad 4 \qquad 7$

Solution: $x > 7$

Only these values satisfy both of the inequalities.

d) $3x + 5 < x + 1 \Rightarrow 2x < -4 \Rightarrow x < -2$

and $6x - 1 \geq 3x + 5 \Rightarrow 3x \geq 6 \Rightarrow x \geq 2$

$\qquad x < -2$
$\qquad\qquad\qquad x \geq 2$

$\qquad -2 \qquad 2$

There is no solution that satisfies both inequalities.

The solutions don't overlap on the number line.

Exercise 2.2 — Quadratic inequalities

Q1 **a)** $-3 < x < 1$

b) $x < 0$ or $x > 4$

c) $2x^2 \geq 5 - 9x \Rightarrow 2x^2 + 9x - 5 \geq 0$

$\Rightarrow x \leq -5$ or $x \geq \dfrac{1}{2}$

d) $x < 1 - \sqrt{6}$ or $x > 1 + \sqrt{6}$

Q2 **a)** Solve the equation $x^2 = 4$ to find the x-intercepts:

$x^2 = 4 \Rightarrow x^2 - 4 = 0 \Rightarrow (x - 2)(x + 2) = 0$

$x = -2$ or $x = 2$

Solution: $x^2 \leq 4 \Rightarrow x^2 - 4 \leq 0$

$\Rightarrow -2 \leq x \leq 2$

b) $13x = 3x^2 + 4 \Rightarrow -3x^2 + 13x - 4 = 0$

$\Rightarrow 3x^2 - 13x + 4 = 0 \Rightarrow (3x - 1)(x - 4) = 0$

$\Rightarrow x = \dfrac{1}{3}$ or $x = 4$

Solution: $13x < 3x^2 + 4 \Rightarrow -3x^2 + 13x - 4 < 0$

$\Rightarrow x < \dfrac{1}{3}$ or $x > 4$

c) $x^2 + 4 = 6x \Rightarrow x^2 - 6x + 4 = 0$

$\Rightarrow x = \dfrac{6 \pm \sqrt{36 - 16}}{2} = \dfrac{6 \pm \sqrt{20}}{2} = \dfrac{6 \pm 2\sqrt{5}}{2}$

$\Rightarrow x = 3 \pm \sqrt{5}$

Solution: $x^2 + 4 < 6x \Rightarrow x^2 - 6x + 4 < 0$

$\Rightarrow 3 - \sqrt{5} < x < 3 + \sqrt{5}$

Q3 **a)** $x^2 + 5x - 6 = 0 \Rightarrow (x + 6)(x - 1) = 0$

$\Rightarrow x = -6$ or $x = 1$

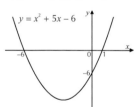

$x^2 + 5x - 6 \geq 0 \Rightarrow x \leq -6$ or $x \geq 1$

b) $x^2 - 3x + 2 = 0 \Rightarrow (x - 1)(x - 2) = 0$

$\Rightarrow x = 1$ or $x = 2$

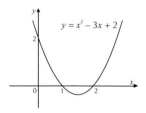

$x^2 - 3x + 2 < 0 \Rightarrow 1 < x < 2$

c) $6 - 5x = 6x^2 \Rightarrow -6x^2 - 5x + 6 = 0$

$\Rightarrow 6x^2 + 5x - 6 = 0 \Rightarrow (3x - 2)(2x + 3) = 0$

$\Rightarrow x = \dfrac{2}{3}$ or $x = -\dfrac{3}{2}$

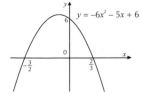

$6 - 5x > 6x^2 \Rightarrow -6x^2 - 5x + 6 > 0$

$\Rightarrow -\dfrac{3}{2} < x < \dfrac{2}{3}$

You could have rearranged the inequality into $6x^2 + 5x - 6 < 0$ and sketched the corresponding graph. You'd get the same final answer, but the graph would be the other way up.

d) $x^2 - 5x + 24 = 5x + 3 \Rightarrow x^2 - 10x + 21 = 0$

$\Rightarrow (x - 3)(x - 7) = 0 \Rightarrow x = 3$ or $x = 7$

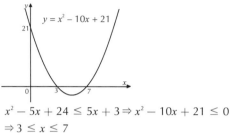

$x^2 - 5x + 24 \leq 5x + 3 \Rightarrow x^2 - 10x + 21 \leq 0$

$\Rightarrow 3 \leq x \leq 7$

e) $36 - 4x^2 = 0 \Rightarrow 9 - x^2 = 0$

$\Rightarrow (3 - x)(3 + x) = 0 \Rightarrow x = \pm 3$

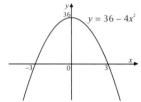

$36 - 4x^2 \leq 0 \Rightarrow x \leq -3$ or $x \geq 3$

f) $x^2 - 6x + 3 = 0 \Rightarrow x = \dfrac{6 \pm \sqrt{36 - 12}}{2}$

$\Rightarrow x = \dfrac{6 \pm \sqrt{24}}{2} = \dfrac{6 \pm 2\sqrt{6}}{2} = 3 \pm \sqrt{6}$

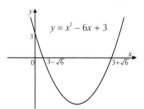

$x^2 - 6x + 3 > 0 \Rightarrow x < 3 - \sqrt{6}$ or $x > 3 + \sqrt{6}$

g) $x^2 - x + 3 = 0 \Rightarrow x = \dfrac{1 \pm \sqrt{1 - 12}}{2}$

$\Rightarrow$ no roots ($\sqrt{-11}$ is not real)

so the graph doesn't cross the x-axis.

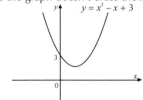

$x^2 - x + 3 > 0 \Rightarrow x$ can take any real value

h) $6 = 5x^2 + 13x \Rightarrow -5x^2 - 13x + 6 = 0$

$\Rightarrow 5x^2 + 13x - 6 = 0 \Rightarrow (5x - 2)(x + 3) = 0$

$\Rightarrow x = \dfrac{2}{5}$ or $x = -3$

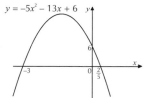

$y = -5x^2 - 13x + 6$

$6 \geq 5x^2 + 13x \Rightarrow -5x^2 - 13x + 6 \geq 0$

$\Rightarrow -3 \leq x \leq \dfrac{2}{5}$

Again, you might have rearranged the inequality differently and ended up with the graph the other way up.

Q4 $(x - 9)(x - 6) > 28 \Rightarrow x^2 - 15x + 54 > 28$

$\Rightarrow x^2 - 15x + 26 > 0$

Now $x^2 - 15x + 26 = 0 \Rightarrow (x - 2)(x - 13) = 0$

$\Rightarrow x = 2$ or $x = 13$

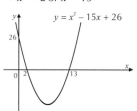

$y = x^2 - 15x + 26$

$x^2 - 15x + 26 > 0 \Rightarrow x < 2$ or $x > 13$

But $x < 2$ would make the sides have negative lengths, so $x > 13$.

Q5 $x^2 - 6x + k = 0 \Rightarrow$

$a = 1$, $b = -6$, $c = k$

$b^2 - 4ac = (-6)^2 - (4 \times 1 \times k) = 36 - 4k$

The original equation has two distinct real solutions, so the discriminant must be > 0.

So $36 - 4k > 0 \Rightarrow 36 > 4k \Rightarrow 9 > k$, so $k < 9$.

Q6 $x^2 - kx + k = 0 \Rightarrow$

$a = 1$, $b = -k$, $c = k$

$b^2 - 4ac = (-k)^2 - (4 \times 1 \times k) = k^2 - 4k$

The original equation has no real solutions, so the discriminant must be < 0.

So $k^2 - 4k < 0$

Factorise the quadratic: $k^2 - 4k = k(k - 4)$

So the solutions of the equation are $k = 0$ and $k = 4$.

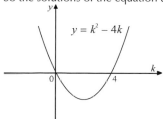

$y = k^2 - 4k$

Solution: $0 < k < 4$

Q7 $4(3 - x) \geq 13 - 5x \Rightarrow 12 - 4x \geq 13 - 5x \Rightarrow x \geq 1$

and

$7x + 6 \geq 3x^2 \Rightarrow -3x^2 + 7x + 6 \geq 0$

$-3x^2 + 7x + 6 = 0 \Rightarrow 3x^2 - 7x - 6 = 0$

$\Rightarrow (3x + 2)(x - 3) = 0$

$\Rightarrow x = -\dfrac{2}{3}$ or $x = 3$

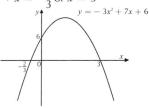

$y = -3x^2 + 7x + 6$

$\Rightarrow -\dfrac{2}{3} \leq x \leq 3$

So, for both inequalities:

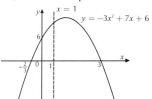

$x = 1$

$y = -3x^2 + 7x + 6$

Solution that satisfies both inequalities:

$\Rightarrow 1 \leq x \leq 3$

Your graphs might be the other way up if you rearranged the inequality differently at the start.

Review Exercise — Chapter 3

Q1 a) (1) $\qquad 3x - 4y = 7$

(2) $\qquad -2x + 7y = -22$

(1) $\times 2$ $\quad 6x - 8y = 14 \quad$ (3)

(2) $\times 3$ $\quad -6x + 21y = -66 \quad$ (4)

(3) + (4) $\quad 13y = -52 \Rightarrow y = -4$

$y = -4$ in (1) $3x + 16 = 7 \Rightarrow x = -3$

So the solution is $x = -3$, $y = -4$

b) (1) $\qquad 2x - 3y = \dfrac{11}{12}$

(2) $\qquad x + y = -\dfrac{7}{12}$

(2) $\times 2$ $\quad 2x + 2y = -\dfrac{14}{12} \quad$ (3)

(1) $-$ (3) $\quad -5y = \dfrac{25}{12} \Rightarrow y = -\dfrac{5}{12}$

$y = -\dfrac{5}{12}$ in (2) $\Rightarrow x - \dfrac{5}{12} = -\dfrac{7}{12} \Rightarrow x = -\dfrac{1}{6}$

So the solution is $x = -\dfrac{1}{6}$, $y = -\dfrac{5}{12}$

Q2 a) (1) $y = 3x - 4$

(2) $y = /x - 5$

Sub (2) in (1) $7x - 5 = 3x - 4 \Rightarrow x = \dfrac{1}{4}$

when $x = \dfrac{1}{4}$, $y = 3\left(\dfrac{1}{4}\right) - 4 = -\dfrac{13}{4}$

So they intersect at $\left(\dfrac{1}{4}, -\dfrac{13}{4}\right)$

b) (1) $y = 13 - 2x$

(2) $7x - y - 23 = 0$

Sub (1) in (2) $7x - (13 - 2x) - 23 = 0$

$\Rightarrow x = 4$

when $x = 4$, $y = 13 - 2(4) = 5$

So they intersect at (4, 5)

c) (1) $2x - 3y + 4 = 0$

Rearrange (2) $x = 2y - 1$

Sub (2) in (1) $2(2y - 1) - 3y + 4 = 0$

$\Rightarrow y = -2$

when $y = -2$, $x = 2(-2) - 1 = -5$

So they intersect at (−5, −2)

Q3 a) (1) $y = x^2 - 7x + 4$

Rearrange (2) $y = 2x - 10$ (3)

Sub (3) in (1) $x^2 - 9x + 14 = 0$

$\Rightarrow (x - 2)(x - 7) = 0 \Rightarrow x = 2$ or $x = 7$

when $x = 2$, $y = 2(2) - 10 = -6$

when $x = 7$, $y = 2(7) - 10 = 4$

The line and the curve meet at the points (2, –6) and (7, 4).

b) (1) $y = 30 - 6x + 2x^2$

(2) $y = 2(x + 11)$

Sub (2) in (1) $2x^2 - 8x + 8 = 0$

$\Rightarrow x^2 - 4x + 4 = 0$

$\Rightarrow (x - 2)^2 = 0 \Rightarrow x = 2$

when $x = 2$, $y = 2(2 + 11) = 26$

The line is a tangent to the parabola at the point (2, 26).

c) (1) $2x^2 + 2y^2 - 3 = 0$

(2) $y = x + 4$

Sub (2) in (1) to get $2x^2 + 2(x + 4)^2 - 3 = 0$

$\Rightarrow 4x^2 + 16x + 29 = 0$

$b^2 - 4ac = 16^2 - (4 \times 4 \times 29)$

$= 16^2 - (16 \times 29) < 0$

The equations have no solution and so the line and the curve never meet.

Q4 (1) $y = x^2 - 2x - 3$

(2) $y = 3x + 11$

Sub (2) in (1) to get $x^2 - 5x - 14 = 0$

Subbing into $b^2 - 4ac$ gives $b^2 - 4ac = 81 > 0$

There will be two points of intersection as the discriminant is greater than zero.

Q5 a) $7x - 4 > 2x - 42 \Rightarrow 5x > -38 \Rightarrow x > -\frac{38}{5}$

b) $12y - 3 \leq 4y + 4 \Rightarrow 8y \leq 7 \Rightarrow y \leq \frac{7}{8}$

c) $9y - 4 \geq 17y + 2 \Rightarrow -8y \geq 6 \Rightarrow y \leq -\frac{3}{4}$

d) $x + 6 < 5x - 4 \Rightarrow -4x < -10 \Rightarrow x > \frac{5}{2}$

e) $4x - 2 > x - 14 \Rightarrow 3x > -12 \Rightarrow x > -4$

f) $7 - x \leq 4 - 2x \Rightarrow x \leq -3$

Q6 a) $3x^2 - 5x - 2 = 0 \Rightarrow (3x + 1)(x - 2) = 0$

$\Rightarrow x = -\frac{1}{3}$ or $x = 2$

$3x^2 - 5x - 2 \leq 0 \Rightarrow -\frac{1}{3} \leq x \leq 2$

b) $x^2 + 2x + 7 = 4x + 9 \Rightarrow x^2 - 2x - 2 = 0$

$\Rightarrow x = \dfrac{2 \pm \sqrt{4 - (-8)}}{2} = \dfrac{2 \pm \sqrt{12}}{2} = \dfrac{2 \pm 2\sqrt{3}}{2}$

$\Rightarrow x = 1 \pm \sqrt{3}$

$x^2 - 2x - 2 > 0$

$\Rightarrow x < 1 - \sqrt{3}$ or $x > 1 + \sqrt{3}$

c) $3x^2 + 7x + 4 = 2(x^2 + x - 1) \Rightarrow x^2 + 5x + 6 = 0$

$\Rightarrow (x + 3)(x + 2) = 0 \Rightarrow x = -3$ or $x = -2$

$x^2 + 5x + 6 \geq 0 \Rightarrow x \leq -3$ or $x \geq -2$

d) $x^2 + 3x - 1 = x + 2 \Rightarrow x^2 + 2x - 3 = 0$

$\Rightarrow (x + 3)(x - 1) = 0 \Rightarrow x = -3$ or $x = 1$

$x^2 + 3x - 1 \geq x + 2 \Rightarrow x \leq -3$ or $x \geq 1$

e) $2x^2 = x + 1 \Rightarrow 2x^2 - x - 1 = 0$

$\Rightarrow (2x + 1)(x - 1) = 0 \Rightarrow x = -\frac{1}{2}$ or $x = 1$

$2x^2 > x + 1 \Rightarrow x < -\frac{1}{2}$ or $x > 1$

f) $3x^2 - 12 = x^2 - 2x \Rightarrow 2x^2 + 2x - 12 = 0$

$\Rightarrow x^2 + x - 6 = 0 \Rightarrow (x - 2)(x + 3) = 0$

$\Rightarrow x = 2$ or $x = -3$

$3x^2 - 12 < x^2 - 2x \Rightarrow -3 < x < 2$

Exam-Style Questions — Chapter 3

Q1 a) $3x + 2 \leq x + 6$

$\quad 2x \leq 4$ **[1 mark]**

$\quad\quad x \leq 2$ **[1 mark]**

b) $\quad 20 - x - x^2 > 0$

$\quad (4 - x)(5 + x) > 0$ **[1 mark]**

The graph crosses the x-axis at $x = 4$ and $x = -5$ **[1 mark]**. The coefficient of x^2 is negative so the graph is n-shaped **[1 mark]**. So $20 - x - x^2 > 0$ when $-5 < x < 4$ **[1 mark]**.

c) From above, x will satisfy both inequalities when $-5 < x \leq 2$ **[1 mark]**.

For this bit, all you need to do is use your answers to parts a) and b) and work out which values of x fit in them both.

Q2 (1) $\quad\quad 2x + 3y = 5$

(2) $\quad\quad 5x + 4y = 2$

(1) × 4 $\quad 8x + 12y = 20$

(2) × 3 $\quad 15x + 12y = 6$ **[1 mark]**

Subtract: $\quad -7x = 14 \Rightarrow x = -2$ **[1 mark]**

$x = -2$ in (1) $-4 + 3y = 5$

$\quad\quad\quad\quad \Rightarrow 3y = 9 \Rightarrow y = 3$

So the solution is $x = -2$, $y = 3$ **[1 mark]**

Q3 a) $3 \leq 2p + 5 \leq 15$

This inequality has 3 parts. Subtract 5 from each part to give: $-2 \leq 2p \leq 10$ **[1 mark]**.

Now divide each part by 2 to give: $-1 \leq p \leq 5$ **[1 mark for −1 ≤ p and 1 mark for p ≤ 5]**.

b) $q^2 - 9 > 0$

$(q + 3)(q - 3) > 0$ *[1 mark]*

The function is 0 at $q = -3$ and $q = 3$ *[1 mark]*.
The coefficient of q^2 is positive
so the graph is u-shaped. So
$q^2 - 9 > 0$ when $q < -3$ or $q > 3$
[1 mark for each correct inequality].

Use the difference of two squares to factorise the quadratic — remember that $a^2 - b^2 = (a + b)(a - b)$.

Q4 a) $(3x + 2)(x - 5)$ *[1 mark]*

b) $(3x + 2)(x - 5) \leq 0$

The function is 0 at $x = -\frac{2}{3}$ and $x = 5$ *[1 mark]*.

The coefficient of x^2 is positive so the graph is u-shaped, meaning the function is less than or equal to 0 between these x-values.

i.e. $3x^2 - 13x - 10 \leq 0$ when $-\frac{2}{3} \leq x \leq 5$

[2 marks, 1 for $-\frac{2}{3} \leq x$ and 1 for $x \leq 5$].

Q5 Rearrange (1) $5x + y = 6$

Rearrange (2) $7x + 2y = 6$ *[1 mark]*

(1) × 2 $\quad 10x + 2y = 12$ (3) *[1 mark]*

(2) − (3) $\quad -3x = -6 \Rightarrow x = 2$ *[1 mark]*

$x = 2$ in (1) $10 + y = 6 \Rightarrow y = -4$
So the solution is $x = 2$, $y = -4$ *[1 mark]*

For this question, you could have eliminated x first to find y, or used the substitution method instead.

Q6 a) (1) $\quad x^2 + y^2 = 13$

Rearrange (2) $\quad x = 5y - 13$

Sub (2) in (1) $\quad (5y - 13)^2 + y^2 = 13$ *[1 mark]*

$\Rightarrow 25y^2 - 130y + 169 + y^2 - 13 = 0$ *[1 mark]*

$\Rightarrow 26y^2 - 130y + 156 = 0$

$\Rightarrow y^2 - 5y + 6 = 0$ *[1 mark]*

b) $(y - 2)(y - 3) = 0$ *[1 mark]*

$\Rightarrow y = 2$ or $y = 3$ *[1 mark]*

When $y = 2$, $x = 10 - 13 = -3$, and
when $y = 3$, $x = 15 - 13 = 2$
So $x = -3$, $y = 2$ or $x = 2$, $y = 3$ *[1 mark]*

Q7 First, take the linear equation and rearrange it to get x on its own: $x = 6 - y$ *[1 mark]*. Now substitute the equation for x into the quadratic equation:

$(6 - y)^2 + 2y^2 = 36$ *[1 mark]*

$36 - 12y + y^2 + 2y^2 = 36$

$3y^2 - 12y = 0$

$y^2 - 4y = 0$

$y(y - 4) = 0$ *[1 mark]*

so $y = 0$ and $y = 4$.
Now you've got the y-values, put them back into the equation for x ($x = 6 - y$) to find the x-values.
When $y = 0$, $x = 6 - y = 6 - 0 = 6$.
When $y = 4$, $x = 6 - y = 6 - 4 = 2$.
So the line and the curve intersect at (6, 0) *[1 mark]* and (2, 4) *[1 mark]*.

You could have substituted $y = 6 - x$ into the quadratic instead and solved it that way.

Q8 a) At points of intersection,

$-2x + 4 = -x^2 + 3$ *[1 mark]*

$x^2 - 2x + 1 = 0$

$(x - 1)^2 = 0$ *[1 mark]*

so $x = 1$ *[1 mark]*. When $x = 1$, $y = -2x + 4 = 2$, so there is one point of intersection at (1, 2) *[1 mark]*.

b)

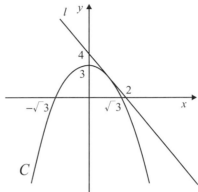

[5 marks available — 1 mark for drawing n-shaped curve, 1 mark for x-axis intercepts at $\pm\sqrt{3}$, 1 mark for maximum point of curve and y-axis intercept at (0, 3). 1 mark for line crossing the y-axis at (0, 4) and the x-axis at (2, 0). 1 mark for line and curve touching in one place.]

Q9 a)

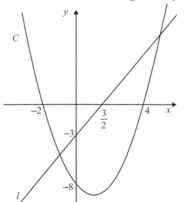

[5 marks available — 1 mark for drawing u-shaped curve, 1 mark for x-axis intercepts at −2 and 4 , 1 mark for y-axis intercept at (0, −8). 1 mark for line crossing the y-axis at (0, −3) and the x-axis at (3/2, 0). 1 mark for line and curve intersecting in two places.]

b) At points of intersection,

$2x - 3 = (x + 2)(x - 4)$

$2x - 3 = x^2 - 2x$ 8 *[1 mark]*

$0 = x^2 - 4x - 5$ *[1 mark]*

c) $x^2 - 4x - 5 = 0$

$(x - 5)(x + 1) = 0$ *[1 mark]*

so $x = 5$, $x = -1$.
When $x = 5$, $y = (2 \times 5) - 3 = 7$ and when $x = -1$, $y = (2 \times -1) - 3 = -5$, so the points of intersection are (5, 7) *[1 mark]* and (−1, −5) *[1 mark]*.

Chapter 4: Algebraic Division

1. Algebraic Division

Exercise 1.1 — Algebraic division

Q1 a)

$$\begin{array}{r} x^2 + x - 1 \\ x - 3 \overline{\smash{)}\, x^3 - 2x^2 - 4x + 8} \\ -\underline{x^3 - 3x^2} \\ x^2 - 4x \\ -\underline{x^2 - 3x} \\ -x + 8 \\ -\underline{-x + 3} \\ 5 \end{array}$$

Quotient: $x^2 + x - 1$
Remainder: 5

b)

$$\begin{array}{r} x^2 - 3x - 5 \\ x + 2 \overline{\smash{)}\, x^3 - x^2 - 11x - 10} \\ -\underline{x^3 + 2x^2} \\ -3x^2 - 11x \\ -\underline{-3x^2 - 6x} \\ -5x - 10 \\ -\underline{-5x - 10} \\ 0 \end{array}$$

Quotient: $x^2 - 3x - 5$
Remainder: 0

c)

$$\begin{array}{r} x^2 + x - 1 \\ x - 2 \overline{\smash{)}\, x^3 - x^2 - 3x + 3} \\ -\underline{x^3 - 2x^2} \\ x^2 - 3x \\ -\underline{x^2 - 2x} \\ -x + 3 \\ -\underline{-x + 2} \\ 1 \end{array}$$

Quotient: $x^2 + x - 1$
Remainder: 1

d)

$$\begin{array}{r} x^2 - 5x + 10 \\ x + 3 \overline{\smash{)}\, x^3 - 2x^2 - 5x + 6} \\ -\underline{x^3 + 3x^2} \\ -5x^2 - 5x \\ -\underline{-5x^2 - 15x} \\ 10x + 6 \\ -\underline{10x + 30} \\ -24 \end{array}$$

Quotient: $x^2 - 5x + 10$
Remainder: –24

e)

$$\begin{array}{r} x^2 - 11x + 29 \\ x + 2 \overline{\smash{)}\, x^3 - 9x^2 + 7x + 33} \\ -\underline{x^3 + 2x^2} \\ -11x^2 + 7x \\ -\underline{-11x^2 - 22x} \\ 29x + 33 \\ -\underline{29x + 58} \\ -25 \end{array}$$

Quotient: $x^2 - 11x + 29$
Remainder: –25

Q2

$$\begin{array}{r} x^2 + x - 4 \\ x - 1 \overline{\smash{)}\, x^3 + 0x^2 - 5x + 4} \\ -\underline{x^3 - x^2} \\ x^2 - 5x \\ -\underline{x^2 - x} \\ -4x + 4 \\ -\underline{-4x + 4} \\ 0 \end{array}$$

So $(x^3 - 5x + 4) \div (x - 1) = x^2 + x - 4$ remainder 0.

Q3

$$\begin{array}{r} x^2 + 2x + 6 \\ x - 3 \overline{\smash{)}\, x^3 - x^2 + 0x - 11} \\ -\underline{x^3 - 3x^2} \\ 2x^2 + 0x \\ -\underline{2x^2 - 6x} \\ 6x - 11 \\ -\underline{6x - 18} \\ 7 \end{array}$$

So $(x^3 - x^2 - 11) \div (x - 3) = x^2 + 2x + 6$ remainder 7.

Q4 a)

$$\begin{array}{r} 2x^2 + x - 12 \\ x + 1 \overline{\smash{)}\, 2x^3 + 3x^2 - 11x - 6} \\ -\underline{2x^3 + 2x^2} \\ x^2 - 11x \\ -\underline{x^2 + x} \\ -12x - 6 \\ -\underline{-12x - 12} \\ 6 \end{array}$$

So $(2x^3 + 3x^2 - 11x - 6) \div (x + 1) = 2x^2 + x - 12$ remainder 6.

b)

$$\begin{array}{r} 2x^2 - x - 9 \\ x + 2 \overline{\smash{)}\, 2x^3 + 3x^2 - 11x - 6} \\ -\underline{2x^3 + 4x^2} \\ -x^2 - 11x \\ -\underline{-x^2 - 2x} \\ -9x - 6 \\ -\underline{-9x - 18} \\ 12 \end{array}$$

So $(2x^3 + 3x^2 - 11x - 6) \div (x + 2) = 2x^2 - x - 9$ remainder 12.

c)

$$\begin{array}{r} 2x^2 + 5x - 6 \\ x - 1 \overline{\smash{)}\, 2x^3 + 3x^2 - 11x - 6} \\ -\underline{2x^3 - 2x^2} \\ 5x^2 - 11x \\ -\underline{5x^2 - 5x} \\ -6x - 6 \\ -\underline{-6x + 6} \\ -12 \end{array}$$

So $(2x^3 + 3x^2 - 11x - 6) \div (x - 1) = 2x^2 + 5x - 6$ remainder –12.

Q5

$$\begin{array}{r} x^2 + 4x + 1 \\ x - 2 \overline{\smash{)}\, x^3 + 2x^2 - 7x - 2} \\ -\underline{x^3 - 2x^2} \\ 4x^2 - 7x \\ -\underline{4x^2 - 8x} \\ x - 2 \\ -\underline{x - 2} \\ 0 \end{array}$$

So $f(x) = (x - 2)(x^2 + 4x + 1)$.

2. The Remainder and Factor Theorems

Exercise 2.1 — The Remainder Theorem

Q1 **a)** $a = 1$, $f(1) = 2(1)^3 - 3(1)^2 - 39(1) + 20 = -20$

b) $a = -1$, $f(-1) = (-1)^3 - 3(-1)^2 + 2(-1) = -6$

c) $a = -1$, $f(-1) = 6(-1)^3 + (-1)^2 - 5(-1) - 2 = -2$

d) $a = -3$, $f(-3) = (-3)^3 + 2(-3)^2 - 7(-3) - 2 = 10$

e) $a = 2$ and $b = -1$

$f\left(-\frac{1}{2}\right) = 4\left(-\frac{1}{2}\right)^3 - 6\left(-\frac{1}{2}\right)^2 - 12\left(-\frac{1}{2}\right) - 6 = -2$

f) $a = 2$ and $b = 1$

$f\left(\frac{1}{2}\right) = \left(\frac{1}{2}\right)^3 - 3\left(\frac{1}{2}\right)^2 - 6\left(\frac{1}{2}\right) + 8 = \frac{35}{8}$ or $4\frac{3}{8}$

Q2 $a = -2$, $f(-2) = (-2)^3 + p(-2)^2 - 10(-2) - 19 = 5$
$4p - 7 = 5$
$4p = 12 \Rightarrow p = 3$

Q3 $a = -2$, $f(-2) = (-2)^3 - d(-2)^2 + d(-2) + 1 = -25$
$-6d - 7 = -25$
$-6d = -18 \Rightarrow d = 3$

Q4 $a = -1$, $f(-1) = (-1)^3 - 2(-1)^2 + 7(-1) + k = -8$
$-10 + k = -8$
$k = 2$

Q5 $a = 2$, $f(2) = (2)^4 + 5(2)^3 + 2p + 156 = 2p + 212$
$a = -1$, $f(-1) = (-1)^4 + 5(-1)^3 - p + 156 = 152 - p$
$\Rightarrow 2p + 212 = 152 - p$
$3p = -60$
$p = -20$

Exercise 2.2 — The Factor Theorem

Q1 **a)** $a = 1$, find $f(a)$ and show the result is 0:
$f(1) = (1)^3 - (1)^2 - 3(1) + 3 = 1 - 1 - 3 + 3 = 0$
The question asked you to use the Factor Theorem, but you could also show it was a factor by adding the coefficients (1, −1, −3, 3) to get 0. (If the coefficients in a polynomial add up to 0, then $(x - 1)$ is a factor.)

b) $a = -1$, find $f(a)$ and show the result is 0:
$f(-1) = (-1)^3 + 2(-1)^2 + 3(-1) + 2$
$= -1 + 2 - 3 + 2 = 0$

c) $a = -2$, find $f(a)$ and show the result is 0:
$f(-2) = (-2)^3 + 3(-2)^2 - 10(-2) - 24$
$= -8 + 12 + 20 - 24 = 0$

Q2 **a)** If $(2x - 1)$ is a factor then $\left(x - \frac{1}{2}\right)$ is also a factor, so substitute $x = \frac{1}{2}$ and show the result is 0:

$f\left(\frac{1}{2}\right) = 2\left(\frac{1}{2}\right)^3 - \left(\frac{1}{2}\right)^2 - 8\left(\frac{1}{2}\right) + 4$

$= \frac{2}{8} - \frac{1}{4} - 4 + 4 = 0$

b) If $(3x - 2)$ is a factor then $\left(x - \frac{2}{3}\right)$ is also a factor, so substitute $x = \frac{2}{3}$ and show the result is 0:

$f\left(\frac{2}{3}\right) = 3\left(\frac{2}{3}\right)^3 - 5\left(\frac{2}{3}\right)^2 - 16\left(\frac{2}{3}\right) + 12$

$= \frac{8}{9} - \frac{20}{9} - \frac{32}{3} + 12$

$= \frac{8}{9} - \frac{20}{9} - \frac{96}{9} + 12 = 0$

Q3 **a)** $f(3) = (3)^3 - 2(3)^2 - 5(3) + 6$
$= 27 - 18 - 15 + 6 = 0$

b) $1 - 2 - 5 + 6 = 0$. The coefficients add to zero so $(x - 1)$ must be a factor.

Q4 **a)** $f(-4) = 3(-4)^3 - 5(-4)^2 - 58(-4) + 40$
$= -192 - 80 + 232 + 40 = 0$

b) $f\left(\frac{2}{3}\right) = 3\left(\frac{2}{3}\right)^3 - 5\left(\frac{2}{3}\right)^2 - 58\left(\frac{2}{3}\right) + 40$

$= \frac{8}{9} - \frac{20}{9} - \frac{116}{3} + 40 = \frac{-120}{3} + 40 = 0$

Q5 $(x - 3)$ is a factor of $f(x) = qx^3 - 4x^2 - 7qx + 12$, so $f(3) = 0$:
$f(3) = q(3)^3 - 4(3)^2 - 7q(3) + 12$
$= 27q - 36 - 21q + 12 = 6q - 24$
$\Rightarrow 6q - 24 = 0$
$6q = 24$
$q = 4$

Q6 $f(1) = (1)^3 + c(1)^2 + d(1) - 2 = 1 + c + d - 2 = 0$
$\Rightarrow c + d = 1$ (equation 1)
$f(2) = (2)^3 + c(2)^2 + d(2) - 2 = 8 + 4c + 2d - 2 = 0$
$\Rightarrow 4c + 2d = -6$ (equation 2)

Rearrange (1) to get $d = 1 - c$, and sub into (2):
$\Rightarrow 4c + 2(1 - c) = -6$
$4c + 2 - 2c = -6$
$2c = -8$
$c = -4$

Sub c into rearranged (1):
$d = 1 - c = 1 + 4 = 5$

3. Factorising Cubics

Exercise 3.1 — Factorising $ax^3 + bx^2 + cx$

Q1 **a)** $x(x^2 + 5x + 6) = x(x + 2)(x + 3)$

b) $x(x^2 + 6x - 7) = x(x + 7)(x - 1)$

c) $x(x^2 - 18x + 81) = x(x - 9)(x - 9) = x(x - 9)^2$

d) $x(x^2 + 7x + 10) = x(x + 5)(x + 2)$

e) $-x(x^2 - 4x + 3) = -x(x - 3)(x - 1)$

f) $x(2x^2 + 15x + 25) = x(2x + 5)(x + 5)$

g) $x(x^2 - 49) = x(x + 7)(x - 7)$

h) $x\left(x^2 - \frac{9}{4}\right) = x\left(x + \frac{3}{2}\right)\left(x - \frac{3}{2}\right)$

Q2 **a)** $-x^3 + 2x^2 + 24x = 0$
$\Rightarrow -x(x^2 - 2x - 24) = 0$
$\Rightarrow -x(x - 6)(x + 4) = 0$
So either $-x = 0$, $x - 6 = 0$ or $x + 4 = 0$.
So the roots are $x = 0$, $x = 6$ and $x = -4$.

b) $x^3 - \frac{7}{9}x^2 + \frac{10}{81}x = 0$
$\Rightarrow x\left(x^2 - \frac{7}{9}x + \frac{10}{81}\right) = 0$
$\Rightarrow x\left(x - \frac{5}{9}\right)\left(x - \frac{2}{9}\right) = 0$
So either $x = 0$, $x - \frac{5}{9} = 0$ or $x - \frac{2}{9} = 0$.
So the roots are $x = 0$, $x = \frac{5}{9}$ and $x = \frac{2}{9}$.

c) $2x^3 + 9x^2 + 4x = 0$
$\Rightarrow x(2x^2 + 9x + 4) = 0$
$\Rightarrow x(2x + 1)(x + 4) = 0$
So either $x = 0$, $2x + 1 = 0$ or $x + 4 = 0$.
So the roots are $x = 0$, $x = -\frac{1}{2}$ or $x = -4$.

d) $3x^3 - 3x^2 + 4x = 0$
$\Rightarrow x(3x^2 - 3x + 4) = 0$
This quadratic won't factorise — so use the quadratic formula: $a = 3$, $b = -3$, $c = 4$
$$x = \frac{-b \pm \sqrt{b^2 - 4ac}}{2a} = \frac{3 \pm \sqrt{(-3)^2 - 4 \times 3 \times 4}}{2 \times 3}$$
$$= \frac{3 \pm \sqrt{9 - 48}}{6} = \frac{3 \pm \sqrt{-39}}{6}$$
These aren't possible solutions since you can't take the square root of a negative number so the only solution is the one we get from the x that we factorised out at the start, i.e. $x = 0$.

e) $x^2(4x + 3) = x$
$\Rightarrow 4x^3 + 3x^2 = x$
$\Rightarrow 4x^3 + 3x^2 - x = 0$
$\Rightarrow x(4x^2 + 3x - 1) = 0$
$\Rightarrow x(4x - 1)(x + 1) = 0$
So either $x = 0$, $4x - 1 = 0$ or $x + 1 = 0$.
So the roots are $x = 0$, $x = \frac{1}{4}$ or $x = -1$.

f) $2x^3 + 8x^2 = -3x$
$\Rightarrow 2x^3 + 8x^2 + 3x = 0$
$\Rightarrow x(2x^2 + 8x + 3) = 0$
So one root is $x = 0$, but the quadratic won't factorise so use the quadratic formula.
Now $a = 2$, $b = 8$ and $c = 3$.
$$x = \frac{-b \pm \sqrt{b^2 - 4ac}}{2a} = \frac{-8 \pm \sqrt{8^2 - 4 \times 2 \times 3}}{4}$$
$$= \frac{-8 \pm \sqrt{40}}{4} = -2 \pm \frac{1}{2}\sqrt{10}$$
So the roots are $x = 0$ and $x = -2 \pm \frac{1}{2}\sqrt{10}$.

Exercise 3.2 — Factorising $ax^3 + bx^2 + cx + d$

Q1 $(x - 2)$ is a factor, so using the equating coefficients method:
$2x^3 + 3x^2 - 11x - 6 = (x - 2)(px^2 + qx + r)$
$2x^3 + 3x^2 - 11x - 6 = px^3 + (q - 2p)x^2 + (r - 2q)x - 2r$
Equating coefficients of x^3 gives $p = 2$.
Equating constants gives $-2r = -6$, so $r = 3$.
Equating coefficients of x^2 gives $q - 2(2) = 3$, so $q = 7$.
So $2x^3 + 3x^2 - 11x - 6 = (x - 2)(2x^2 + 7x + 3)$.
Factorise the quadratic to get $(x - 2)(x + 3)(2x + 1)$.

Q2 $(x - 1)$ is a factor, so using the equating coefficients method:
$x^3 - 3x^2 + 3x - 1 = (x - 1)(px^2 + qx + r)$
$x^3 - 3x^2 + 3x - 1 = px^3 + (q - p)x^2 + (r - q)x - r$
Equating coefficients of x^3 gives $p = 1$.
Equating constants gives $-r = -1$, so $r = 1$.
Equating coefficients of x^2 gives $q - 1 = -3$, so $q = -2$.
So $x^3 - 3x^2 + 3x - 1 = (x - 1)(x^2 - 2x + 1)$. Factorise the quadratic to get $(x - 1)(x - 1)(x - 1) \Rightarrow (x - 1)^3$.

Q3 a) Adding the coefficients gives you 3, so $(x - 1)$ is not a factor. Trying different values of x you should find that, e.g. $f(-2) = 0$, so $(x + 2)$ is a factor. Factorise (by equating coefficients or by long division) to get:
$(x + 2)(x^2 - 4x + 4) \Rightarrow (x - 2)^2(x + 2)$
You might have found the $(x - 2)$ factor first by doing $f(2) = 0$, but you should still end up with the same answer.

b) So the solutions are $x = 2$ and $x = -2$.

Q4 Add the coefficients $(1 - 1 - 3 + 3)$ to get 0, so $(x - 1)$ is a factor.
Factorise (by equating coefficients or by long division) to get:
$(x - 1)(x^2 - 3)$
So the roots are $x = 1$ and $x = \pm\sqrt{3}$.

Q5 a) $(x - 5)$ is a factor, so $f(5) = 0$
$f(5) = (5)^3 - p(5)^2 + 17(5) - 10$
$= 125 - 25p + 85 - 10 = 200 - 25p$
$\Rightarrow 200 - 25p = 0$
$200 = 25p$
$p = 8$

b) $(x - 5)(x^2 - 3x + 2) \Rightarrow (x - 5)(x - 1)(x - 2)$

c) So the roots are $x = 5$, $x = 1$ and $x = 2$.

Review Exercise — Chapter 4

Q1 a)
$$\begin{array}{r} x^2 - 4x + 9 \\ x + 3 \overline{\smash{)}\ x^3 - x^2 - 3x + 3} \\ -\underline{x^3 + 3x^2} \\ -4x^2 - 3x \\ -\underline{-4x^2 - 12x} \\ 9x + 3 \\ -\underline{9x + 27} \\ -24 \end{array}$$
Quotient: $x^2 - 4x + 9$
Remainder: -24

b)
$$\begin{array}{r} x^2 - x - 7 \\ x - 2 \overline{\smash{)}\ x^3 - 3x^2 - 5x + 6} \\ -\underline{x^3 - 2x^2} \\ -x^2 - 5x \\ -\underline{-x^2 + 2x} \\ -7x + 6 \\ -\underline{-7x + 14} \\ -8 \end{array}$$
Quotient: $x^2 - x - 7$
Remainder: -8

c)
$$\begin{array}{r} x^2 + 0x + 3 \\ x + 2 \overline{\smash{)}\ x^3 + 2x^2 + 3x + 2} \\ -\underline{x^3 + 2x^2} \\ 0 + 3x \\ -\underline{0 + 0} \\ 3x + 2 \\ -\underline{3x + 6} \\ -4 \end{array}$$
Quotient: $x^2 + 3$
Remainder: -4

Q2 a)

$$\begin{array}{r} 3x^2 - 10x + 15 \\ x + 2 \overline{)3x^3 - 4x^2 - 5x - 6} \\ \underline{-\ 3x^3 + 6x^2} \\ -10x^2 - 5x \\ \underline{-\ -10x^2 - 20x} \\ 15x - 6 \\ \underline{-\ 15x + 30} \\ -36 \end{array}$$

So, $f(x) = (x + 2)(3x^2 - 10x + 15) - 36$

b)

$$\begin{array}{r} x^2 - 0x - 3 \\ x + 2 \overline{)x^3 + 2x^2 - 3x + 4} \\ \underline{-\ x^3 + 2x^2} \\ 0 - 3x \\ \underline{-\ 0 - 0} \\ -3x + 4 \\ \underline{-\ -3x - 6} \\ 10 \end{array}$$

So, $f(x) = (x + 2)(x^2 - 3) + 10$

c)

$$\begin{array}{r} 2x^2 - 4x + 14 \\ x + 2 \overline{)2x^3 + 0x^2 + 6x - 3} \\ \underline{-\ 2x^3 + 4x^2} \\ -4x^2 + 6x \\ \underline{-\ -4x^2 - 8x} \\ 14x - 3 \\ \underline{-\ 14x + 28} \\ -31 \end{array}$$

So, $f(x) = (x + 2)(2x^2 - 4x + 14) - 31$

Q3 a) (i) You just need to find $f(-1)$.
This is $-6 - 1 + 3 - 12 = -16$.

(ii) Now find $f(1)$. This is $6 - 1 - 3 - 12 = -10$.

(iii) Now find $f(2)$. This is $48 - 4 - 6 - 12 = 26$.

b) (i) $f(-1) = -1$

(ii) $f(1) = 9$

(iii) $f(2) = 38$

c) (i) $f(-1) = -2$

(ii) $f(1) = 0$

(iii) $f(2) = 37$

Q4 a) You need to find $f(-2)$. This is
$(-2)^4 - 3(-2)^3 + 7(-2)^2 - 12(-2) + 14$
$= 16 + 24 + 28 + 24 + 14 = 106$.

b) You need to find $f(-\frac{4}{2}) = f(-2)$. You found this in part a), so remainder $= 106$. You might also have noticed that $2x + 4$ is a multiple of $x + 2$ (from part a)), so the remainder must be the same.

c) You need to find $f(3)$. This is
$(3)^4 - 3(3)^3 + 7(3)^2 - 12(3) + 14$
$= 81 - 81 + 63 - 36 + 14 = 41$.

d) You need to find $f(-\frac{6}{2}) = f(3)$. You found this in part c), so remainder $= 41$. You might also have noticed that $2x - 6$ is a multiple of $x - 3$, so the remainder must be the same.

Q5 $f(-3) = -16$,
$f(-3) = (-3)^3 + c(-3)^2 + 17(-3) - 10$
$= -27 + 9c - 51 - 10 = -88 + 9c$

$\Rightarrow -88 + 9c = -16$
$9c = 72$
$c = 8$

Q6 a) You need to find $f(1)$ — if $f(1) = 0$, then $(x - 1)$ is a factor:
$f(1) = 1 - 4 + 3 + 2 - 2 = 0$, so $(x - 1)$ is a factor.

b) You need to find $f(-1)$ — if $f(-1) = 0$, then $(x + 1)$ is a factor:
$f(-1) = -1 - 4 - 3 + 2 - 2 = -8$,
so $(x + 1)$ is not a factor.

c) You need to find $f(2)$ — if $f(2) = 0$, then $(x - 2)$ is a factor:
$f(2) = 32 - (4 \times 16) + (3 \times 8) + (2 \times 4) - 2$
$= 32 - 64 + 24 + 8 - 2 = -2$, so $(x - 2)$ is not a factor.

d) The remainder when you divide by $(2x - 2)$ is the same as the remainder when you divide by $x - 1$.
$(x - 1)$ is a factor (i.e. remainder $= 0$), so $(2x - 2)$ is also a factor.

Q7 Sub in $x = -2$. If $(x + 2)$ is a factor, then $f(-2) = 0$.
$f(-2) = (-2 + 5)(-2 - 2)(-2 - 1) + k$
$= (3)(-4)(-3) + k = 36 + k$

$\Rightarrow 36 + k = 0$
$k = -36$

Q8 a) Let $f(x) = g(x)$ to find where the curves intersect:
$5x^3 - 13x^2 + 6x = -5x^3 + 7x^2 + 6x$
$\Rightarrow 5x^3 - 13x^2 + 6x + 5x^3 - 7x^2 - 6x = 0$
$\Rightarrow 10x^3 - 20x^2 = 0$
$\Rightarrow 10x^2(x - 2) = 0$
$\Rightarrow x = 0$ or $x = 2$.
Put $x = 0, 2$ into one of the expressions to find y:
$x = 0$ gives $y = 0$
$x = 2$ gives $y = 5(2^3) - 13(2^2) + 6(2)$
$= 40 - 52 + 12 = 0$
So the intersection points are $(0, 0)$ and $(2, 0)$.

b) In part a), you found that the graph of $y = f(x)$ passes through the points $(0, 0)$ and $(2, 0)$. So you actually found two roots of $f(x)$ since the roots are points where the graph meets the x-axis. These roots tell you that $f(x)$ will have factors of x and $(x - 2)$. So you only need to find one more factor. You know $5x^3 - 13x^2 + 6x = x(x - 2)(.........)$
The third factor is found by noticing that you need $5x$ to make the $5x^3$ and -3 to make the $+6x$.
So $5x^3 - 13x^2 + 6x = x(x - 2)(5x - 3)$.
You could also have found that last factor by algebraic long division $(5x^3 - 13x^2 + 6x \div x^2 - 2x)$ or by equating coefficients.

Q9 a) Set the equations equal to each other to give an equation that can be solved to find the points where they intersect:
$x(x - 6)^2 = -x(2x - 31)$
$\rightarrow x(x^2 - 12x + 36) = -2x^2 + 31x$
$\Rightarrow x^3 - 12x^2 + 36x = -2x^2 + 31x$
$\Rightarrow x^3 - 10x^2 + 5x = 0$

b) Solving the equation in part a):
$x^3 - 10x^2 + 5x = 0 \Rightarrow x(x^2 - 10x + 5) = 0$
This quadratic won't factorise, so use the quadratic formula: $a = 1$, $b = -10$, $c = 5$

$$x = \frac{-b \pm \sqrt{b^2 - 4ac}}{2a}$$

$$= \frac{10 \pm \sqrt{(-10)^2 - 4 \times 1 \times 5}}{2 \times 1}$$

$$= \frac{10 \pm \sqrt{100 - 20}}{2}$$

$$= \frac{10 \pm \sqrt{80}}{2} = \frac{10 \pm 4\sqrt{5}}{2} = 5 \pm 2\sqrt{5}$$

So the points where the two curves meet are at $x = 0$ and $x = 5 \pm 2\sqrt{5}$.

Q10 Since $(x - 3)$ is a factor, $x = 3$ is a solution to $f(x) = 0$. Using long division to find the quadratic factor:

$$
\begin{array}{r}
x^2 - 6x - 11 \\
x - 3 \overline{)\, x^3 - 9x^2 + 7x + 33} \\
-\underline{\ x^3 - 3x^2} \\
-6x^2 + 7x \\
-\underline{\ -6x^2 + 18x} \\
-11x + 33 \\
-\underline{\ -11x + 33} \\
0
\end{array}
$$

So $x^3 - 9x^2 + 7x + 33 = (x - 3)(x^2 - 6x - 11)$.

This quadratic won't factorise, so you will need to use the quadratic formula to find the other two roots: $x = 3 \pm 2\sqrt{5}$.
Remember that the other root is $x = 3$.
You could use the equating coefficients method to fully factorise the cubic instead of long division, but you should still end up with the same answer.

Q11 Find one factor by trying different values of x in $f(x)$ to see whether $f(x) = 0$. E.g.

$f(1) = (1 \times 1) + (6 \times 1) + (11 \times 1) + 6 = 24$

$f(-1) = (1 \times -1) + (6 \times 1) + (11 \times -1) + 6 = 0$

so $(x + 1)$ is a factor. Dividing the cubic by $(x + 1)$, or using the equating coefficients method, gives you:
$f(x) = (x + 1)(x^2 + 5x + 6) = (x + 1)(x + 2)(x + 3)$
So $f(x)$ has roots of $x = -1$, $x = -2$ and $x = -3$.
If you'd found the $(x + 2)$ or $(x + 3)$ factors first the quadratic would be different but the final answer would be the same.

Exam-Style Questions — Chapter 4

Q1 a) (i) Remainder $= f(1) = 2(1)^3 - 5(1)^2 - 4(1) + 3$
[1 mark] $= -4$ *[1 mark]*.

(ii) Remainder $= f\left(-\frac{1}{2}\right)$
$f\left(-\frac{1}{2}\right) = 2\left(-\frac{1}{8}\right) - 5\left(\frac{1}{4}\right) - 4\left(-\frac{1}{2}\right) + 3$
[1 mark]
$= \frac{7}{2}$ *[1 mark]*.

b) If $f(-1) = 0$ then $(x + 1)$ is a factor.
$f(-1) = 2(-1)^3 - 5(-1)^2 - 4(-1) + 3$ *[1 mark]*
$= -2 - 5 + 4 + 3 = 0$, so $(x + 1)$ is a factor of $f(x)$.
[1 mark]

c) $(x + 1)$ is a factor, so divide $2x^3 - 5x^2 - 4x + 3$ by $x + 1$. Using long division:

$$
\begin{array}{r}
2x^2 - 7x + 3 \\
x + 1 \overline{)\, 2x^3 - 5x^2 - 4x + 3} \\
-\underline{\ 2x^3 + 2x^2} \\
-7x^2 - 4x \\
-\underline{\ -7x^2 - 7x} \\
3x + 3 \\
-\underline{\ 3x + 3} \\
0
\end{array}
$$

So $2x^3 - 5x^2 - 4x + 3 = (x + 1)(2x^2 - 7x + 3)$.
Factorising the quadratic expression gives:
$f(x) = (x + 1)(2x - 1)(x - 3)$.
Remember — you can use the equating coefficients method to find the quadratic factor if you're not a fan of long division.
[4 marks available — 1 mark for attempt to find the quadratic factor, 1 mark for correct quadratic factor, 1 mark for attempt to factorise quadratic, 1 mark for correct factorisation of quadratic.]

Q2 a) $f(p) = (4p^2 + 3p + 1)(p - p) + 5$
$= (4p^2 + 3p + 1) \times 0 + 5$
$= 5$ *[1 mark]*.

b) $f(-1) = -1$.
$f(-1) = (4(-1)^2 + 3(-1) + 1)((-1) - p) + 5$
$= (4 - 3 + 1)(-1 - p) + 5$
$= 2(-1 - p) + 5 = 3 - 2p$ *[1 mark]*
So: $3 - 2p = -1$, $p = 2$ *[1 mark]*.

c) $f(x) = (4x^2 + 3x + 1)(x - 2) + 5$
$f(1) = (4 + 3 + 1)(1 - 2) + 5 = -3$ *[1 mark]*.

Q3 a) If $f(-2) = 0$ then $(x + 2)$ is a factor.
$f(-2) = 3(-2)^3 + 8(-2)^2 + 3(-2) - 2$ *[1 mark]*
$= -24 + 32 - 6 - 2 = 0$, so $(x + 2)$ is a factor of $f(x)$. *[1 mark]*

b) $(x + 2)$ is a factor, so using the equating coefficients method:
$3x^3 + 8x^2 + 3x - 2 = (x + 2)(px^2 + qx + r)$
$3x^3 + 8x^2 + 3x - 2 = px^3 + (q + 2p)x^2 + (r + 2q)x + 2r$

Equating coefficients of x^3 gives $p = 3$.
Equating constants gives $2r = -2$, so $r = -1$.
Equating coefficients of x^2 gives $q + 2(3) = 8$, so $q = 2$.

So $3x^3 + 8x^2 + 3x - 2 = (x + 2)(3x^2 + 2x - 1)$.
Factorising the quadratic expression gives:
$f(x) = (x + 2)(x + 1)(3x - 1)$.
[4 marks available — 1 mark for attempt to find quadratic factor, 1 mark for correct quadratic factor, 1 mark for attempt to factorise quadratic, 1 mark for correct factorisation of quadratic.]

c) The solutions to the equation are $x = -2$, $x = -1$ and $x = \frac{1}{3}$. *[1 mark, allow for error carried forward from part b)]*

Chapter 5: Coordinate Geometry

1. The Equation of a Straight Line

Exercise 1.1

— $y - y_1 = m(x - x_1)$ and $y = mx + c$

Q1 **a)** gradient = –4, y-intercept = (0, 11)

b) gradient = –1, y-intercept = (0, 4)

c) gradient = 1.7, y-intercept = (0, –2.3)

Q2 **a)** $y = -3x + 2$

b) $y = 5x - 3$

c) $y = \frac{1}{2}x + 6$

d) $y = 0.8x + 1.2$

Q3 **a)** $c = 8$

$(x_1, y_1) = (-4, 0), (x_2, y_2) = (0, 8)$

$m = \frac{8 - 0}{0 - (-4)} = \frac{8}{4} = 2$

$\Rightarrow y = 2x + 8$

b) $c = -5$

$(x_1, y_1) = (-2, 11), (x_2, y_2) = (0, -5)$

$m = \frac{-5 - 11}{0 - (-2)} = \frac{-16}{2} = -8$

$\Rightarrow y = -8x - 5$

c) $c = -1$

$(x_1, y_1) = (0, -1), (x_2, y_2) = (2, 0)$

$m = \frac{0 - (-1)}{2 - 0} = \frac{1}{2}$

$\Rightarrow y = \frac{1}{2}x - 1$

Q4 **a)** $(x_1, y_1) = (4, 1), (x_2, y_2) = (0, -3)$

$m = \frac{-3 - 1}{0 - 4} = \frac{-4}{-4} = 1$

(i) $y - 1 = 1(x - 4)$

$\Rightarrow y - 1 = x - 4$

(ii) $y = x - 3$

b) $(x_1, y_1) = (12, -3), (x_2, y_2) = (14, 1)$

$m = \frac{1 - (-3)}{14 - 12} = \frac{4}{2} = 2$

(i) $y - (-3) = 2(x - 12)$

$\Rightarrow y + 3 = 2(x - 12)$

(ii) $y = 2x - 27$

c) $(x_1, y_1) = (5, 7), (x_2, y_2) = (-2, 5)$

$m = \frac{5 - 7}{-2 - 5} = \frac{-2}{-7} = \frac{2}{7}$

(i) $y - 7 = \frac{2}{7}(x - 5)$

(ii) $y = \frac{2}{7}x + \frac{39}{7}$

d) $(x_1, y_1) = (-3, 6), (x_2, y_2) = (4, -2)$

$m = \frac{-2 - 6}{4 - (-3)} = -\frac{8}{7}$

(i) $y - 6 = -\frac{8}{7}(x - (-3))$

$\Rightarrow y - 6 = -\frac{8}{7}(x + 3)$

(ii) $y = -\frac{8}{7}x + \frac{18}{7}$

Q5 $y = mx + c$

$\Rightarrow -3 = \frac{1}{4} \times (-4) + c$

$\Rightarrow -3 = -1 + c \Rightarrow c = -2$

$\Rightarrow y = \frac{1}{4}x - 2$

Q6 Find the equation of the line first.

$m = 3$, find c using the point (2, –7) on the line:

$y = mx + c$

$\Rightarrow -7 = 3 \times 2 + c$

$\Rightarrow -7 = 6 + c \Rightarrow c = -13$

$\Rightarrow y = 3x - 13$

The points a), c) and e) lie on the line.

Sub in the x value from each point — if the resulting value for y matches the value of y in the original point, then the point lies on that line.

Exercise 1.2 — $ax + by + c = 0$

Q1 **a)** $5x - y + 2 = 0$

b) $3y = -\frac{1}{2}x + 3$

$\Rightarrow \frac{1}{2}x + 3y - 3 = 0$

$\Rightarrow x + 6y - 6 = 0$

c) $2(x - 1) = 4y - 1$

$\Rightarrow 2x - 2 = 4y - 1$

$\Rightarrow 2x - 4y - 1 = 0$

d) $7x - 2y - 9 = 0$

e) $\frac{1}{2}(4x + 3) = 3(y - 2)$

$\Rightarrow 2x + \frac{3}{2} = 3y - 6$

$\Rightarrow 2x - 3y + \frac{15}{2} = 0$

$\Rightarrow 4x - 6y + 15 = 0$

f) $3(y - 4) = 4(x - 3)$

$\Rightarrow 3y - 12 = 4x - 12$

$\Rightarrow 4x - 3y = 0$

Q2 **a)** $6x - 2y + 3 = 0$

$\Rightarrow 2y = 6x + 3$

$\Rightarrow y = 3x + \frac{3}{2}$

$m = 3$, y-intercept = $(0, \frac{3}{2})$

b) $-9x + 3y - 12 = 0$

$\Rightarrow 3y = 9x + 12$

$\Rightarrow y = 3x + 4$

$m = 3$, y-intercept = (0, 4)

c) $-x - 4y - 2 = 0$

$\Rightarrow -4y = x + 2$

$\Rightarrow y = -\frac{1}{4}x - \frac{1}{2}$

$m = -\frac{1}{4}$, y-intercept $= (0, -\frac{1}{2})$

d) $7x + 8y + 11 = 0$

$\Rightarrow 8y = -7x - 11$

$\Rightarrow y = -\frac{7}{8}x - \frac{11}{8}$

$m = -\frac{7}{8}$, y-intercept $= (0, -\frac{11}{8})$

Q3 a) $(x_1, y_1) = (5, 2)$, $(x_2, y_2) = (3, 4)$

$m = \frac{4 - 2}{3 - 5} = \frac{2}{-2} = -1$

$y - y_1 = m(x - x_1)$

$\Rightarrow y - 2 = -1(x - 5) \Rightarrow y - 2 = -x + 5$

$\Rightarrow x + y - 7 = 0$

b) $(x_1, y_1) = (9, -1)$, $(x_2, y_2) = (7, 2)$

$m = \frac{2 - (-1)}{7 - 9} = -\frac{3}{2}$

$y - y_1 = m(x - x_1)$

$\Rightarrow y - (-1) = -\frac{3}{2}(x - 9)$

$\Rightarrow y + 1 = -\frac{3}{2}x + \frac{27}{2}$

$\Rightarrow \frac{3}{2}x + y - \frac{25}{2} = 0$

$\Rightarrow 3x + 2y - 25 = 0$

c) $(x_1, y_1) = (-6, 1)$, $(x_2, y_2) = (4, 0)$

$m = \frac{0 - 1}{4 - (-6)} = -\frac{1}{10}$

$y - y_1 = m(x - x_1)$

$\Rightarrow y - 1 = -\frac{1}{10}(x - (-6))$

$\Rightarrow y - 1 = -\frac{1}{10}x - \frac{6}{10}$

$\Rightarrow \frac{1}{10}x + y - \frac{4}{10} = 0$

$\Rightarrow x + 10y - 4 = 0$

d) $(x_1, y_1) = (-12, 3)$, $(x_2, y_2) = (5, 7)$

$m = \frac{7 - 3}{5 - (-12)} = \frac{4}{17}$

$y - y_1 = m(x - x_1)$

$\Rightarrow y - 3 = \frac{4}{17}(x - (-12))$

$\Rightarrow y - 3 = \frac{4}{17}x + \frac{48}{17}$

$\Rightarrow -\frac{4}{17}x + y - \frac{99}{17} = 0$

$\Rightarrow -4x + 17y - 99 = 0$

$\Rightarrow 4x - 17y + 99 = 0$

Q4 a) $(x_1, y_1) = (0, -5)$, $(x_2, y_2) = (-5, 0)$

$m = \frac{0 - (-5)}{-5 - 0} = -1$

$y - y_1 = m(x - x_1)$

$\Rightarrow y - (-5) = -1(x - 0)$

$\Rightarrow y + 5 = -x$

$\Rightarrow x + y + 5 = 0$

b) $(x_1, y_1) = (0, -2)$, $(x_2, y_2) = (3, 0)$

$m = \frac{0 - (-2)}{3 - 0} = \frac{2}{3}$

$y - y_1 = m(x - x_1)$

$\Rightarrow y - (-2) = \frac{2}{3}(x - 0)$

$\Rightarrow y + 2 = \frac{2}{3}x$

$\Rightarrow -\frac{2}{3}x + y + 2 = 0$

$\Rightarrow 2x - 3y - 6 = 0$

Exercise 1.3 — Finding the midpoint of a line segment

Q1 a) $(3.5, 3)$

b) $(-0.5, 0.5)$

c) $(5, 2)$

d) $(-10.5, -25)$

e) $(2, -2)$

f) $(0.5, -0.5)$

Q2 $\frac{5 + x}{2} = 4$

$\Rightarrow 5 + x = 8$

$\Rightarrow x = 3$

Q3 $\frac{-1 + x}{2} = 2.5$

$\Rightarrow -1 + x = 5$

$\Rightarrow x = 6$

$\frac{2 + y}{2} = 1$

$\Rightarrow 2 + y = 2$

$\Rightarrow y = 0$

So Q is at $(6, 0)$.

Q4 a) $\frac{1 + x}{2} = 1$

$\Rightarrow 1 + x = 2$

$\Rightarrow x = 1$

$\frac{4 + y}{2} = 1$

$\Rightarrow 4 + y = 2$

$\Rightarrow y = -2$

So B is at $(1, -2)$.

b) $\frac{3 + x}{2} = 1$

$\Rightarrow 3 + x = 2$

$\Rightarrow x = -1$

$\frac{0 + y}{2} = 1$

$\Rightarrow 0 + y = 2$

$\Rightarrow y = 2$

So B is at $(-1, 2)$.

c) $\dfrac{6+x}{2}=1$

$\Rightarrow 6+x=2$

$\Rightarrow x=-4$

$\dfrac{2+y}{2}=1$

$\Rightarrow 2+y=2$

$\Rightarrow y=0$

So B is at $(-4, 0)$.

d) $\dfrac{-1+x}{2}=1$

$\Rightarrow -1+x=2$

$\Rightarrow x=3$

$\dfrac{-4+y}{2}=1$

$\Rightarrow -4+y=2$

$\Rightarrow y=6$

So B is at $(3, 6)$.

Exercise 1.4 — Finding the distance between two points

Q1 a) $d=\sqrt{(3--2)^2+(4-6)^2}$

$=\sqrt{5^2+(-2)^2}$

$=\sqrt{25+4}$

$=\sqrt{29}$

b) $d=\sqrt{(7-8)^2+(12-1)^2}$

$=\sqrt{(-1)^2+11^2}$

$=\sqrt{1+121}$

$=\sqrt{122}$

c) $d=\sqrt{(6--3)^2+(2--2)^2}$

$=\sqrt{9^2+4^2}$

$=\sqrt{81+16}$

$=\sqrt{97}$

d) $d=\sqrt{(0--6)^2+(0--8)^2}$

$=\sqrt{6^2+8^2}$

$=\sqrt{36+64}$

$=\sqrt{100}$

$=10$

e) $d=\sqrt{(2--6)^2+(-4--3)^2}$

$=\sqrt{8^2+(-1)^2}$

$=\sqrt{64+1}$

$=\sqrt{65}$

f) $d=\sqrt{(10-20)^2+(20--10)^2}$

$=\sqrt{(-10)^2+(30)^2}$

$=\sqrt{100+900}$

$=\sqrt{1000}$

$=\sqrt{100\times10}$

$=10\sqrt{10}$

Q2 $5=\sqrt{(4-x)^2+(10-6)^2}=\sqrt{(4-x)^2+4^2}$

$5=\sqrt{(4-x)^2+16}$

$25=(4-x)^2+16$

$9=(4-x)^2$

$\pm3=4-x$

$x=1$ or $x=7$

Q3 $13=\sqrt{(-5-0)^2+(8-y)^2}=\sqrt{(-5)^2+(8-y)^2}$

$13=\sqrt{25+(8-y)^2}$

$169=25+(8-y)^2$

$144=64-16y+y^2$

$0=y^2-16y-80$

$0=(y+4)(y-20)$

$y=-4$ or $y=20$

Q4 a) $AB=\sqrt{(4-1)^2+(6-2)^2}=\sqrt{3^2+4^2}$

$=\sqrt{25}$

$=5$

b) $CD=\sqrt{(3-0)^2+(7-0)^2}=\sqrt{3^2+7^2}$

$=\sqrt{58}$

c) $EF=\sqrt{(-8-2)^2+(3-5)^2}$

$=\sqrt{(-10)^2+(-2)^2}$

$=\sqrt{104}=2\sqrt{26}$

d) $GH=\sqrt{(20-12)^2+(-10--5)^2}$

$=\sqrt{8^2+(-5)^2}$

$=\sqrt{89}$

2. Parallel and Perpendicular Lines

Exercise 2.1 — Parallel lines

Q1 a), c) and e) are parallel.

Rearrange each equation so it's in the form $y = mx + c$ and then compare gradients. If a line is parallel to $y = -3x + c$, then it'll have a gradient of -3.

Q2 a) $y=4x+c$

Sub in $x=3$ and $y=2$

$\Rightarrow 2=4\times3+c\Rightarrow-10=c$

So $y=4x-10$

$\Rightarrow 4x-y-10=0$

b) First rearrange the given equation:

$4x-2y-1=0$

$-2y=-4x+1$

$y=2x-\dfrac{1}{2}$

So the equation of the line we want is:

$y=2x+c$

Sub in $x=-4$, $y=-5\Rightarrow-5=2(-4)+c\Rightarrow c=3$

So $y=2x+3\Rightarrow 2x-y+3=0$.

Q3 a) no

b) yes (they both have a gradient of $\frac{2}{3}$).

c) yes (they both have a gradient of $\frac{5}{4}$).

Q4 a) Find the gradient of the other line first:

Rearrange $2x - 4y + 3 = 0$

$\Rightarrow 4y = 2x + 3 \Rightarrow y = \frac{1}{2}x + \frac{3}{4}$

So gradient, $m = \frac{1}{2}$

$y = \frac{1}{2}x + c$

Sub in $x = 4$ and $y = 3$

$\Rightarrow 3 = \frac{1}{2} \times 4 + c \Rightarrow c = 1$

$\Rightarrow y = \frac{1}{2}x + 1$

b) Rearrange $y = \frac{1}{2}x + 1$

$\Rightarrow \frac{1}{2}x - y + 1 = 0 \Rightarrow x - 2y + 2 = 0$

Exercise 2.2 — Perpendicular lines

Q1 a) $m = -1 \div 2 = -\frac{1}{2} \Rightarrow y = -\frac{1}{2}x + c$

Sub in $(-2, 5)$

$\Rightarrow 5 = \left(-\frac{1}{2}\right) \times (-2) + c \Rightarrow c = 5 - 1 = 4$

$\Rightarrow y = -\frac{1}{2}x + 4$

b) Rearrange $x - 5y - 30 = 0 \Rightarrow y = \frac{1}{5}x - 6$

$m = -1 \div \frac{1}{5} = -5 \Rightarrow y = -5x + c$

Sub in $(5, 2)$

$\Rightarrow 2 = -5 \times 5 + c \Rightarrow c = 2 + 25 = 27$

$\Rightarrow y = -5x + 27$

Q2 a) $m = -1 \div \frac{1}{4} = -4$

$\Rightarrow y = -4x + c$

Sub in $(-1, 2)$

$\Rightarrow 2 = (-4) \times (-1) + c \Rightarrow c = 2 - 4 = -2$

$\Rightarrow y = -4x - 2$

$\Rightarrow 4x + y + 2 = 0$

b) Rearrange to get $y = -\frac{2}{3}x + \frac{1}{3}$

$m = -1 \div -\frac{2}{3} = \frac{3}{2} \Rightarrow y = \frac{3}{2}x + c$

Sub in $(-3, -1)$

$\Rightarrow -1 = \frac{3}{2} \times (-3) + c \Rightarrow c = -1 + \frac{9}{2} = \frac{7}{2}$

$\Rightarrow y = \frac{3}{2}x + \frac{7}{2} \Rightarrow 2y = 3x + 7$

$\Rightarrow 3x - 2y + 7 = 0$

c) Rearrange to get $y = \frac{1}{2}x + \frac{1}{10}$

$m = -1 \div \frac{1}{2} = -2 \Rightarrow y = -2x + c$

Sub in $(6, -5)$

$\Rightarrow -5 = -2 \times 6 + c \Rightarrow c = -5 + 12 = 7$

$\Rightarrow y = -2x + 7 \Rightarrow 2x + y - 7 = 0$

d) $m = -1 \div \frac{3}{2} = -\frac{2}{3} \Rightarrow y = -\frac{2}{3}x + c$

Sub in $(2, 1)$

$\Rightarrow 1 = -\frac{2}{3} \times 2 + c \Rightarrow c = 1 + \frac{4}{3} = \frac{7}{3}$

$\Rightarrow y = -\frac{2}{3}x + \frac{7}{3} \Rightarrow 3y = -2x + 7$

$\Rightarrow 2x + 3y - 7 = 0$

Q3 a) Rearrange $3x + 4y - 1 = 0 \Rightarrow y = -\frac{3}{4}x + \frac{1}{4}$

Multiply the gradients of both lines:

$\frac{4}{3} \times -\frac{3}{4} = -1$

So the lines are perpendicular.

Remember, if you multiply the gradients of two perpendicular lines you get −1.

b) Rearrange $3x + 2y - 3 = 0 \Rightarrow y = -\frac{3}{2}x + \frac{3}{2}$

Multiply the gradients of both lines:

$\frac{3}{2} \times -\frac{3}{2} = -\frac{9}{4}$

So the lines are not perpendicular.

c) Rearrange $4x - y + 3 = 0 \Rightarrow y = 4x + 3$

Rearrange $2x + 8y + 1 = 0 \Rightarrow y = -\frac{1}{4}x - \frac{1}{8}$

Multiply the gradients of both lines:

$4 \times -\frac{1}{4} = -1$

So the lines are perpendicular.

Q4 a) $AB: m = \frac{3 - 2}{4 - 0} = \frac{1}{4} \Rightarrow y = \frac{1}{4}x + c$

Sub in $(0, 2) \Rightarrow 2 = 0 + c \Rightarrow c = 2$

$\Rightarrow y = \frac{1}{4}x + 2$

$BC: m = \frac{-1 - 3}{5 - 4} = -4 \Rightarrow y = -4x + c$

Sub in $(4, 3) \Rightarrow 3 = -4 \times 4 + c \Rightarrow c = 19$

$\Rightarrow y = -4x + 19$

$AC: m = \frac{-1 - 2}{5 - 0} = -\frac{3}{5} \Rightarrow y = -\frac{3}{5}x + c$

Sub in $(0, 2) \Rightarrow 2 = 0 + c \Rightarrow c = 2$

$\Rightarrow y = -\frac{3}{5}x + 2$

b) The triangle is right-angled, as AB is perpendicular to BC:

$m_{AB} \times m_{BC} = \frac{1}{4} \times -4 = -1$

Q5 $3x - 2y = 6$

Rearrange into $y = mx + c$:

$\Rightarrow -2y = -3x + 6$

$\Rightarrow y = \frac{3}{2}x - 3$

So the line we want will have gradient

$m = -1 \div \frac{3}{2} = -\frac{2}{3}$

Now sub in (a, b) to find c:

$y = -\frac{2}{3}x + c$

$b = -\frac{2}{3}a + c$

$c = b + \frac{2}{3}a$

So the equation of line A is $y = -\frac{2}{3}x + \frac{2}{3}a + b$

You could also have given the line in the form
$2x + 3y - 2a - 3b = 0$ as the question didn't
tell you which form to use.

3. Curve Sketching
Exercise 3.1 — Sketching cubic functions
Q1 **a)**

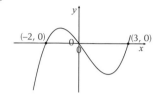

b)

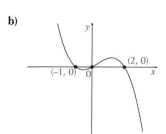

c)

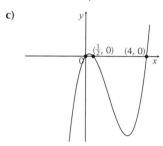

Your graphs don't need to look exactly like these,
e.g. you don't need to get the size of the 'dips' right
— as long as you've shown the rough shape and
intercept points with the axes.

Q2 **a)**

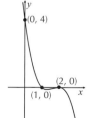

b)

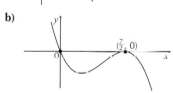

Remember — putting in values for x near the key points
can really help understand the shape of the graphs.
E.g. for part b) above, pop in x = 3 and 4 to check that
both give negative values for y.

Q3 **a)**

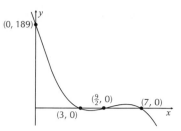

b)

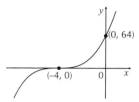

Q4 **a)** First take out a factor of x:
$x^3 - 7x^2 + 12x = x(x^2 - 7x + 12)$

Then factorise the quadratic:
$x^2 - 7x + 12 = (x - 3)(x - 4)$

So $x^3 - 7x^2 + 12x = x(x - 3)(x - 4)$.

b)

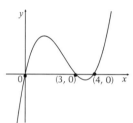

Q5 **a)** $x^3 - 16x = x(x^2 - 16) = x(x + 4)(x - 4)$

Using this information we can sketch the graph:

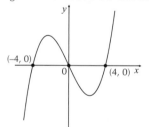

b) $2x^3 - 12x^2 + 18x = 2x(x^2 - 6x + 9)$
$= 2x(x - 3)^2$

Using this information we can sketch the graph:

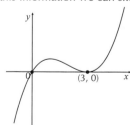

Q6 **a)**

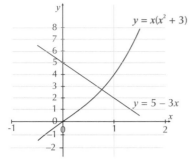

b) The x-coordinates of the points of intersection of the curve and the line are found by setting them equal to each other: $x(x^2 + 3) = 5 - 3x$

Rearranging: $x^3 + 3x = 5 - 3x$
$\Rightarrow x^3 + 3x - 5 + 3x = 0 \Rightarrow x^3 + 6x - 5 = 0$

So the intersection point of the curve and the line is the real solution to $x^3 + 6x - 5 = 0$.

c) Looking at the graph from part a) — particularly at the point where the curve and the line cross, you can estimate the x-value of the real solution to the equation.

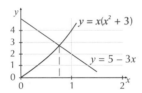

It looks like the solution is at about $x = 0.7$. The exact solution is actually close to 0.76 but anything between 0.6 and 0.9 would be a good answer.

Q7 **a)** $y = x(x^2 - 3x + 12)$
Look at the discriminant to see if the quadratic has any roots:
$b^2 - 4ac = 9 - 4(12) < 0$, so there are no real roots, which means the only root of the cubic is $x = 0$.

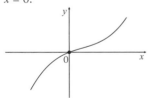

b) The discriminant of the quadratic factor is negative, so it has no real roots — so the cubic has just one root:

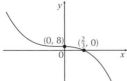

These graphs flatten rather than 'dip' — putting in lots of values for x will help you see this. But don't worry if you didn't get them exactly right.

In chapter 7 you'll look at ways of finding the max / min points of graphs, which will help you to do sketches like this more accurately.

c) The discriminant of the quadratic factor is negative, so it has no real roots — so the cubic has just one root:

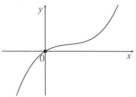

4. Transformations

Exercise 4.1 — Translations

Q1 **a)**

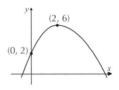

b)

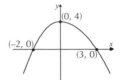

Q2 The graph of $y = g(x - 1)$ is the graph of $y = g(x)$ translated 1 unit in the positive x-direction so it must be graph B.

Q3 $y = (x - 2)^2(x - 6) = (x - 2)^2 ((x - 2) - 4)$ so it is the curve $y = x^2(x - 4)$ with x replaced by $x - 2$ so it will be translated 2 units in the positive x-direction.

Q4 $y = x^3 + 3x + 2 = (x^3 + 3x + 7) - 5$ so the translation will be -5 in the y-direction, i.e. 5 units down.

Q5 The equation will be $y = (x + 1)^2 - 3(x + 1) + 7$
$= x^2 + 2x + 1 - 3x - 3 + 7 = x^2 - x + 5$.

Q6 **a)** and **b)**

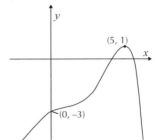

Q7 **a)**

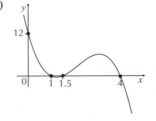

b) The equation of the translated graph would be
$$y = ((x-2)-1)(2(x-2)-3)(4-(x-2))$$
$$= (x-3)(2x-4-3)(4-x+2)$$
$$= (x-3)(2x-7)(6-x)$$

c)

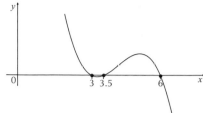

Review Exercise — Chapter 5

Q1 a) (i) $y + 1 = 3(x-2)$

(ii) $y = 3x - 7$

(iii) $3x - y - 7 = 0$

b) (i) $y + \dfrac{1}{3} = \dfrac{1}{5}x$

(ii) $y = \dfrac{1}{5}x - \dfrac{1}{3}$

(iii) $3x - 15y - 5 = 0$

Q2 a) $M = \left(\dfrac{2+12}{2}, \dfrac{5-1}{2}\right) = (7, 2)$

b) $d = \sqrt{(7-2)^2 + (2-5)^2} = \sqrt{25+9} = \sqrt{34}$

Q3 a) Substitute $(1, k)$ into $5y - x = 9$:
$5k - 1 = 9 \Rightarrow 5k = 10 \Rightarrow k = 2$.

b) $d = \sqrt{(x_2 - x_1)^2 + (y_2 - y_1)^2}$
$= \sqrt{(6-1)^2 + (3-2)^2} = \sqrt{26}$
Midpoint $= \left(\dfrac{1+6}{2}, \dfrac{2+3}{2}\right) = (3.5, 2.5)$.

c) First find the equation of the line BC:
The gradient of BC is $m = \dfrac{3-0}{6+1} = \dfrac{3}{7}$, and so BC has equation:
$y - y_1 = m(x - x_1)$
$y - 0 = \dfrac{3}{7}(x + 1)$
$\Rightarrow 7y = 3x + 3$
Now substitute $(2p + 3, p + 1)$ into your equation to find p:
$7(p + 1) = 3(2p + 3) + 3$
$7p + 7 = 6p + 12$
$\Rightarrow p = 5$

Q4 a) $y = \dfrac{3}{2}x + c$ since it is parallel to l_1.
Substitute in $x = 4$ and $y = 2$ to get $c = -4$
So $y = \dfrac{3}{2}x - 4$

b) l_2 can be rearranged to the form $y = 2x - 7$. So it has gradient 2 and so a perpendicular line will have gradient $-\dfrac{1}{2}$. So $y = -\dfrac{1}{2}x + d$.
Substitute in $x = 6$ and $y = 1$ to get $d = 4$
So $y = -\dfrac{1}{2}x + 4$

Q5 The gradient of the line RS is $\dfrac{9-3}{1-10} = \dfrac{6}{-9} = -\dfrac{2}{3}$
so the gradient of the perpendicular line is $\dfrac{3}{2}$.
So $y = \dfrac{3}{2}x + c$.
Substituting in $x = 1$ and $y = 9$ gives $c = \dfrac{15}{2}$.
The equation of the required line is $y = \dfrac{3}{2}x + \dfrac{15}{2}$.

Q6 a)

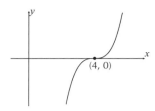

b)

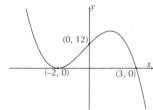

c)

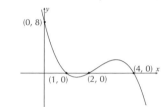

d)

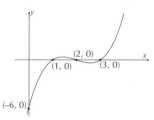

Q7 a)

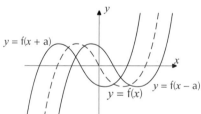

b)

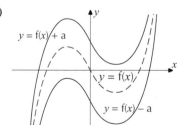

Q8 a)

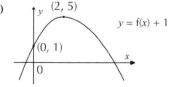

b)

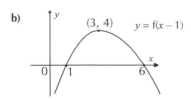

Exam-Style Questions — Chapter 5

Q1 a) Rearrange into $y = mx + c$ form and read off m:

$3y = 15 - 4x$

$y = -\dfrac{4}{3}x + 5$ *[1 mark]*

so the gradient of the line PQ is $-\dfrac{4}{3}$ *[1 mark]*.

b) Gradient of line $= -1 \div -\dfrac{4}{3} = \dfrac{3}{4}$ *[1 mark]*

So $y = \dfrac{3}{4}x + c$.

Now use the x- and y- values of R to find C:

$1 = \dfrac{3}{4}(3) + c$

$1 = \dfrac{9}{4} + c$

$\Rightarrow c = -\dfrac{5}{4}$ *[1 mark]*

so the equation is $y = \dfrac{3}{4}x - \dfrac{5}{4}$ *[1 mark]*

Q2 When the brackets are multiplied out, the first term is $2x^3$, so the graph is a positive cubic graph.

$y = 0$ when $x = 2$ or $x = -\frac{1}{2}$: the graph touches the x-axis at $(2, 0)$ and crosses it at $(-\frac{1}{2}, 0)$.

When $x = 0$, $y = (1)(-2)^2 = 4$.

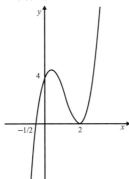

[4 marks available — 1 mark for correct shape, 1 mark for x-axis intercept at −1/2, 1 mark for graph touching the x-axis at 2 and 1 mark for correct y-axis intercept at 4.]

Q3 a)

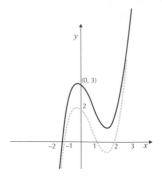

[2 marks available — 1 mark for vertical translation up, 1 mark for correct y-axis intercept.]

b)

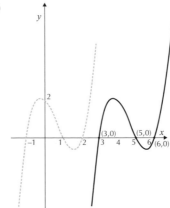

[2 marks available — 1 mark for horizontal translation to the right, 1 mark for correct intercepts.]

Q4 a)

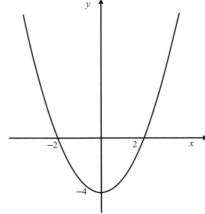

[2 marks available — 1 mark for x-axis intercepts at −2 and 2, 1 mark for correct y-axis intercept (0, −4)]

b) The curve is translated 1 unit in the negative x-direction *[1 mark]* and 3 units in the negative y-direction *[1 mark]*.

c) $y = f(x) + 2$ *[1 mark]*

Q5 a) You can use either the formula $y - y_1 = m(x - x_1)$ or $y = mx + c$, with the coordinates of point S for the x- and y- values and $m = -2$.
Using $y - y_1 = m(x - x_1)$:
$$y - (-3) = -2(x - 7) \quad \textbf{\textit{[1 mark]}}$$
$$y + 3 = -2x + 14 \quad \textbf{\textit{[1 mark]}}$$
$$y = -2x + 11 \quad \textbf{\textit{[1 mark]}}$$

OR using $y = mx + c$:
$$-3 = (-2 \times 7) + c \quad \textbf{\textit{[1 mark]}}$$
$$c = -3 + 14 = 11 \quad \textbf{\textit{[1 mark]}}$$
$$y = -2x + 11 \quad \textbf{\textit{[1 mark]}}$$
There are sometimes two different ways to tackle a problem — as long as you show your working and get the right answer, you'll pick up the marks.

b) When $x = 5$, $y = (-2 \times 5) + 11 = 1$ **[1 mark]**, so $T(5, 1)$ must lie on the line.

Q6 a) Gradient of $LK = \dfrac{8 - 6}{5 - 2} = \dfrac{2}{3}$ **[1 mark]**

so gradient of $l_1 = -1 \div \dfrac{2}{3} = -\dfrac{3}{2}$ **[1 mark]**.

Now, putting this gradient and the x- and y-coordinates of L into the formula $y - y_1 = m(x - x_1)$ gives:
$$y - 6 = -\frac{3}{2}(x - 2)$$
$$y = -\frac{3}{2}x + 3 + 6$$
$$y = -\frac{3}{2}x + 9 \quad \textbf{\textit{[1 mark]}}$$
$$\Rightarrow 3x + 2y - 18 = 0 \quad \textbf{\textit{[1 mark]}}$$

b) Putting $x = 0$ into $y = -\dfrac{3}{2}x + 9$ gives $y = 9$ so $M = (0, 9)$ **[1 mark]**.

c) Putting $y = 0$ into $3x + 2y - 18 = 0$ gives $x = 6$, so $N = (6, 0)$ **[1 mark]**.

d) $\left(\dfrac{2 + 6}{2}, \dfrac{6 + 0}{2}\right)$ **[1 mark]**
$= (4, 3)$ **[1 mark]**

Chapter 6: Circles
1. Equation of a Circle
Exercise 1.1 — Equation of a circle with centre (a, b)

Q1 $x^2 + y^2 = 25$

Q2 $x^2 + y^2 = 49$

Q3 a) $a = 2, b = 5, r = 3$
$(x - 2)^2 + (y - 5)^2 = 9$

b) $a = -3, b = 2, r = 5$
$(x + 3)^2 + (y - 2)^2 = 25$

c) $a = -2, b = -3, r = 7$
$(x + 2)^2 + (y + 3)^2 = 49$

d) $a = 3, b = 0, r = 4$
$(x - 3)^2 + y^2 = 16$

Q4 a) $a = 1, b = 5, r = \sqrt{4}$
So the centre is $(1, 5)$ and the radius is 2.

b) $a = 3, b = 5, r = \sqrt{64}$
So the centre is $(3, 5)$ and the radius is 8.

c) $a = 3, b = -2, r = \sqrt{25}$
So the centre is $(3, -2)$ and the radius is 5.

Q5 $a = 5, b = 3, r = 8 \Rightarrow (x - 5)^2 + (y - 3)^2 = 64$.
This is a translation of the circle with radius 8 and centre $(0, 0)$ 5 units in the positive x-direction and 3 units in the positive y-direction.

Q6 $a = 3, b = 1, r = \sqrt{31} \Rightarrow (x - 3)^2 + (y - 1)^2 = 31$

Q7 a) $a = 6, b = 4$, so the centre is $(6, 4)$.

b) Radius $= \sqrt{20} = \sqrt{4 \times 5} = 2\sqrt{5}$

Q8 $a = -3, b = -2, r = \sqrt{5}$
$(x + 3)^2 + (y + 2)^2 = 5$
$\Rightarrow x^2 + 6x + 9 + y^2 + 4y + 4 = 5$
$\Rightarrow x^2 + y^2 + 6x + 4y + 8 = 0$

Exercise 1.2 — Rearranging circle equations

Q1 a) Complete the square for the x's and y's:
$x^2 + y^2 + 2x - 6y - 6 = 0$
$x^2 + 2x + y^2 - 6y - 6 = 0$
$(x + 1)^2 - 1 + (y - 3)^2 - 9 - 6 = 0$
$(x + 1)^2 + (y - 3)^2 = 16$
Radius = 4, centre is $(-1, 3)$.

b) Complete the square for the x's and y's:
$x^2 + y^2 - 2y - 4 = 0$
$x^2 + (y - 1)^2 - 1 - 4 = 0$
$x^2 + (y - 1)^2 = 5$
Radius $= \sqrt{5}$, centre is $(0, 1)$.

c) Complete the square for the x's and y's:
$x^2 + y^2 - 6x - 4y = 12$
$x^2 - 6x + y^2 - 4y = 12$
$(x - 3)^2 - 9 + (y - 2)^2 - 4 = 12$
$(x - 3)^2 + (y - 2)^2 = 25$
Radius = 5, centre is $(3, 2)$.

d) Complete the square for the x's and y's:
$x^2 + y^2 - 10x + 6y + 13 = 0$
$x^2 - 10x + y^2 + 6y + 13 = 0$
$(x - 5)^2 - 25 + (y + 3)^2 - 9 + 13 = 0$
$(x - 5)^2 + (y + 3)^2 = 21$
Radius $= \sqrt{21}$, centre is $(5, -3)$.

Q2 a) Complete the square for the x's and y's:
$x^2 + y^2 + 2x - 4y - 3 = 0$
$x^2 + 2x + y^2 - 4y - 3 = 0$
$(x + 1)^2 - 1 + (y - 2)^2 - 4 - 3 = 0$
$(x + 1)^2 + (y - 2)^2 = 8$
Centre is $(-1, 2)$.

b) Radius $= \sqrt{8} = \sqrt{2 \times 4} = 2\sqrt{2}$

Q3 a) Complete the square for the x's and y's:
$x^2 + y^2 - 3x + 1 = 0$
$x^2 - 3x + y^2 + 1 = 0$
$\left(x - \dfrac{3}{2}\right)^2 - \dfrac{9}{4} + y^2 + 1 = 0$
$\left(x - \dfrac{3}{2}\right)^2 + y^2 = \dfrac{5}{4}$
Centre is $\left(\dfrac{3}{2}, 0\right)$

b) Radius $= \sqrt{\dfrac{5}{4}} = \dfrac{\sqrt{5}}{2}$

2. Circle Properties

Exercise 2.1 — Using circle properties

Q1 **a)** Centre is (3, 1).

b) Gradient of radius $= \dfrac{4-1}{4-3} = \dfrac{3}{1} = 3$

c) The tangent at A is perpendicular to the radius at A, so the gradient of the tangent is $-\dfrac{1}{3}$.

Use $y - y_1 = m(x - x_1)$ to find equation of tangent:

$y - 4 = -\dfrac{1}{3}(x - 4)$

$3y - 12 = -x + 4$

$x + 3y = 16$

You're asked for the equation in a particular form, so don't forget to rearrange it.

Q2 Centre of the circle is (–1, 2).

Gradient of radius $= \dfrac{2 - (-1)}{-1 - (-3)} = \dfrac{3}{2}$

Gradient of the tangent $= -\dfrac{2}{3}$

Use $y - y_1 = m(x - x_1)$ to find equation of tangent:

$y - (-1) = -\dfrac{2}{3}(x - (-3))$

$3y + 3 = -2(x + 3)$

$3y + 3 = -2x - 6$

$2x + 3y + 9 = 0$

Q3 Centre of the circle is (3, 4).

Gradient of radius $= \dfrac{4-1}{3-7} = -\dfrac{3}{4}$

Gradient of the tangent $= \dfrac{4}{3}$

Use $y - y_1 = m(x - x_1)$ to find equation of tangent:

$y - 1 = \dfrac{4}{3}(x - 7)$

$3y - 3 = 4x - 28$

$4x - 3y = 25$

Q4 Rearrange $x^2 + y^2 + 2x - 7 = 0$ and complete the square for the x and y terms, to get:

$(x + 1)^2 + y^2 = 8$

Centre of the circle is (–1, 0).

Gradient of radius $= \dfrac{0 - 2}{-1 - (-3)} = \dfrac{-2}{2} = -1$

Gradient of the tangent $= 1$

Use $y - y_1 = m(x - x_1)$ to find equation of tangent:

$y - 2 = 1(x - (-3))$

$y - 2 = x + 3$

$y = x + 5$

Q5 Rearrange $x^2 + y^2 + 2x + 4y = 5$ and complete the square for the x and y terms to get:

$(x + 1)^2 + (y + 2)^2 = 10$

Centre of the circle is (–1, –2).

Gradient of the radius $= \dfrac{-2 - (-5)}{-1 - 0} = \dfrac{3}{-1} = -3$

Gradient of the tangent $= \dfrac{1}{3}$

Use $y - y_1 = m(x - x_1)$ to find equation of tangent:

$y - (-5) = \dfrac{1}{3}(x - 0)$

$3y + 15 = x$

$x - 3y = 15$

Q6 **a)** The line l is perpendicular to the chord AB. So find the gradient of AB:

Gradient of $AB = \dfrac{1-7}{-1-(-3)} = -\dfrac{6}{2} = -3$

So the gradient of l is $\dfrac{1}{3}$.

Then sub the gradient of l and point M (–1, 1) into $y - y_1 = m(x - x_1)$ to find the equation:

$y - 1 = \dfrac{1}{3}(x - (-1))$

$3y - 3 = x + 1$

$x - 3y + 4 = 0$

b) The centre is (2, 2), so $a = 2$ and $b = 2$ in the equation $(x - a)^2 + (y - b)^2 = r^2$.

The radius is the length CA, which can be found using Pythagoras:

$r^2 = CA^2 = (-3 - 2)^2 + (7 - 2)^2 = (-5^2) + 5^2 = 50$

So the equation of the circle is:

$(x - 2)^2 + (y - 2)^2 = 50$

Q7 If AC is a diameter, the angle ABC will be 90°. So find out if AB and BC are perpendicular.

Gradient of AB $= \dfrac{14 - 12}{4 - (-2)} = \dfrac{2}{6} = \dfrac{1}{3}$

Gradient of BC $= \dfrac{2 - 14}{8 - 4} = \dfrac{-12}{4} = -3$

Use the gradient rule to check:

$m_1 \times m_2 = -1$

$\dfrac{1}{3} \times -3 = -1$

As AB and BC are perpendicular, the angle ABC must be 90° and so AC must be a diameter of the circle.

Review Exercise — Chapter 6

Q1 **a)** Radius = 3, centre = (0, 0)

b) Radius = 2, centre = (2, –4)

c) Complete the square for the x's and y's:

$x(x + 6) = y(8 - y)$

$x^2 + 6x = 8y - y^2$

$x^2 + 6x + y^2 - 8y = 0$

$(x + 3)^2 - 9 + (y - 4)^2 - 16 = 0$

$(x + 3)^2 + (y - 4)^2 = 25$

Radius = 5, centre = (–3, 4)

Q2 **a)** $(x - 3)^2 + (y - 2)^2 = 36$

b) $(x + 4)^2 + (y + 8)^2 = 64$

c) $x^2 + (y + 3)^2 = 14$

Q3 Complete the square for the x's and y's:

$x^2 + y^2 - 4x + 6y - 68 = 0$

$x^2 - 4x + y^2 + 6y - 68 = 0$

$(x - 2)^2 - 4 + (y + 3)^2 - 9 - 68 = 0$

$(x - 2)^2 + (y + 3)^2 = 81$

Centre is (2, –3), radius = 9

Q4 CD is a radius that bisects the chord, so it must be perpendicular to it.

C is at (2, 1) (from the equation of the circle).

Gradient of CD $= \dfrac{-5 - 1}{10 - 2} = \dfrac{-6}{8} = -\dfrac{3}{4}$

So gradient of $l = \dfrac{4}{3}$.

Using $y - y_1 = m(x - x_1)$ for line l, passing through (10, 7):

$y - 7 = \frac{4}{3}(x - 10)$

$3y - 21 = 4x - 40$

$4x - 3y - 19 = 0$

Q5 Rearrange $x^2 + y^2 - 12x + 2y + 11 = 0$ and complete the square for the x and y terms to get:

$(x - 6)^2 + (y + 1)^2 = 26$

Centre is (6, –1).

Gradient of the radius = $\frac{-1 - (-2)}{6 - 1} = \frac{1}{5}$

Gradient of the tangent = –5

Use $y - y_1 = m(x - x_1)$ to find equation of tangent:

$y - (-2) = -5(x - 1)$

$y + 2 = -5x + 5$

$y = 3 - 5x$

Exam-Style Questions — Chapter 6

Q1 a) Rearrange equation and complete the square:

$x^2 - 2x + y^2 - 10y + 21 = 0$

$(x - 1)^2 - 1 + (y - 5)^2 - 25 + 21 = 0$ *[1 mark]*

$(x - 1)^2 + (y - 5)^2 = 5$ *[1 mark]*

Compare with $(x - a)^2 + (y - b)^2 = r^2$:

centre = (1, 5) *[1 mark]*,

radius = $\sqrt{5}$ *[1 mark]*.

b) The point (3, 6) and centre (1, 5) both lie on the diameter.

Gradient of the diameter = $\frac{6 - 5}{3 - 1} = \frac{1}{2}$.

$Q(q, 4)$ also lies on the diameter, so $\frac{4 - 6}{q - 3} = \frac{1}{2}$.

$-2 = \frac{1}{2}q - \frac{3}{2}$

So $q = (-2 + \frac{3}{2}) \div \frac{1}{2} = -1$.

You could have done this question by realising that the x-coordinate of the centre will be the average of the x-coordinates of P and Q, but you'll need the gradient for the next part so it makes sense to do it this way.

[3 marks available — 1 mark for finding the gradient of the diameter, 1 mark for linking this with the point Q, and 1 mark for correct calculation of q.]

c) Tangent at Q is perpendicular to the diameter at Q, so gradient $m = -\frac{1}{0.5} = -2$

$y - y_1 = m(x - x_1)$, and (–1, 4) is a point on the line, so:

$y - 4 = -2(x + 1)$

$y - 4 = -2x - 2$

$2x + y - 2 = 0$ is the equation of the tangent.

[4 marks available — 1 mark for gradient = –1 ÷ gradient of diameter, 1 mark for correct value for gradient, 1 mark for substituting Q in straight-line equation, 1 mark for equation in the correct form.]

Q2 a) Centre of $C = (-4, 4)$, so $a = -4$ and $b = 4$ *[1 mark]*. Radius r is the length of MJ. Using Pythagoras, $r^2 = (0 - -4)^2 + (7 - 4)^2$ *[1 mark]* = 25

So substituting into the equation gives:

$(x + 4)^2 + (y - 4)^2 = 25$ *[1 mark]*

b) Angle MJH between the radius and tangent is a right angle, so use trig ratios to calculate angle JMH (or θ).

E.g. Length $MJ = r = \sqrt{25} = 5$. Using Pythagoras, Length $JH = \sqrt{(6 - 0)^2 + (-1 - 7)^2} = 10$.

$\tan\theta = \frac{10}{5} = 2$

$\theta = \tan^{-1} 2$

[4 marks available — 1 mark for identifying that MJH is a right angle and that trig ratios can be used, 1 mark for calculation of two lengths of the triangle, 1 mark for correct substitution into a trig ratio, and 1 mark for correct answer.]

Q3 a) The line through P is a diameter, and as such is perpendicular to the chord AB at the midpoint M.

Gradient of AB = Gradient of $AM = \frac{(7 - 10)}{(11 - 9)}$

$= -\frac{3}{2}$.

$\Rightarrow$ Gradient of $PM = \frac{2}{3}$.

Gradient of $PM = \frac{(7 - 3)}{(11 - p)} = \frac{2}{3}$

$\Rightarrow 3(7 - 3) = 2(11 - p)$

$\Rightarrow 12 = 22 - 2p \Rightarrow p = 5$.

[4 marks available — 1 mark for identifying that PM and AM are perpendicular, 1 mark for correct gradient of AM, 1 mark for correct gradient of PM and 1 mark for substitution of the y-value of P into the gradient or equation of the line.]

b) The centre of C is $P(5, 3)$, so $a = 5$ and $b = 3$ *[1 mark]* in the equation

$(x - a)^2 + (y - b)^2 = r^2$.

The radius is the length of AP, which can be found using Pythagoras as follows:

$r^2 = AP^2 = (9 - 5)^2 + (10 - 3)^2$ *[1 mark]* = 65

So the equation of C is:

$(x - 5)^2 + (y - 3)^2 = 65$ *[1 mark]*.

Chapter 7: Differentiation

1. The Gradient of a Curve
Exercise 1.1
— Differentiating from first principles

Q1 *The gradient of the straight line joining points (x_1, y_1) and (x_2, y_2) is given by $\frac{y_2 - y_1}{x_2 - x_1}$.*

a) (i) When $x = 1$, $y = 1$ and when $x = 2$, $y = 8$ so the gradient is $\frac{8 - 1}{2 - 1} = \frac{7}{1} = 7$.

(ii) When $x = 1$, $y = 1$ and when $x = 1.5$, $y = 3.375$ so the gradient is $\frac{3.375 - 1}{1.5 - 1} = \frac{2.375}{0.5} = 4.75$.

(iii) When $x = 1$, $y = 1$ and when $x = 1.1$, $y = 1.331$ so the gradient is $\frac{1.331 - 1}{1.1 - 1} = \frac{0.331}{0.1} = 3.31$.

b) The gradients of the straight lines in part a) move closer to 3 as the value of x moves closer to 1.

Q2 a) $\dfrac{dy}{dx} = \lim_{h \to 0}\left[\dfrac{(x+h)-x}{(x+h)-x}\right] = \lim_{h \to 0}[1] = 1$

b) $f'(x) = \lim_{h \to 0}\left[\dfrac{(x+h)^3 - x^3}{(x+h)-x}\right]$

$= \lim_{h \to 0}\left[\dfrac{(x+h)^2(x+h) - x^3}{(x+h)-x}\right]$

$= \lim_{h \to 0}\left[\dfrac{(x^2 + 2xh + h^2)(x+h) - x^3}{(x+h)-x}\right]$

$= \lim_{h \to 0}\left[\dfrac{x^3 + 3x^2h + 3xh^2 + h^3 - x^3}{(x+h)-x}\right]$

$= \lim_{h \to 0}\left[\dfrac{3x^2h + 3xh^2 + h^3}{h}\right]$

$= \lim_{h \to 0}[3x^2 + 3xh + h^2] = 3x^2$

c) $f'(x) = \lim_{h \to 0}\left[\dfrac{2(x+h)-2x}{(x+h)-x}\right] = \lim_{h \to 0}\left[\dfrac{2x + 2h - 2x}{h}\right]$

$= \lim_{h \to 0}\left[\dfrac{2h}{h}\right] = \lim_{h \to 0}[2] = 2$

2. Differentiating $y = f(x)$
Exercise 2.1 — Differentiating x^n

Q1 a) $\dfrac{dy}{dx} = 6x^5$ **b)** $\dfrac{dy}{dx} = 3x^2$

c) $\dfrac{dy}{dx} = 0$ **d)** $\dfrac{dy}{dx} = 6x$

e) $\dfrac{dy}{dx} = 7$ **f)** $\dfrac{dy}{dx} = 0$

g) $\dfrac{dy}{dx} = 15x^2$ **h)** $\dfrac{dy}{dx} = 11$

Remember that $x^0 = 1$, so you can use this fact when differentiating any constant.

Q2 a) $f'(x) = 5x^4$ **b)** $f'(x) = 7x^6$

c) $f'(x) = 4x^3$ **d)** $f'(x) = 12x^2$

e) $f'(x) = 8$ **f)** $f'(x) = 15x^4$

g) $f'(x) = 0$ **h)** $f'(x) = 8x$

Q3 a) $\dfrac{dy}{dx} = 4x \Rightarrow$ At $x = 4, \dfrac{dy}{dx} = 16$

b) $\dfrac{dy}{dx} = 1 \Rightarrow$ At $x = 2, \dfrac{dy}{dx} = 1$

c) $\dfrac{dy}{dx} = -20x^4 \Rightarrow$ At $x = 1, \dfrac{dy}{dx} = -20$

d) $f'(x) = 4x \Rightarrow f'(9) = 36$

e) $f'(x) = 4x^3 \Rightarrow f'(-2) = -32$

f) $f(x) = -250, -250 = -2x^3$
$\Rightarrow 125 = x^3 \Rightarrow x = 5$
$f'(x) = -6x^2 \Rightarrow f'(5) = -150$

Exercise 2.2 — Differentiating functions

Q1 a) $\dfrac{dy}{dx} = 12x^2 - 2x$

b) $\dfrac{dy}{dx} = 1$

c) $\dfrac{dy}{dx} = 6x + 1$

d) $f'(x) = -10x^4 + 4$

e) $f'(x) = 4x^3 - 1$

f) $f'(x) = 5 - 6x^2$

Q2 a) $\dfrac{d}{dx}(x(x^6 - 1)) = \dfrac{d}{dx}(x^7 - x) = 7x^6 - 1$

b) $\dfrac{d}{dx}((x-3)(x+4)) = \dfrac{d}{dx}(x^2 - 3x + 4x - 12)$

$= \dfrac{d}{dx}(x^2 + x - 12)$

$= 2x + 1$

c) $\dfrac{d}{dx}(x(x-1)(x-2)) = \dfrac{d}{dx}(x(x^2 - x - 2x + 2))$

$= \dfrac{d}{dx}(x(x^2 - 3x + 2))$

$= \dfrac{d}{dx}(x^3 - 3x^2 + 2x)$

$= 3x^2 - 3(2x) + 2$

$= 3x^2 - 6x + 2$

d) $\dfrac{d}{dx}((x-3)(x+4)(x-1))$

$= \dfrac{d}{dx}((x-3)(x^2 + 3x - 4))$

$= \dfrac{d}{dx}(x^3 + 3x^2 - 4x - 3x^2 - 9x + 12)$

$= \dfrac{d}{dx}(x^3 - 13x + 12)$

$= 3x^2 - 13$

e) $\dfrac{d}{dx}(x^2(x-4)(3-x^3))$

$= \dfrac{d}{dx}(x^2(3x - x^4 - 12 + 4x^3))$

$= \dfrac{d}{dx}(3x^3 - x^6 - 12x^2 + 4x^5)$

$= 9x^2 - 6x^5 - 24x + 20x^4$

f) $\dfrac{d}{dx}((x-3)^2(x^2 - 2))$

$= \dfrac{d}{dx}((x^2 - 3x - 3x + 9)(x^2 - 2))$

$= \dfrac{d}{dx}((x^2 - 6x + 9)(x^2 - 2))$

$= \dfrac{d}{dx}((x^4 - 6x^3 + 9x^2) + (-2x^2 + 12x - 18))$

$= \dfrac{d}{dx}(x^4 - 6x^3 + 7x^2 + 12x - 18)$

$= 4x^3 - 18x^2 + 14x + 12$

Q3 a) $\dfrac{dy}{dx} = 4x^3 - 2x$. At $x = 3, \dfrac{dy}{dx} = 102$.

b) $\dfrac{dy}{dx} = 10x^4$. At $x = -2, \dfrac{dy}{dx} = 160$.

c) $y = x(x-1)(x-2) = x(x^2 - 3x + 2)$
$= x^3 - 3x^2 + 2x$
$\dfrac{dy}{dx} = 3x^2 - 6x + 2$. At $x = -3, \dfrac{dy}{dx} = 47$.

d) $y = 5(x^2 - 1)(3 - x) = 5(-x^3 + 3x^2 + x - 3)$
$= -5x^3 + 15x^2 + 5x - 15$
$\dfrac{dy}{dx} = -15x^2 + 30x + 5$. At $x = 0, \dfrac{dy}{dx} = 5$.

e) $y = x(x - 1) = x^2 - x$

$\dfrac{dy}{dx} = 2x - 1$.

At $x = 4$, $\dfrac{dy}{dx} = 7$.

f) $f(x) = x^3(x^2 - 5) = x^5 - 5x^3$

$f'(x) = 5x^4 - 15x^2$. $f'(-1) = -10$

g) $f(x) = \dfrac{1}{3x^2}(x^5 - 3x^3) = \dfrac{x^3}{3} - x$

$f'(x) = x^2 - 1$. $f'(5) = 24$.

h) $f(x) = \dfrac{3x^3 + 18x^2 + 24x}{x + 4}$

$= \dfrac{3x(x + 4)(x + 2)}{x + 4} = 3x(x + 2) = 3x^2 + 6x$

$f'(x) = 6x + 6$. $f'(-2) = -6$.

Q4 a) $y = (x + 3)(x + 4) = x^2 + 7x + 12$

$\dfrac{dy}{dx} = 2x + 7$. If $2x + 7 = 3 \Rightarrow 2x = -4 \Rightarrow x = -2$.

So $y = (-2 + 3)(-2 + 4) = 2$.

Coordinates are $(-2, 2)$.

b) $y = (x + 3)(x - 5) = x^2 - 2x - 15$

$\dfrac{dy}{dx} = 2x - 2$. If $2x - 2 = 2 \Rightarrow 2x = 4 \Rightarrow x = 2$

So $y = (2 + 3)(2 - 5) = -15$.

Coordinates are $(2, -15)$.

c) $\dfrac{dy}{dx} = 2x + 8$. If $2x + 8 = 4 \Rightarrow 2x = -4 \Rightarrow x = -2$

So $y = (-2)^2 + 8(-2) = -12$.

Coordinates are $(-2, -12)$.

d) $y = \dfrac{x^3 - 3x^2 + 2x}{x - 1} = \dfrac{x(x - 1)(x - 2)}{x - 1} = x^2 - 2x$

$\dfrac{dy}{dx} = 2x - 2$. If $2x - 2 = -6 \Rightarrow 2x = -4 \Rightarrow x = -2$

So $y = (-2)^2 - 2(-2) = 8$. Coordinates are $(-2, 8)$.

Q5 a) $\dfrac{dy}{dx} = 2x - 2$. If $2x - 2 = 0 \Rightarrow 2x = 2 \Rightarrow x = 1$.

So $y = (1)^2 - 2(1) = -1$. Coordinates are $(1, -1)$.

b) $\dfrac{dy}{dx} = 6x + 4$. If $6x + 4 = 0 \Rightarrow 6x = -4$

$\Rightarrow x = -\dfrac{4}{6} = -\dfrac{2}{3}$.

So $y = 3(-\dfrac{2}{3})^2 + 4(-\dfrac{2}{3}) = -\dfrac{4}{3}$.

Coordinates are $(-\dfrac{2}{3}, -\dfrac{4}{3})$.

c) $\dfrac{dy}{dx} = 10x - 3$. If $10x - 3 = 0 \Rightarrow 10x = 3$

$\Rightarrow x = \dfrac{3}{10} \Rightarrow y = 5(\dfrac{3}{10})^2 - 3(\dfrac{3}{10}) = -\dfrac{9}{20}$.

Coordinates are $(\dfrac{3}{10}, -\dfrac{9}{20})$.

d) $\dfrac{dy}{dx} = 9 - 9x^2$. If $9 - 9x^2 = 0 \Rightarrow 9 = 9x^2 \Rightarrow 1 = x^2$

$\Rightarrow x = 1$ or -1

$\Rightarrow y = 9(1) - 3(1)^3 = 6$ or $y = 9(-1) - 3(-1)^3 = -6$.

Coordinates of points are $(1, 6)$ and $(-1, -6)$.

e) $\dfrac{dy}{dx} = 6x^2 - 2x$. If $6x^2 - 2x = 0 \Rightarrow 2x(3x - 1) = 0$

$\Rightarrow 2x = 0$ or $3x - 1 = 0 \Rightarrow x = 0$ or $x = \dfrac{1}{3}$

So $y = 2(0)^3 - (0)^2 = 0$ or $y = 2(\dfrac{1}{3})^3 - (\dfrac{1}{3})^2 = -\dfrac{1}{27}$.

So points are $(0, 0)$ and $(\dfrac{1}{3}, -\dfrac{1}{27})$.

f) $\dfrac{dy}{dx} = 6x^2 + 6x - 12$. If $6x^2 + 6x - 12 = 0$

$\Rightarrow 6(x^2 + x - 2) = 0 \Rightarrow x^2 + x - 2 = 0$

$\Rightarrow (x + 2)(x - 1) = 0 \Rightarrow x = -2$ or $x = 1$.

So $y = 2(-2)^3 + 3(-2)^2 - 12(-2) = 20$ or

$y = 2(1)^3 + 3(1)^2 - 12(1) = -7$.

So the points are $(-2, 20)$ and $(1, -7)$.

Q6 a) $y = \dfrac{x^2 - 3x - 4}{x + 1} = \dfrac{(x - 4)(x + 1)}{x + 1} = x - 4$

$\Rightarrow \dfrac{dy}{dx} = 1$

b) $f(x) = \dfrac{x^4 - 9}{x^2 + 3} = \dfrac{(x^2 + 3)(x^2 - 3)}{x^2 + 3} = x^2 - 3$

$\Rightarrow f'(x) = 2x$

Exercise 2.3
— Finding tangents and normals

Q1 a) $\dfrac{dy}{dx} = 9 - 4x$. At $(1, 7)$, $\dfrac{dy}{dx} = 5$

$\Rightarrow$ tangent has a gradient of 5 and has an equation of the form $y = 5x + c$.

Using the point $(1, 7)$, $7 = 5 + c$

$\Rightarrow c = 2$. So the tangent's equation is $y = 5x + 2$.

b) $\dfrac{dy}{dx} = 3x^2 - 2$. At $(2, 7)$, $\dfrac{dy}{dx} = 10$

$\Rightarrow$ tangent has a gradient of 10 and has an equation of the form $y = 10x + c$.

Using the point $(2, 7)$, $7 = 20 + c \Rightarrow c = -13$.

So the tangent's equation is $y = 10x - 13$.

c) $y = (x + 2)(2x - 3) = 2x^2 + x - 6$

$\dfrac{dy}{dx} = 4x + 1$. At $(2, 4)$, $\dfrac{dy}{dx} = 9$

$\Rightarrow$ tangent has a gradient of 9 and has an equation of the form $y = 9x + c$.

Using the point $(2, 4)$, $4 = 18 + c \Rightarrow c = -14$.

So the tangent's equation is $y = 9x - 14$.

d) $y = x(x - 1)^2 = x(x^2 - 2x + 1) = x^3 - 2x^2 + x$

$\dfrac{dy}{dx} = 3x^2 - 4x + 1$. At $(-1, -4)$, $\dfrac{dy}{dx} = 8$

$\Rightarrow$ tangent has a gradient of 8 and has an equation of the form $y = 8x + c$.

Using the point $(-1, -4)$, $-4 = -8 + c \Rightarrow c = 4$.

So the tangent's equation is $y = 8x + 4$.

e) $y = x^2(x + 3) - 10 = x^3 + 3x^2 - 10$

$\dfrac{dy}{dx} = 3x^2 + 6x$. At $(2, 10)$, $\dfrac{dy}{dx} = 24$

$\Rightarrow$ tangent has a gradient of 24 and has an equation of the form $y = 24x + c$.

Using the point $(2, 10)$, $10 = 48 + c \Rightarrow c = -38$.

So the tangent's equation is $y = 24x - 38$.

f) $y = x(2x^2 - 2x - 12) = 2x^3 - 2x^2 - 12x$

$\frac{dy}{dx} = 6x^2 - 4x - 12$. At $(-1, 8)$, $\frac{dy}{dx} = -2$

$\Rightarrow$ tangent has a gradient of –2 and has an equation of the form $y = -2x + c$.
Using the point $(-1, 8)$, $8 = 2 + c \Rightarrow c = 6$.
So the tangent's equation is $y = -2x + 6$.

Q2 a) $\frac{dy}{dx} = 6x - 4$. At $(2, 6)$, $\frac{dy}{dx} = 8$.

So the normal has a gradient of $-\frac{1}{8}$ and an equation of the form $y = -\frac{1}{8}x + c$.

Don't forget — the gradient of the normal to a curve at a point is $-\frac{1}{Gradient\ of\ the\ curve}$.

Using the point $(2, 6)$, $6 = -\frac{1}{4} + c \Rightarrow c = 6\frac{1}{4}$.

So the normal's equation is $y = -\frac{1}{8}x + 6\frac{1}{4}$

$\Rightarrow 8y = -x + 50 \Rightarrow x + 8y - 50 = 0$.

b) $y = x^3 + 4x^2 - 5x$

$\frac{dy}{dx} = 3x^2 + 8x - 5$. At $(-1, 8)$, $\frac{dy}{dx} = -10$.
So the normal has a gradient of $\frac{1}{10}$ and an equation of the form $y = \frac{1}{10}x + c$.

Using the point $(-1, 8)$, $8 = -\frac{1}{10} + c \Rightarrow c = \frac{81}{10}$.

So the normal's equation is $y = \frac{1}{10}x + \frac{81}{10}$

$\Rightarrow 10y = x + 81 \Rightarrow x - 10y + 81 = 0$.

c) $y = x(x^2 - 3x + 2) = x^3 - 3x^2 + 2x$

$\frac{dy}{dx} = 3x^2 - 6x + 2$. At $(3, 6)$, $\frac{dy}{dx} = 11$.
So the normal has a gradient of $-\frac{1}{11}$ and an equation of the form $y = -\frac{1}{11}x + c$.

Using the point $(3, 6)$, $6 = -\frac{3}{11} + c \Rightarrow c = \frac{69}{11}$.

So the normal's equation is $y = -\frac{1}{11}x + \frac{69}{11}$

$\Rightarrow 11y = -x + 69 \Rightarrow x + 11y - 69 = 0$.

d) $y = x(x^2 + x - 12) - 10 = x^3 + x^2 - 12x - 10$

$\frac{dy}{dx} = 3x^2 + 2x - 12$. At $(-2, 10)$, $\frac{dy}{dx} = -4$.
So the normal has a gradient of $\frac{1}{4}$ and an equation of the form $y = \frac{1}{4}x + c$.

Using the point $(-2, 10)$, $10 = -\frac{1}{2} + c \Rightarrow c = \frac{21}{2}$.

So the normal's equation is $y = \frac{1}{4}x + \frac{21}{2}$

$\Rightarrow 4y = x + 42 \Rightarrow x - 4y + 42 = 0$.

e) $y = \frac{(x + 2)(x^2 - 7x)}{x + 2} = x^2 - 7x$

$\frac{dy}{dx} = 2x - 7$. At $(5, -10)$, $\frac{dy}{dx} = 3$.
So the normal has a gradient of $-\frac{1}{3}$ and an equation of the form $y = -\frac{1}{3}x + c$.

Using the point $(5, -10)$, $-10 = -\frac{5}{3} + c$

$\Rightarrow c = -\frac{25}{3}$.

So the normal's equation is $y = -\frac{1}{3}x - \frac{25}{3}$

$\Rightarrow 3y = -x - 25 \Rightarrow x + 3y + 25 = 0$.

Q3 a) $f'(x) = 3x^2 - 6x$. If $f'(x) = 9$, $3x^2 - 6x = 9$

$\Rightarrow 3x^2 - 6x - 9 = 0 \Rightarrow x^2 - 2x - 3 = 0$
$\Rightarrow (x - 3)(x + 1) = 0 \Rightarrow x = 3$ or $x = -1$. So $x = 3$
since $x > 0$. So $y = f(3) = 3^3 - 3(3)^2 + 3 = 3$.
The coordinates are $(3, 3)$.

b) The gradient of the tangent at $(3, 3)$ is 9 from part a). So the equation is of the form $y = 9x + c$. You know the tangent goes through $(3, 3)$ so use this point: $3 = 27 + c \Rightarrow c = -24$.
So the equation is $y = 9x - 24$.

c) The gradient of the normal is $-\frac{1}{9}$ so the equation has the form $y = -\frac{1}{9}x + c$. Again, use the point $(3, 3)$, so $3 = -\frac{1}{3} + c \Rightarrow c = \frac{10}{3}$.

So the equation is $y = -\frac{1}{9}x + \frac{10}{3} \Rightarrow 9y = -x + 30$
$\Rightarrow x + 9y - 30 = 0$

Q4 a) Putting $x = -2$ into the equation gives:

$y = x^3 + x^2 + x + 5$
$= (-2)^3 + (-2)^2 + (-2) + 5$
$= -8 + 4 - 2 + 5$
$= -1$

so $(-2, -1)$ is a point on the curve.

b) $y = x^3 + x^2 + x + 5$

$\frac{dy}{dx} = 3x^2 + 2x + 1$

At $(-2, -1)$, $\frac{dy}{dx} = 9$. So the gradient of the tangent at this point is 9 and it has equation $y = 9x + c$. Using the point $(-2, -1)$,
$-1 = -18 + c \Rightarrow c = 17$.
So the equation of the tangent is $y = 9x + 17$
$\Rightarrow 9x - y + 17 = 0$.

c) The gradient of the normal at $(-2, -1)$ is $-\frac{1}{9}$ and so it has equation $y = -\frac{1}{9}x + c$. Using the point $(-2, -1)$, $-1 = \frac{2}{9} + c \Rightarrow c = -\frac{11}{9}$. So the equation of the normal is $y = -\frac{1}{9}x - \frac{11}{9} \Rightarrow 9y = -x - 11$

$\Rightarrow x + 9y + 11 = 0$.

3. Using Differentiation

Exercise 3.1
— Finding second order derivatives

Q1 a) $\frac{dy}{dx} = 3x^2$ and $\frac{d^2y}{dx^2} = 6x$.

b) $\frac{dy}{dx} = 5x^4$ and $\frac{d^2y}{dx^2} = 20x^3$.

c) $\frac{dy}{dx} = 4x^3$ and $\frac{d^2y}{dx^2} = 12x^2$.

d) $\frac{dy}{dx} = 1$ and $\frac{d^2y}{dx^2} = 0$.

e) $\frac{dy}{dx} = 6x$ and $\frac{d^2y}{dx^2} = 6$.

f) $\frac{dy}{dx} = 20x^3$ and $\frac{d^2y}{dx^2} = 60x^2$.

g) $\frac{dy}{dx} = 2$ and $\frac{d^2y}{dx^2} = 0$.

h) $\frac{dy}{dx} = 4x^3 + 4$ and $\frac{d^2y}{dx^2} = 12x^2$.

Q2 a) $f(x) = x(3x^2 + 2) = 3x^3 + 2x$
$f'(x) = 9x^2 + 2$
$f''(x) = 18x$

b) $f(x) = x(4x^2 - x) = 4x^3 - x^2$
$f'(x) = 12x^2 - 2x$
$f''(x) = 24x - 2$

c) $f(x) = x(x^3 - x^2 + 7x) = x^4 - x^3 + 7x^2$
$f'(x) = 4x^3 - 3x^2 + 14x$
$f''(x) = 12x^2 - 6x + 14$

d) $f(x) = \frac{1}{x}(3x^4 - 2x^3) = 3x^3 - 2x^2$
$f'(x) = 9x^2 - 4x$
$f''(x) = 18x - 4$

e) $f(x) = (x^2 - 3)(x - 4) = x^3 - 4x^2 - 3x + 12$
$f'(x) = 3x^2 - 8x - 3$
$f''(x) = 6x - 8$

f) $f(x) = \dfrac{4x^5 + 12x^3 - 40x}{4(x^2 + 5)} = \dfrac{4x(x^4 + 3x^2 - 10)}{4(x^2 + 5)}$

$= \dfrac{4x(x^2 + 5)(x^2 - 2)}{4(x^2 + 5)} = x(x^2 - 2) = x^3 - 2x$

$f'(x) = 3x^2 - 2$
$f''(x) = 6x$

Q3 a) $f'(x) = 3x^2 - 2x$ and so $f''(x) = 6x - 2$.
$f''(3) = 16$.

b) $\frac{dy}{dx} = 5x^4 - 1$

and $\frac{d^2y}{dx^2} = 20x^3$.

At $x = 2$, $\frac{d^2y}{dx^2} = 160$.

c) $f'(x) = 18x + 3$ and
$f''(x) = 18$.
$f''(1) = 18$.

d) $y = (x^2 + x)(5 - x) = 5x^2 - x^3 + 5x - x^2 = 4x^2 - x^3 + 5x$

so $\frac{dy}{dx} = 8x - 3x^2 + 5$

and $\frac{d^2y}{dx^2} = 8 - 6x$.
At $x = -3$, $\frac{d^2y}{dx^2} = 26$

e) $f(x) = x^2(x^3 - 4x^2 - 5x) = x^5 - 4x^4 - 5x^3$
so $f'(x) = 5x^4 - 16x^3 - 15x^2$ and
$f''(x) = 20x^3 - 48x^2 - 30x$.
$f''(-1) = -38$.

f) $y = \dfrac{x^3(x + 6)(x - 2)}{(x + 6)} = x^3(x - 2) = x^4 - 2x^3$

so $\frac{dy}{dx} = 4x^3 - 6x^2$, $\frac{d^2y}{dx^2} = 12x^2 - 12x$.

At $x = 5$, $\frac{d^2y}{dx^2} = 240$.

Q4 a) $\frac{dx}{dt} = 6t - 7$.

b) (i) $t = 2 \Rightarrow \frac{dx}{dt} = 12 - 7 = 5$ ms^{-1}

(ii) $t = 5 \Rightarrow \frac{dx}{dt} = 30 - 7 = 23$ ms^{-1}

c) If $\frac{dx}{dt} = 17 \Rightarrow 6t - 7 = 17 \Rightarrow 6t = 24 \Rightarrow t = 4$ s.

d) $\frac{d^2x}{dt^2} = 6$ ms^{-2}

Q5 a) $\frac{dx}{dt} = 6t^2 - 8t$

b) If $\frac{dx}{dt} = 30$ then $6t^2 - 8t = 30 \Rightarrow 6t^2 - 8t - 30 = 0$
$\Rightarrow 3t^2 - 4t - 15 = 0 \Rightarrow (3t + 5)(t - 3) = 0$
$\Rightarrow t = 3$ or $t = -\frac{5}{3}$. But $t > 0$ so $t = 3$.
If $t = 3$, $x = 2t^3 - 4t^2 = 18$.
So $t = 3$ s and $x = 18$ m.

c) $\frac{d^2x}{dt^2} = 12t - 8$.

d) $t = 5 \Rightarrow \frac{d^2x}{dt^2} = 52$ ms^{-2}

e) If $\frac{d^2x}{dt^2} = 16 \Rightarrow 12t - 8 = 16 \Rightarrow 12t = 24 \Rightarrow t = 2$.
$\frac{dx}{dt} = 6t^2 - 8t = 8$ ms^{-1}.

Exercise 3.2 — Stationary points

Q1 a) The graph has 2 stationary points — a minimum and a point of inflection.

b) The graph has 3 stationary points — a maximum, a minimum and a point of inflection.

Q2 a) $\frac{dy}{dx} = 2x + 3$. When $\frac{dy}{dx} = 0$, $2x + 3 = 0 \Rightarrow x = -\frac{3}{2}$

b) $y = (3 - x)(4 + 2x) = 12 + 2x - 2x^2$
$\frac{dy}{dx} = 2 - 4x$. When $\frac{dy}{dx} = 0$, $2 - 4x = 0 \Rightarrow x = \frac{1}{2}$

Q3 a) $\frac{dy}{dx} = 4x - 8$. When $\frac{dy}{dx} = 0$, $4x - 8 = 0 \Rightarrow x = 2$
When $x = 2$, $y = 2(2)^2 - 8(2) + 2 = -6$

So the coordinates are $(2, -6)$.

b) $\frac{dy}{dx} = -2x + 6$. When $\frac{dy}{dx} = 0$, $-2x + 6 = 0$
$\Rightarrow x = 3$. When $x = 3$, $y = -(3)^2 + 6(3) - 4 = 5$

So the coordinates are $(3, 5)$.

c) $\frac{dy}{dx} = -6 - 6x$. When $\frac{dy}{dx} = 0$, $-6 - 6x = 0 \Rightarrow$
$x = -1$. When $x = -1$, $y = 7 - 6(-1) - 3(-1)^2 = 10$.
So the coordinates are $(-1, 10)$.

d) $y = (x - 12)(x + 2) = x^2 - 10x - 24$
$\frac{dy}{dx} = 2x - 10$. When $\frac{dy}{dx} = 0$, $2x - 10 = 0 \Rightarrow x = 5$
When $x = 5$, $y = (5 - 12)(5 + 2) = -49$.

So the coordinates are (5, –49).

Q4 a) $\frac{dy}{dx} = 3x^2 - 3$. When $\frac{dy}{dx} = 0$, $3x^2 - 3 = 0$
$\Rightarrow x = \pm 1$. When $x = 1$, $y = 1^3 - 3(1) + 2 = 0$.
When $x = -1$, $y = (-1)^3 - 3(-1) + 2 = 4$.
So the coordinates are (1, 0) and (–1, 4).

b) $\frac{dy}{dx} = 12x^2$. When $\frac{dy}{dx} = 0$, $12x^2 = 0 \Rightarrow x = 0$
When $x = 0$, $y = 4(0)^3 + 5 = 5$.
So the coordinates are (0, 5).

Q5 $f'(x) = 5x^4 + 3$. When $f'(x) = 0$, $5x^4 + 3 = 0 \Rightarrow x^4 = -\frac{3}{5}$.
There are no stationary points as $x^4 = (x^2)^2$, and $x^2 \geq 0$,
so $x^4 \geq 0$ (i.e. there is no solution for $x^4 = -\frac{3}{5}$).

Q6 a) $\frac{dy}{dx} = 3x^2 - 14x - 5$

b) When $\frac{dy}{dx} = 0$, $3x^2 - 14x - 5 = 0$
$\Rightarrow (3x + 1)(x - 5) = 0$, so either $x = -\frac{1}{3}$ or $x = 5$.
When $x = -\frac{1}{3}$, $y = (-\frac{1}{3})^3 - 7(-\frac{1}{3})^2 - 5(-\frac{1}{3}) + 2$
$= \frac{77}{27}$.
When $x = 5$, $y = 5^3 - 7(5)^2 - 5(5) + 2 = -73$.
So the coordinates are $(-\frac{1}{3}, \frac{77}{27})$ and (5, –73).

Q7 For stationary points to occur, $f'(x)$ must equal zero,
so $f'(x) = 3x^2 + k = 0 \Rightarrow -\frac{k}{3} = x^2$. For this equation to
have a solution, k can't be positive (or it would be
taking the square root of a negative number), so $k \leq 0$.
Therefore, if the graph has no stationary points, $k > 0$.

Exercise 3.3
— Maximum and minimum points

Q1 a) maximum **b)** minimum **c)** maximum
d) maximum **e)** minimum

Q2 a) $\frac{dy}{dx} = -2x$. When $\frac{dy}{dx} = 0$, $x = 0$.
When $x = 0$, $y = 5 - 0 = 5$.
So the coordinates are (0, 5).
$\frac{d^2y}{dx^2} = -2$, so it's a maximum turning point.

b) $\frac{dy}{dx} = 6x^2 - 6$. When $\frac{dy}{dx} = 0$, $6x^2 = 6 \Rightarrow x = \pm 1$
When $x = 1$, $y = 2 - 6 + 2 = -2$.
When $x = -1$, $y = -2 + 6 + 2 = 6$.
So the coordinates are (1, –2) and (–1, 6).
$\frac{d^2y}{dx^2} = 12x$.
At (1, –2), $\frac{d^2y}{dx^2} = 12$, so it's a minimum.
At (–1, 6), $\frac{d^2y}{dx^2} = -12$, so it's a maximum.

c) $\frac{dy}{dx} = 3x^2 - 6x - 24$. When $\frac{dy}{dx} = 0$, $x^2 - 2x - 8 = 0$
$\Rightarrow (x - 4)(x + 2) = 0 \Rightarrow x = 4$ or –2.
When $x = 4$, $y = 64 - 48 - 96 + 15 = -65$.
When $x = -2$, $y = -8 - 12 + 48 + 15 = 43$.
So the coordinates are (4, –65) and (–2, 43).
$\frac{d^2y}{dx^2} = 6x - 6$. At (4, –65), $\frac{d^2y}{dx^2} = 24 - 6 = 18$,
so it's a minimum.
At (–2, 43), $\frac{d^2y}{dx^2} = -12 - 6 = -18$, so it's a
maximum.

d) $\frac{dy}{dx} = 4x^3 + 12x^2 + 8x$.
When $\frac{dy}{dx} = 0$, $x^3 + 3x^2 + 2x = 0$
$\Rightarrow x(x + 2)(x + 1) = 0$, so $x = 0$, –1 or –2.
When $x = 0$, $y = 0 + 0 + 0 - 10 = -10$.
When $x = -1$, $y = 1 - 4 + 4 - 10 = -9$.
When $x = -2$, $y = 16 - 32 + 16 - 10 = -10$.
So the stationary points are (0, –10), (–1, –9)
and (–2, –10).
$\frac{d^2y}{dx^2} = 12x^2 + 24x + 8$.
At (0, –10), $\frac{d^2y}{dx^2} = 0 + 0 + 8 = 8$,
so it's a minimum.
At (–1, –9), $\frac{d^2y}{dx^2} = 12 - 24 + 8 = -4$,
so it's a maximum.
At (–2, –10), $\frac{d^2y}{dx^2} = 48 - 48 + 8 = 8$,
so it's a minimum.

Q3 a) (1, 3)
All the clues are in the question — the derivative when
x = 1 is zero so you know it's a stationary point, and the
y-value when x = 1 is 3.

b) The second derivative is positive, so it's a
minimum.

Q4 a) $f'(x) = 24x^2 + 32x + 8$.
When $f'(x) = 0$, $3x^2 + 4x + 1 = 0$
$\Rightarrow (3x + 1)(x + 1) = 0$, so $x = -1$ or $-\frac{1}{3}$.
When $x = -1$, $f(x) = -8 + 16 - 8 + 1 = 1$.
When $x = -\frac{1}{3}$, $f(x) = -\frac{8}{27} + \frac{16}{9} - \frac{8}{3} + 1 = -\frac{5}{27}$.
So the coordinates are (–1, 1) and $(-\frac{1}{3}, -\frac{5}{27})$.
$f''(x) = 48x + 32$.
At (–1, 1) $f''(x) = -48 + 32 = -16$,
so it's a maximum.
At $(-\frac{1}{3}, -\frac{5}{27})$, $f''(x) = -\frac{48}{3} + 32 = 16$,
so it's a minimum.

b) $f'(x) = 8x^3 + 1$. When $f'(x) = 0$, $8x^3 + 1 = 0$
$\Rightarrow 8x^3 = -1$, so $x = -\frac{1}{2}$.
When $x = -\frac{1}{2}$, $f(x) = -\frac{3}{8}$, so the coordinates of the
stationary point are $(-\frac{1}{2}, -\frac{3}{8})$.
$f''(x) = 24x^2$. At $(-\frac{1}{2}, -\frac{3}{8})$, $f''(x) = 6$,
so it's a minimum.

Q5 a) $f'(x) = 3x^2 - 6x$. $f''(x) = 6x - 6$.

b) When $f'(x) = 0$, $3x^2 - 6x = 0 \Rightarrow x(x - 2) = 0$,
so $x = 0$ or $x = 2$.
When $x = 0$, $f(x) = 0 - 0 + 4 = 4$.
When $x = 2$, $f(x) = 8 - 12 + 4 = 0$.
So the coordinates are $(0, 4)$ and $(2, 0)$.
At $(0, 4)$ $f''(x) = 0 - 6 = -6$, so it's a maximum.
At $(2, 0)$ $f''(x) = 12 - 6 = 6$, so it's a minimum.

Q6 a) $V = 4r^3 - 12r^2 \Rightarrow \dfrac{dV}{dr} = 12r^2 - 24r$.
When $\dfrac{dV}{dr} = 0$, $12r(r - 2) = 0 \Rightarrow r = 0$ or $r = 2$.
$r > 0$ so $r = 2$.

b) $\dfrac{d^2V}{dr^2} = 24r - 24$. When $r = 2$,
$\dfrac{d^2V}{dr^2} = 48 - 24 = 24$, so it's a minimum.

Q7 $f(x) = x^3 + ax^2 + bx + c \Rightarrow f'(x) = 3x^2 + 2ax + b$.
$\Rightarrow f''(x) = 6x + 2a$.
At the point $(3, 10)$, $f(3) = 10$ so:
$10 = 3^3 + a(3^2) + b(3) + c \Rightarrow 10 = 27 + 9a + 3b + c$
As $(3, 10)$ is a stationary point, $f'(3) = 0$ and so:
$0 = 3(3^2) + 2a(3) + b \Rightarrow 0 = 27 + 6a + b$.
We know that $f''(3) = 0$, so $0 = 6(3) + 2a$
$\Rightarrow 0 = 18 + 2a \Rightarrow a = -9$.
Then $0 = 27 + 6a + b = 27 + 6(-9) + b \Rightarrow b = 27$
And $10 = 27 + 9a + 3b + c = 27 + 9(-9) + 3(27) + c$
$\Rightarrow c = -17$. So $f(x) = x^3 - 9x^2 + 27x - 17$.

Q8 a) $\dfrac{dy}{dx} = 4x^3 + 3kx^2 + 2x$.
Stationary points occur when $\dfrac{dy}{dx} = 0$,
so $4x^3 + 3kx^2 + 2x = 0 \Rightarrow x(4x^2 + 3kx + 2) = 0$
so $x = 0$ or $4x^2 + 3kx + 2 = 0$. As you know the
only stationary point occurs at $x = 0$, the part in
brackets can't have any solutions.
This gives you information about the discriminant
of the quadratic equation:
$b^2 - 4ac < 0 \Rightarrow 9k^2 - 32 < 0 \Rightarrow k^2 < \dfrac{32}{9}$.

Have a look back at Chapter 2 if you need a reminder about the discriminant.

b) When $x = 0$, $y = 0 + 0 + 0 + 17 = 17$, so the
coordinates are $(0, 17)$.
$\dfrac{d^2y}{dx^2} = 12x^2 + 6kx + 2$. When $x = 0$, $\dfrac{d^2y}{dx^2} = 2$, so
it's a minimum.

Exercise 3.4 — Increasing and decreasing functions

Q1 a) $\dfrac{dy}{dx} = 2x + 7$. If the function is increasing, $\dfrac{dy}{dx} > 0$
$\Rightarrow 2x > -7 \Rightarrow x > -\dfrac{7}{2}$

b) $\dfrac{dy}{dx} = 10x + 3$.
If the function is increasing,
$\dfrac{dy}{dx} > 0 \Rightarrow 10x > -3 \Rightarrow x > -\dfrac{3}{10}$.

c) $\dfrac{dy}{dx} = -18x$. If the function is increasing, $\dfrac{dy}{dx} > 0$
$\Rightarrow -18x > 0 \Rightarrow x < 0$.
*Be careful with the direction of the inequality sign if
you're dividing by a negative number.*

Q2 a) $f'(x) = -3 - 4x$.
If the function is decreasing,
$f'(x) < 0 \Rightarrow -4x < 3 \Rightarrow x > -\dfrac{3}{4}$.

b) $f(x) = (6 - 3x)(6 + 3x) = 36 - 9x^2$
$f'(x) = -18x$.
If the function is decreasing,
$f'(x) < 0 \Rightarrow -18x < 0 \Rightarrow x > 0$.

c) $f(x) = (1 - 2x)(7 - 3x) = 7 - 17x + 6x^2$
$f'(x) = -17 + 12x$.
If the function is decreasing,
$f'(x) < 0 \Rightarrow 12x < 17 \Rightarrow x < \dfrac{17}{12}$.

Q3 a) $\dfrac{dy}{dx} = 3x^2 - 12x - 15$.
If the function is increasing,
$\dfrac{dy}{dx} > 0 \Rightarrow 3x^2 - 12x - 15 > 0$
$\Rightarrow x^2 - 4x - 5 > 0 \Rightarrow (x - 5)(x + 1) > 0$
The coefficient of x^2 is positive, so the graph of
the quadratic is u-shaped. It crosses the x-axis at
$x = -1$ and $x = 5$, so $x > 0$ when $x < -1$ and
when $x > 5$ (from the shape of the graph).
This means the function is increasing when $x < -1$
and when $x > 5$.
The method for solving quadratic inequalities is on p.53.

b) $\dfrac{dy}{dx} = 3x^2 + 12x + 12$.
If the function is increasing, $\dfrac{dy}{dx} > 0$
$\Rightarrow 3x^2 + 12x + 12 > 0 \Rightarrow x^2 + 4x + 4 > 0$
$\Rightarrow (x + 2)^2 > 0 \Rightarrow$ either $x + 2 > 0$ or $x + 2 < 0$
so either $x > -2$ or $x < -2$. So the function is
increasing for all $x \neq -2$.

Q4 a) $f'(x) = 3x^2 - 6x - 9$.
If the function is decreasing, $f'(x) < 0$
$\Rightarrow 3x^2 - 6x - 9 < 0 \Rightarrow x^2 - 2x - 3 < 0$
$\Rightarrow (x - 3)(x + 1) < 0$.
The coefficient of x^2 is positive, so the graph of
the quadratic is u-shaped. It crosses the x-axis at
$x = -1$ and $x = 3$, so $x < 0$ when $-1 < x < 3$ (from
the shape of the graph). This means the function
is decreasing when $-1 < x < 3$.

b) $f'(x) = 3x^2 - 8x + 4$.
If the function is decreasing, $f'(x) < 0$
$\Rightarrow 3x^2 - 8x + 4 < 0 \Rightarrow (3x - 2)(x - 2) < 0$.
The coefficient of x^2 is positive, so the graph of
the quadratic is u-shaped. It crosses the x-axis
at $x = \dfrac{2}{3}$ and $x = 2$, so $x < 0$ when $\dfrac{2}{3} < x < 2$ (from
the shape of the graph). This means the function
is decreasing when $\dfrac{2}{3} < x < 2$.

Q5 $f'(x) = 3x^2 + 1$.
x^2 can't be negative ($x^2 \geq 0$), so $f'(x)$ must always be
positive and so $f(x)$ is always an increasing function.

Q6 $f'(x) = -3 - 3x^2$. x^2 can't be negative ($x^2 \geq 0$), so $f'(x)$
must always be less than -3 (hence negative), so $f(x)$
is a decreasing function.

Q7 a) $\frac{dy}{dx} = 8x^3 + 1$. If the function is decreasing,

$\frac{dy}{dx} < 0 \Rightarrow 8x^3 + 1 < 0 \Rightarrow x^3 < -\frac{1}{8} \Rightarrow x < -\frac{1}{2}$

b) $\frac{dy}{dx} = 4x^3 - 6x^2 - 10x$. From the hint, it's a good idea to use the nature of the stationary points to work out this question.

$\frac{dy}{dx} = 4x^3 - 6x^2 - 10x = 2x(2x^2 - 3x - 5)$
$\qquad\qquad = 2x(x + 1)(2x - 5)$

is equal to 0 when $x = -1$, $x = 0$ and $x = \frac{5}{2}$.

$\frac{d^2y}{dx^2} = 12x^2 - 12x - 10$.

At $x = -1$, $\frac{d^2y}{dx^2} = 14 > 0$ so it's a minimum.

At $x = 0$, $\frac{d^2y}{dx^2} = -10 < 0$ so it's a maximum.

At $x = \frac{5}{2}$, $\frac{d^2y}{dx^2} = 35 < 0$ so it's a minimum.

The function is decreasing when approaching a minimum and increasing when approaching a maximum so it is decreasing for $x < -1$ and $0 < x < \frac{5}{2}$.

Q8 If the function is decreasing, $\frac{dy}{dx} < 0$. $\frac{dy}{dx} = -3 - 5ax^4$
$\Rightarrow -3 - 5ax^4 < 0 \Rightarrow ax^4 > -\frac{3}{5}$. The right-hand side is negative, so as $x^4 \geq 0$, a must also be positive to make the LHS > RHS for all x. So $a > 0$.

Q9 If the function is increasing, $\frac{dy}{dx}$ will always be greater than 0. $\frac{dy}{dx} = kx^{k-1} + 1 \Rightarrow kx^{k-1} + 1 > 0$.

When $k = 1$, $x^0 + 1 > 0$ — true for all x
When $k = 2$, $2x^1 + 1 > 0$ — not true for all x
When $k = 3$, $3x^2 + 1 > 0$ — true for all x
When $k = 4$, $4x^3 + 1 > 0$ — not true for all x etc.
So k must be an odd number greater than zero.

Exercise 3.5 — Curve sketching

Q1 a) The roots of the equation are where
$(2x - 1)(x + 1)(x - 3) = 0 \Rightarrow x = \frac{1}{2}$, $x = -1$
and $x = 3$ and so the curve will meet the x-axis at these points.

Letting $x = 0$ gives $y = 3$ so the graph crosses the y-axis at $y = 3$.

$y = 2x^3 - 5x^2 - 4x + 3$, so $\frac{dy}{dx} = 6x^2 - 10x - 4$.

Setting this equal to 0 and solving for x:
$6x^2 - 10x - 4 = 0 \Rightarrow (3x + 1)(x - 2) = 0$, so $x = -\frac{1}{3}$
or $x = 2$. When $x = -\frac{1}{3}$, $y = \frac{100}{27}$ and when

$x = 2$, $y = -9$. Differentiate again to check if they're maximums or minimums: $\frac{d^2y}{dx^2} = 12x - 10$.

When $x = -\frac{1}{3}$, $\frac{d^2y}{dx^2} = -14$ so it's a maximum

and when $x = 2$, $\frac{d^2y}{dx^2} = 14$ so it's a minimum.

So the graph looks like this:

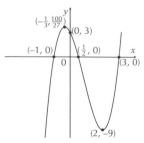

b) The roots of the equation are where $x^2(2x - 5) = 0$
$\Rightarrow x = 0$ or $x = \frac{5}{2}$. The graph will meet the x-axis at these points.

$y = 2x^3 - 5x^2$, so $\frac{dy}{dx} = 6x^2 - 10x$.

Setting this equal to 0 and solving for x:
$6x^2 - 10x = 0 \Rightarrow x(3x - 5) = 0$, so $x = 0$ or $x = \frac{5}{3}$

When $x = 0$, $y = 0$ and when $x = \frac{5}{3}$, $y = -\frac{125}{27}$.

Differentiate again to check if they're maximums or minimums: $\frac{d^2y}{dx^2} = 12x - 10$.

When $x = 0$, $\frac{d^2y}{dx^2} = -10$ so it's a maximum and

when $x = \frac{5}{3}$, $\frac{d^2y}{dx^2} = 10$ so it's a minimum.

So the graph looks like this:

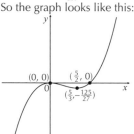

c) The roots of the equation are found by letting $x(5 - x)^2 = 0 \Rightarrow x = 0$ or $x = 5$, so these are the points where the graph meets the x-axis.

$y = x^3 - 10x^2 + 25x$, so $\frac{dy}{dx} = 3x^2 - 20x + 25$.

Setting this equal to 0 and solving for x:
$3x^2 - 20x + 25 = 0 \Rightarrow (3x - 5)(x - 5) = 0$, so $x = \frac{5}{3}$
or $x = 5$. When $x = \frac{5}{3}$, $y = \frac{500}{27}$ and when

$x = 5$, $y = 0$. Differentiate again to check if they're maximums or minimums: $\frac{d^2y}{dx^2} = 6x - 20$.

When $x = \frac{5}{3}$, $\frac{d^2y}{dx^2} = -10$ so it's a maximum

and when $x = 5$, $\frac{d^2y}{dx^2} = 10$ so it's a minimum.

So the graph looks like this:

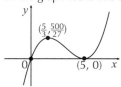

d) The roots of the equation are found by letting $-5x^2(3x - 2) = 0 \Rightarrow x = 0$ or $x = \frac{2}{3}$, so these are the points where the graph meets the x-axis.

$y = 10x^2 - 15x^3$, so $\dfrac{dy}{dx} = 20x - 45x^2$.

Setting this equal to 0 and solving for x:
$20x - 45x^2 = 0 \Rightarrow x(4 - 9x) = 0$, so $x = 0$ or
$x = \dfrac{4}{9}$. When $x = 0$, $y = 0$ and when $x = \dfrac{4}{9}$,
$y = \dfrac{160}{243}$. Differentiate again to check if they're
maximums or minimums: $\dfrac{d^2y}{dx^2} = 20 - 90x$.

When $x = 0$, $\dfrac{d^2y}{dx^2} = 20$ so it's a minimum and

when $x = \dfrac{4}{9}$, $\dfrac{d^2y}{dx^2} = -20$ so it's a maximum.

So the graph looks like this:

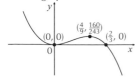

4. Real-Life Problems
Exercise 4.1 — Differentiation in real-life problems

Q1 Let the length of fence parallel to the wall be x and
the lengths perpendicular to the wall be y.
We want to maximise area, i.e $A = xy$.
Total length of fence $= 66 = x + 2y \Rightarrow y = \dfrac{66 - x}{2}$

So we want to maximise $A = x\left(\dfrac{66 - x}{2}\right) = 33x - \dfrac{x^2}{2}$.

$\dfrac{dA}{dx} = 33 - x$, so when $\dfrac{dA}{dx} = 0$, $x = 33$.

Check that this is a maximum by differentiation
again: $\dfrac{d^2A}{dx^2} = -1$, so it's a maximum.
When $x = 33$, $y = \dfrac{66 - 33}{2} = 16.5$.
Area $= 33 \times 16.5 = 544.5$ m^2.
*If you'd labelled the sides the other way round, your working
would be different but you'd still get the same answer.*

Q2 $\dfrac{dh}{dt} = 30 - 15t$. When $\dfrac{dh}{dt} = 0$, $30 - 15t = 0$
$\Rightarrow t = 2$. Check this is a maximum point:
$\dfrac{d^2h}{dt^2} = -15$, so it's a maximum. So the maximum
value of $h = 30(2) - 7.5(2)^2 = 30$ m.

Q3 a) Volume of the box $=$ length $\times$ width $\times$ height
$= (30 - 2x) \times (30 - 2x) \times x = 4x^3 - 120x^2 + 900x$

b) $\dfrac{dV}{dx} = 12x^2 - 240x + 900$.
When $\dfrac{dV}{dx} = 0$, $12x^2 - 240x + 900 = 0$
$\Rightarrow x^2 - 20x + 75 = 0 \Rightarrow (x - 5)(x - 15) = 0$
$\Rightarrow x = 5$ or $x = 15$.

Differentiate again to find which of these is a
maximum: $\dfrac{d^2V}{dx^2} = 24x - 240$. When $x = 5$,
$\dfrac{d^2V}{dx^2} = -120$, and when $x = 15$, $\dfrac{d^2V}{dx^2} = 120$,
so V is a maximum when $x = 5$.
So the maximum volume is:
$4(5)^3 - 120(5)^2 + 900(5) = 2000$ cm^3.

Q4 a) $\dfrac{dh}{dx} = \dfrac{1}{100}\left(\dfrac{x^3}{300} - \dfrac{11}{30}x^2 + 8x\right)$

b) $\dfrac{dh^2}{d^2x} = \dfrac{1}{100}\left(\dfrac{x^2}{100} - \dfrac{11}{15}x + 8\right)$

c) For $x = 0$ to be a stationary point, $\dfrac{dh}{dx} = 0$ when
$x = 0$, so put this into the equation:
$\dfrac{1}{100}\left(\dfrac{0^3}{300} - \dfrac{11}{30}(0)^2 + 8(0)\right) = 0$,
so this is a stationary point.

d) Set $\dfrac{dh}{dx}$ equal to 0 and solve for x:
$\dfrac{1}{100}\left(\dfrac{x^3}{300} - \dfrac{11}{30}x^2 + 8x\right) = 0$
$\Rightarrow \dfrac{x^3}{300} - \dfrac{11}{30}x^2 + 8x = 0$
$\Rightarrow x^3 - 110x^2 + 2400x = 0$
$\Rightarrow x(x^2 - 110x + 2400) = 0$
$\Rightarrow x(x^2 - 80)(x - 30) = 0$

So ride photos can be taken at $x = 30$ m and
$x = 80$ m.

e) At $h = 30$, $\dfrac{d^2h}{dx^2} = \dfrac{1}{100}\left(\dfrac{30^2}{100} - \dfrac{11}{15}(30) + 8\right)$
$= -0.05$, so this is a maximum.

At $h = 80$, $\dfrac{d^2V}{dh^2} = \dfrac{1}{100}\left(\dfrac{80^2}{100} - \dfrac{11}{15}(80) + 8\right)$
$= 0.13$, so this is a minimum.

The ride photo should be taken at 80 m.

Review Exercise — Chapter 7

Q1 a) $\dfrac{dy}{dx} = \lim_{h \to 0}\left[\dfrac{f(x + h) - f(x)}{(x + h) - x}\right]$
$= \lim_{h \to 0}\left[\dfrac{(x + h + 1) - (x + 1)}{(x + h) - x}\right]$
$= \lim_{h \to 0}\left[\dfrac{x + h + 1 - x - 1}{x + h - x}\right]$
$= \lim_{h \to 0}\left[\dfrac{h}{h}\right] = \lim_{h \to 0}[1] = 1$

b) $\dfrac{dy}{dx} = \lim_{h \to 0}\left[\dfrac{f(x + h) - f(x)}{(x + h) - x}\right]$
$= \lim_{h \to 0}\left[\dfrac{4(x + h)^2 - 4x^2}{(x + h) - x}\right]$
$= \lim_{h \to 0}\left[\dfrac{4x^2 + 8xh + 4h^2 - 4x^2}{x + h - x}\right]$
$= \lim_{h \to 0}\left[\dfrac{8xh + 4h^2}{h}\right] = \lim_{h \to 0}[8x + 4h] = 8x$

c) $\dfrac{dy}{dx} = \lim_{h \to 0}\left[\dfrac{3(x + h) - 3x}{(x + h) - x}\right]$
$= \lim_{h \to 0}\left[\dfrac{3x + 3h - 3x}{x + h - x}\right]$
$= \lim_{h \to 0}\left[\dfrac{3h}{h}\right] = \lim_{h \to 0}[3] = 3$

Q2 a) $\dfrac{dy}{dx} = 2x$ **b)** $\dfrac{dy}{dx} = 4x^3 + 2x$

c) $\dfrac{dy}{dx} = 2x - 3 + 36x^2$

Q3 They're the same.

Q4 The gradient of the normal to the curve at a point and the gradient of the curve multiply to give –1.

Q5 a) $\dfrac{dy}{dx} = 4x = 8$

b) $\dfrac{dy}{dx} = 8x - 1 = 15$

c) $\dfrac{dy}{dx} = 3x^2 - 14x = -16$

Q6 a) When $t = 0$, $v = 3(0)^2 + 4 = 4$ ml.

b) Differentiate $v = 3t^2 + 4$ to give: $\dfrac{dv}{dt} = 6t$
so, when $t = 4$, $\dfrac{dv}{dt} = 24$ ml/s.

Q7 If $x = 1$ $y = 1 + 4 + 2$ so the tangent must go through (1, 7).
Differentiate to find $\dfrac{dy}{dx} = 3x^2 + 8x + 2$, so gradient at (1, 7) is 13.
Therefore tangent can be written $y = 13x + c$.
Putting $x = 1$ and $y = 7$ gives $7 = 13 + c$, so $c = -6$, and the equation of the tangent is $y = 13x - 6$.

Q8 If $x = 3$, then $y = 27 - 9 - 10 = 8$ so the tangent and normal must go through (3, 8).
Differentiate to find $\dfrac{dy}{dx} = 3x^2 - 3$, so gradient at (3, 8) is 24.
Therefore tangent can be written $y_T = 24x + c_T$; putting $x = 3$ and $y = 8$ gives $8 = 24 \times 3 + c_T$, so $c_T = -64$, and the equation of the tangent is $y = 24x - 64$.

The gradient of the normal must be $-\dfrac{1}{24}$, so the equation of the normal is $y_N = -\dfrac{1}{24}x + c_N$
Substituting in the coordinates of the point (3, 8) gives
$8 = -\dfrac{3}{24} + c_N \Rightarrow c_N = \dfrac{195}{24}$; so the normal is
$y = -\dfrac{1}{24}x + \dfrac{195}{24} \Rightarrow x + 24y - 195 = 0$.

Q9 a) C and L intersect when $x^2 - 6 = 3 \Rightarrow x^2 = 9$
$\Rightarrow x = \pm 3$. If $x = 3$, $y = 3$. If $x = -3$, $y = 3$. So the points are $A = (3, 3)$ and $B = (-3, 3)$.

Note — you might have A and B the other way round.

b) For C, $\dfrac{dy}{dx} = 2x$.
At point A, $\dfrac{dy}{dx} = 6$. At point B, $\dfrac{dy}{dx} = -6$

c) At A, the gradient of the normal is $-\dfrac{1}{6}$. The normal has an equation of the form $y = -\dfrac{1}{6}x + c$.
Letting $x = 3$ and $y = 3$, $3 = -\dfrac{1}{2} + c$, so $c = \dfrac{7}{2}$.
So the normal at A is given by $y = -\dfrac{1}{6}x + \dfrac{7}{2}$
At B, the gradient of the normal is $\dfrac{1}{6}$. The normal has an equation of the form $y = \dfrac{1}{6}x + c$.
Letting $x = -3$ and $y = 3$, $3 = -\dfrac{1}{2} + c$, so $c = \dfrac{7}{2}$.
So the normal at B is given by $y = \dfrac{1}{6}x + \dfrac{7}{2}$.

d) From part c), you know that both tangents cross the y-axis at the same point ($y = \dfrac{7}{2}$). So $D = (0, \dfrac{7}{2})$.

Q10 a) The gradient of the line L is 0 for any x since the line is horizontal.

b) The gradient of C is given by $\dfrac{dy}{dx} = 3x^2 - 4x$. If $\dfrac{dy}{dx} = 0$, then $3x^2 - 4x = 0$, so $x(3x - 4) = 0$.
So $x = 0$, which is not possible since $x > 0$, or $3x = 4$ so $x = \dfrac{4}{3}$. $y = x^3 - 2x^2 + 1 = -\dfrac{5}{27}$.
So the point is $(\dfrac{4}{3}, -\dfrac{5}{27})$.

c) The tangent at this point will have gradient 0, so it will be a horizontal line, and it goes through $(\dfrac{4}{3}, -\dfrac{5}{27})$, so the tangent line will be $y = -\dfrac{5}{27}$.

You could also have worked this out in the usual way. However when the gradient is 0, you can work out the equation easily from the point that it goes through.

Q11 $\dfrac{dy}{dx} = 3x^2$. At $x = 2$, $\dfrac{dy}{dx} = 3(2^2) = 12$.
For the tangent, the gradient is 12 and it has equation $y = 12x + c$. At $x = 2$, $y = 9$, so
$9 = 24 + c \Rightarrow c = -15$. So the equation of the tangent is $y = 12x - 15$.
For the normal, the gradient is $-\dfrac{1}{12}$ and it has equation $y = -\dfrac{1}{12}x + c$. At $x = 2$, $y = 9$, so
$9 = -\dfrac{1}{6} + c \Rightarrow c = \dfrac{55}{6}$. So the equation of the normal is $y = -\dfrac{1}{12}x + \dfrac{55}{6} \Rightarrow x + 12y - 110 = 0$.

Q12 a) $\dfrac{dx}{dt} = 3t^2 - 8$.

b) If $\dfrac{dx}{dt} = 19$, then $3t^2 - 8 = 19 \Rightarrow 3t^2 = 27 \Rightarrow t^2 = 9$
$\Rightarrow t = \pm 3$. But t must be non–negative so $t = 3$ s.
When $t = 3$ $x = t^3 - 8t = 3$. So $t = 3$ s and $x = 3$ m.

c) $\dfrac{d^2x}{dt^2} = 6t$

d) If $t = 2$, then $\dfrac{d^2x}{dt^2} = 12$ ms^{-2}.

e) $\dfrac{d^2x}{dt^2} = 24 \Rightarrow 6t = 24 \Rightarrow t = 4$ s. The speed when $t = 4$ is $\dfrac{dx}{dt} = 3t^2 - 8 = 40$ ms^{-1}.

Q13 a) $f'(x) = 3x^2 - 3$. Gradient $= f'(-1) = 0$.

b) $f''(x) = 6x$ so,
$$2f''(x) - 3f'(x) + f(x)$$
$$= 2(6x) - 3(3x^2 - 3) + (x^3 - 3x)$$
$$= 12x - 9x^2 + 9 + x^3 - 3x$$
$$= x^3 - 9x^2 + 9x + 9$$
$$= x^3 + 9(1 + x - x^2)$$

Q14 $f''(x) + 2f'(x) - 4f(x) = (12x^2) + 2(4x^3) - 4(x^4)$
$$= 12x^2 + 8x^3 - 4x^4$$

Q15 $\frac{dy}{dx} = 3x^2 - 12x - 63$

When $\frac{dy}{dx} = 0$, $3x^2 - 12x - 63 = 0$

$\Rightarrow x^2 - 4x - 21 = 0 \Rightarrow (x - 7)(x + 3) = 0$

So $x = 7$ or $x = -3$. When $x = 7$,
$y = 7^3 - 6(7)^2 - 63(7) + 21 = -371$. When $x = -3$,
$y = (-3)^3 - 6(-3)^2 - 63(-3) + 21 = 129$. So the
stationary points are $(7, -371)$ and $(-3, 129)$.

Q16 $\frac{dy}{dx} = 8x^3 - 2x$. When $\frac{dy}{dx} = 0$, $8x^3 - 2x = 0$

$\Rightarrow x(4x^2 - 1) = 0$ so either $x = 0$ or $4x^2 - 1 \Rightarrow x^2 = \frac{1}{4}$

$\Rightarrow x = \pm\frac{1}{2}$. When $x = 0$, $y = 0 - 0 + 4 = 4$.

When $x = \frac{1}{2}$, $y = 2(\frac{1}{2})^4 - (\frac{1}{2})^2 + 4 = \frac{31}{8}$.

When $x = -\frac{1}{2}$, $y = 2(-\frac{1}{2})^4 - (-\frac{1}{2})^2 + 4 = \frac{31}{8}$.

So the coordinates are $(0, 4)$, $(\frac{1}{2}, \frac{31}{8})$ and $(-\frac{1}{2}, \frac{31}{8})$.

$\frac{d^2y}{dx^2} = 24x^2 - 2$. At $(0, 4)$, $\frac{d^2y}{dx^2} = -2$, so it's

a maximum. At $(\frac{1}{2}, \frac{31}{8})$ and $(-\frac{1}{2}, \frac{31}{8})$, $\frac{d^2y}{dx^2} = 4$,

so they're minimums.

Q17 $y = 6(x + 2)(x - 3) = 6x^2 - 6x - 36$

$\frac{dy}{dx} = 12x - 6$. It's increasing when $\frac{dy}{dx} > 0$,

i.e. when $12x - 6 > 0 \Rightarrow x > \frac{1}{2}$ and it's decreasing

when $12x - 6 < 0 \Rightarrow x < \frac{1}{2}$.

Q18 First find where it crosses the axes:
When $x = 0$, $y = 0 - 0 = 0$. When $y = 0$,
$3x^3 - 16x = 0 \Rightarrow x(3x^2 - 16) = 0$, so $x = 0$ and
$x = \pm\frac{4}{\sqrt{3}}$ ($\approx \pm2.3$).

Then differentiate to find the stationary points:
$\frac{dy}{dx} = 9x^2 - 16 = 0 \Rightarrow x^2 = \frac{16}{9} \Rightarrow x = \pm\frac{4}{3}$ ($\approx \pm1.3$)

When $x = \frac{4}{3}$, $y = -\frac{128}{9}$ (≈ -14.2) and when

$x = -\frac{4}{3}$, $y = \frac{128}{9}$ (≈ 14.2).

Differentiate again to find if they're maximum or
minimum points:
$\frac{d^2y}{dx^2} = 18x$, so when $x = \frac{4}{3}$ it's a minimum and when

$x = -\frac{4}{3}$ it's a maximum.

It's a positive cubic, so will go from bottom left to top
right.

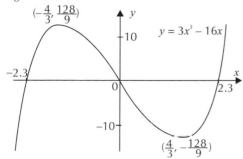

Q19 First find where it crosses the axes:
When $x = 0$, $y = 0 + 0 = 0$.
When $y = 0$, $-3x^3 + 6x^2 = 0 \Rightarrow 3x^2(2 - x) = 0$,
so $x = 0$ and $x = 2$.
Then differentiate to find the stationary points:
$\frac{dy}{dx} = -9x^2 + 12x = 0 \Rightarrow 3x(4 - 3x) = 0 \Rightarrow x = 0$ and

$x = \frac{4}{3}$. When $x = 0$, $y = 0$ and when $x = \frac{4}{3}$, $y = \frac{32}{9}$.

Differentiate again to find if they're maximum or
minimum points:
$\frac{d^2y}{dx^2} = -18x + 12$.

At $(0, 0)$ $\frac{d^2y}{dx^2} = 12$, so it's a minimum.

At $(\frac{4}{3}, \frac{32}{9})$ $\frac{d^2y}{dx^2} = -12$, so it's a maximum.

It's a negative cubic, so will go from top left to
bottom right.

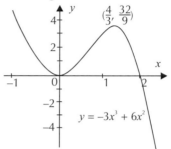

Q20 We need to find when h is at its maximum value, i.e.

when $\frac{dh}{dm} = 0$, so differentiate:

$\frac{dh}{dm} = \frac{m}{5} - \frac{3m^2}{800} = 0 \Rightarrow \frac{1}{5}m(1 - \frac{3m}{160}) = 0$

So $m = 0$ and $m = \frac{160}{3}$.

The answer can't be $m = 0$ since $0 < m$, so the max

height is reached when $m = \frac{160}{3}$. To check it's a

maximum, differentiate again:
$\frac{d^2h}{dm^2} = \frac{1}{5} - \frac{3m}{400}$. At $m = \frac{160}{3}$, $\frac{d^2h}{dm^2} = -\frac{1}{5}$,

so it's a maximum.

When $m = \frac{160}{3}$, $h = \frac{1}{10}(\frac{160}{3})^2 - \frac{1}{800}(\frac{160}{3})^3 = 94.8$ m

(3 s.f.).

Exam-Style Questions — Chapter 7

Q1 **a)** $\frac{dy}{dx} = 6x^2 - 8x - 4$

*[2 marks for all 3 terms correct or 1 mark for 2
terms.]*

b) To find the gradient, put $x = 2$ into the answer
to part (a): $6(2^2) - 8(2) - 4 = 24 - 16 - 4 = 4$
[1 mark].

c) The gradient of the normal is $-1 \div$ the gradient of

the tangent $= -1 \div 4 = -\frac{1}{4}$ *[1 mark]*.

At $x = 2$, the y-value is $2(2^3) - 4(2^2) - 4(2) + 12$

$= 16 - 16 - 8 + 12 = 4$ *[1 mark]*. Putting these

values into the formula $y - y_1 = m(x - x_1)$ gives:

$y - 4 = -\frac{1}{4}(x - 2)$

$$y = -\frac{1}{4}x + \frac{1}{2} + 4$$

$$y = -\frac{1}{4}x + 4\frac{1}{2} \text{ [1 mark]}.$$

You could have left your answer in the form $y - y_1 = m(x - x_1)$ as the question didn't ask for a specific form.

Q2 a) $\frac{dy}{dx} = 12x^2 - 30x + 12$

[2 marks for all 3 terms correct or 1 mark for 2 terms.]

b) Stationary points occur when $12x^2 - 30x + 12 = 0$ **[1 mark]**. Factorising the equation gives: $(2x - 1)(x - 2) = 0$, so stationary points occur when $x = 2$ **[1 mark]** and $x = \frac{1}{2}$ **[1 mark]**.
When $x = 2$:
$y = 4(2)^3 - 15(2)^2 + 12(2) + 6 = 2$ **[1 mark]**
When $x = \frac{1}{2}$:
$y = 4(\frac{1}{2})^3 - 15(\frac{1}{2})^2 + 12(\frac{1}{2}) + 6 = \frac{35}{4}$ **[1 mark]**
So coordinates of the stationary points on the curve are $(2, 2)$ and $(\frac{1}{2}, \frac{35}{4})$.

c) Differentiate again to find $\frac{d^2y}{dy^2} = 24x - 30$ **[1 mark]**.
When $x = 2$ this gives $\Rightarrow 24(2) - 30 = 18$, which is positive, therefore the curve has a minimum at $(2, 2)$. **[1 mark]**
When $x = \frac{1}{2}$ this gives $24(\frac{1}{2}) - 30 = -18$, which is negative, so the curve has a maximum at $(\frac{1}{2}, \frac{35}{4})$. **[1 mark]**

Q3 a) Surface area
$= [2 \times (d \times x)] + [2 \times (d \times \frac{x}{2})] + [x \times \frac{x}{2}]$
$= 2dx + \frac{2dx}{2} + \frac{x^2}{2}$ **[1 mark]**
Surface area $= 72$, so $3dx + \frac{x^2}{2} = 72$
$\Rightarrow x^2 + 6dx = 144$ **[1 mark]**
$d = \frac{144 - x^2}{6x}$ **[1 mark]**
Volume $=$ length $\times$ width $\times$ height
$= \frac{x}{2} \times x \times d = \frac{x^2}{2} \times \frac{144 - x^2}{6x} = \frac{144x^2 - x^4}{12x}$
$= 12x - \frac{x^3}{12}$ **[1 mark]**

b) Differentiate V and then solve for when $\frac{dV}{dx} = 0$:
$\frac{dV}{dx} = 12 - \frac{x^2}{4}$ **[1 mark for each correct term]**
$12 - \frac{x^2}{4} = 0$ **[1 mark]** $\Rightarrow \frac{x^2}{4} = 12 \Rightarrow x = 4\sqrt{3}$ **[1 mark]**

c) $\frac{d^2V}{dx^2} = -\frac{x}{2}$ **[1 mark]** so when $x = 4\sqrt{3}$,
$\frac{d^2V}{dx^2} = -2\sqrt{3}$ **[1 mark]**. $\frac{d^2V}{dx^2}$ is negative, so it's a maximum point. **[1 mark]**
$x = 4\sqrt{3}$ at V_{max}, so $V_{max} = (12 \times 4\sqrt{3}) - \frac{(4\sqrt{3})^3}{12}$
$= 32\sqrt{3}$ m³ **[1 mark]**

Q4 a) $f'(x) = 3 + 4x^3$ **[1 mark]**

b) If $f'(x) = 111$, then $3 + 4x^3 = 111$ **[1 mark]**, so $4x^3 = 108$, so $x^3 = \frac{108}{4} = 27$ so $x = 3$ **[1 mark]**.

Q5 a) $\frac{dy}{dx} = m(3x^2) - 2x + 8$
$= 3mx^2 - 2x + 8$
[2 marks for all 3 terms correct or 1 mark for 2 terms.]

b) Rearranging the equation of the line parallel to the normal gives the equation: $y = 3 - 4x$, so it has a gradient of -4 **[1 mark]**. The normal also has gradient -4 because it is parallel to this line **[1 mark]**.
The gradient of the tangent is $-1 \div$ the gradient of the normal $= -1 \div -4 = \frac{1}{4}$, so the gradient of the curve at P is also $\frac{1}{4}$ **[1 mark]**.

c) (i) So you know that when $x = 5$, the gradient $3mx^2 - 2x + 8 = \frac{1}{4}$. **[1 mark]**
Now find the value of m:
$m(3 \times 5^2) - (2 \times 5) + 8 = \frac{1}{4}$ **[1 mark]**
$75m - 2 = \frac{1}{4}$
$m = \frac{9}{4} \times \frac{1}{75} = \frac{9}{300} = \frac{3}{100} = 0.03$ **[1 mark]**

(ii) When $x = 5$, then:
$y = (\frac{3}{100} \times 5^3) - (5^2) + (8 \times 5) + 2$
[1 mark]
$= \frac{375}{100} - 25 + 40 + 2$
$= 3.75 + 17$
$= 20.75$ **[1 mark]**

Q6 a) $f'(x) = 2x^3 - 2 = 0$ at the stationary point. **[1 mark]**
$2x^3 = 2 \Rightarrow x = 1$ **[1 mark]**, which gives:
$y = f(1) = \frac{1}{2}(1)^4 - 2(1) = -1.5$ **[1 mark]**. So coordinates of the stationary point are $(1, -1.5)$.

b) $f''(x) = 6x^2$ **[1 mark]** so at the stationary point: $f''(1) = 6$, which is positive, so it's a minimum **[1 mark]**.

c) (i) As the stationary point is a minimum, $f'(x) > 0$ to the right of the stationary point. So the function is increasing when $x > 1$ **[1 mark]**.

(ii) As the stationary point is a minimum, $f'(x) < 0$ to the left of the stationary point. So the function is decreasing when $x < 1$ **[1 mark]**.

Q7 a) First, multiply out the function to get $y = x^3 + 4x^2 - 3x$, so $\frac{dy}{dx} = 3x^2 + 8x - 3 = 0$ at the stationary point **[2 marks for all three terms correct]**.
Solve the equation to find x: $3x^2 + 8x - 3 = 0$
$\Rightarrow (3x - 1)(x + 3) = 0 \Rightarrow x = \frac{1}{3}$ or $x = -3$ **[1 mark]**.
Substituting these values for x into the original equation for y gives: $y = -\frac{14}{27}$ and $y = 18$.
So the stationary points have coordinates: $(\frac{1}{3}, -\frac{14}{27})$ and $(-3, 18)$ **[1 mark]**

b) $\frac{d^2y}{dx^2} = 6x + 8$ *[1 mark]*

At $x = \frac{1}{3}$, $\frac{d^2y}{dx^2} = 10 > 0$, so it's a minimum
[1 mark]

At $x = -3$, $\frac{d^2y}{dx^2} = -10 < 0$, so it's a maximum
[1 mark].

c) y is a positive cubic function, with stationary points as found in parts a) and b). The curve crosses the y-axis when $x = 0$, so $y = 0$. The initial cubic equation can be solved by completing the square to find where it intersects the x-axis:

$x(x^2 + 4x - 3) = 0 \Rightarrow x = 0$ and $x = -2 \pm \sqrt{7}$.

So the graph looks like this.

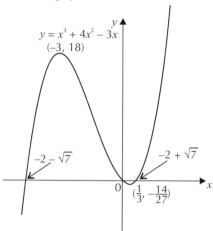

[3 marks available — 1 mark for shape and 1 mark for each x-intercept]

Q8 a) Rearrange $2x - y = 6$ into an expression for y:
$y = 2x - 6$. *[1 mark]*.
Now find W in terms of x:
$W = x^2(2x - 6)^2 = x^2(4x^2 - 24x + 36)$
$= 4x^4 - 24x^3 + 36x^2$ *[1 mark]*

b) (i) $\frac{dW}{dx} = 16x^3 - 72x^2 + 72x$

[2 marks for all three terms, or 1 mark for two]
$= 8(2x^3 - 9x^2 + 9x)$ *[1 mark]*
So $k = 8$

(ii) At $x = 1$,
$\frac{dW}{dx} = 8(2(1)^3 - 9(1)^2 + 9(1)) = 8(2 - 9 + 9)$
$= 16$ *[1 mark]*.

c) $\frac{d^2W}{dx^2} = 48x^2 - 144x + 72$ *[1 mark]*

So for $x = 1 : \frac{d^2W}{dx^2} = 48 - 144 + 72$
$= -24$ *[1 mark]*

Chapter 8: Integration

1. Indefinite Integration
Exercise 1.1 — Integrating x^n

Q1 a) $y = \int \frac{dy}{dx}\, dx = \int x^7\, dx = \frac{x^8}{8} + C$

b) $y = \int \frac{dy}{dx}\, dx = \int 2x^3\, dx = 2\int x^3\, dx$
$= 2\left(\frac{x^4}{4}\right) + C = \frac{x^4}{2} + C$

c) $y = \int \frac{dy}{dx}\, dx = \int 8x\, dx = 8\int x\, dx$
$= 8\left(\frac{x^2}{2}\right) + C = 4x^2 + C$

d) $y = \int \frac{dy}{dx}\, dx = \int -5x^4\, dx = -5\int x^4\, dx$
$= -5\left(\frac{x^5}{5}\right) + C = -x^5 + C$

e) $y = \int \frac{dy}{dx}\, dx = \int x^6\, dx = \frac{x^7}{7} + C$

f) $y = \int \frac{dy}{dx}\, dx = \int 4x^4\, dx = 4\int x^4\, dx$
$= 4\left(\frac{x^5}{5}\right) + C = \frac{4x^5}{5} + C$

g) $y = \int \frac{dy}{dx}\, dx = \int -6x^5\, dx = -6\int x^5\, dx$
$= -6\left(\frac{x^6}{6}\right) + C = -x^6 + C$

h) $y = \int \frac{dy}{dx}\, dx = \int -12\, dx = -12x + C$
$= -12x + C$

i) $y = \int \frac{dy}{dx}\, dx = \int x^0\, dx = x + C$

j) $y = \int \frac{dy}{dx}\, dx = \int 40\, dx = 40x + C$

Q2 a) $\int x^2\, dx = \frac{x^3}{3} + C$

b) $\int 7x^4\, dx = 7\int x^4\, dx = \frac{7x^5}{5} + C$

c) $\int \frac{x}{2}\, dx = \frac{x^2}{4} + C$

d) $\int 3x^3\, dx = 3\int x^3\, dx = 3\left(\frac{x^4}{4}\right) + C = \frac{3x^4}{4} + C$

e) $\int 14x\, dx = 14\int x\, dx = 14\left(\frac{x^2}{2}\right) + C$
$= 7x^2 + C$

f) $\int -1.2x^2\, dx = -1.2\int x^2\, dx$
$= -1.2\left(\frac{x^3}{3}\right) + C = -0.4x^3 + C$

g) $\int -2x^4\, dx = -2\int x^4\, dx = -\frac{2x^5}{5} + C$

h) $\int -\frac{3}{2}x^2\,dx = -\frac{3}{2}\int x^2\,dx = -\frac{3}{2}\left(\frac{x^3}{3}\right) + C$

$\qquad = -\frac{x^3}{2} + C$

i) $\int -\frac{4}{3}x^3\,dx = -\frac{4}{3}\int x^3\,dx = -\frac{4}{3}\left(\frac{x^4}{4}\right) + C$

$\qquad = -\frac{x^4}{3} + C$

Exercise 1.2 — Integrating functions

Q1 **a)** $f(x) = \int f'(x)\,dx = \int (5x + 3x^4)\,dx$

$\qquad = 5\int x\,dx + 3\int x^4\,dx$

$\qquad = 5\left(\frac{x^2}{2}\right) + 3\left(\frac{x^5}{5}\right) + C$

$\qquad = \frac{5x^2}{2} + \frac{3x^5}{5} + C$

b) $f(x) = \int f'(x)\,dx = \int 4x(x^2 - 1)\,dx$

$\qquad = \int (4x^3 - 4x)\,dx$

$\qquad = 4\left(\frac{x^4}{4}\right) - 4\left(\frac{x^2}{2}\right) + C = x^4 - 2x^2 + C$

c) $f(x) = \int f'(x)\,dx = \int (x - 3)^2\,dx$

$\qquad = \int (x^2 - 6x + 9)\,dx$

$\qquad = \frac{x^3}{3} - 6\left(\frac{x^2}{2}\right) + 9\left(\frac{x^1}{1}\right) + C$

$\qquad = \frac{x^3}{3} - 3x^2 + 9x + C$

d) $f(x) = \int f'(x)\,dx = \int x\left(6x^2 + \frac{1}{4}x\right)dx$

$\qquad = \int \left(6x^3 + \frac{x^2}{4}\right)dx$

$\qquad = 6\left(\frac{x^4}{4}\right) + \frac{1}{4}\left(\frac{x^3}{3}\right) + C$

$\qquad = \frac{3}{2}x^4 + \frac{x^3}{12} + C$

e) $f(x) = \int f'(x)\,dx = \int \left(x + \frac{1}{2}\right)^2 dx$

$\qquad = \int \left(x^2 + x + \frac{1}{4}\right)dx$

$\qquad = \frac{x^3}{3} + \frac{x^2}{2} + \frac{1}{4}\left(\frac{x^1}{1}\right) + C$

$\qquad = \frac{x^3}{3} + \frac{x^2}{2} + \frac{x}{4} + C$

f) $f(x) = \int f'(x)\,dx = \int x(3x - 2)\,dx$

$\qquad = \int (3x^2 - 2x)\,dx$

$\qquad = 3\left(\frac{x^3}{3}\right) - 2\left(\frac{x^2}{2}\right) + C$

$\qquad = x^3 - x^2 + C$

g) $f(x) = \int f'(x)\,dx = \int (6x^3 - x^5)\,dx$

$\qquad = 6\left(\frac{x^4}{4}\right) - \frac{x^6}{6} + C$

$\qquad = \frac{3}{2}x^4 - \frac{x^6}{6} + C$

h) $f(x) = \int f'(x)\,dx = \int (-2 - 7x^2x^4)\,dx$

$\qquad = \int (-2 - 7x^6)\,dx$

$\qquad = -2\left(\frac{x^1}{1}\right) - 7\left(\frac{x^7}{7}\right) + C$

$\qquad = -2x - x^7 + C$

i) $f(x) = \int f'(x)\,dx = \int (5x^3 - 3x + 7)\,dx$

$\qquad = 5\left(\frac{x^4}{4}\right) - 3\left(\frac{x^2}{2}\right) + 7\left(\frac{x^1}{1}\right) + C$

$\qquad = \frac{5}{4}x^4 - \frac{3}{2}x^2 + 7x + C$

Q2 **a)** $\int (0.8x - 3x^2)\,dx = 0.8\left(\frac{x^2}{2}\right) - 3\left(\frac{x^3}{3}\right) + C$

$\qquad = 0.4x^2 - x^3 + C$

b) $\int (8x^3 - 2x + 5x^2)\,dx$

$\qquad = 8\left(\frac{x^4}{4}\right) - 2\left(\frac{x^2}{2}\right) + 5\left(\frac{x^3}{3}\right) + C$

$\qquad = 2x^4 - x^2 + \frac{5x^3}{3} + C$

c) $\int ((x^2)^3 + x)\,dx = \int (x^6 + x)\,dx$

$\qquad = \frac{x^7}{7} + \frac{x^2}{2} + C$

d) $\int (x(7x^2 - 1 - 2x))\,dx$

$\qquad = \int (7x^3 - x - 2x^2)\,dx$

$\qquad = 7\left(\frac{x^4}{4}\right) - \frac{x^2}{2} - 2\left(\frac{x^3}{3}\right) + C$

$\qquad = \frac{7x^4}{4} - \frac{x^2}{2} - \frac{2x^3}{3} + C$

e) $\int ((3x^2 - 5x)^2)\,dx = \int (9x^4 - 30x^3 + 25x^2)\,dx$

$\qquad = 9\left(\frac{x^5}{5}\right) - 30\left(\frac{x^4}{4}\right) + 25\left(\frac{x^3}{3}\right) + C$

$\qquad = \frac{9x^5}{5} - \frac{15x^4}{2} + \frac{25x^3}{3} + C$

f) $\int \left(\frac{2x^3 - x}{x}\right)dx = \int (2x^2 - 1)\,dx$

$\qquad = 2\left(\frac{x^3}{3}\right) - x + C$

$\qquad = \frac{2}{3}x^3 - x + C$

g) $\int (10x^2 + x + 4)\,dx$

$\qquad = 10\left(\frac{x^3}{3}\right) + \frac{x^2}{2} + \frac{4x^1}{1} + C$

$\qquad = \frac{10x^3}{3} + \frac{x^2}{2} + 4x + C$

h) $\int ((5x - 3)^2)\,dx = \int (25x^2 - 30x + 9)\,dx$

$\qquad = 25\left(\frac{x^3}{3}\right) - 30\left(\frac{x^2}{2}\right) + \frac{9x^1}{1} + C$

$\qquad = \frac{25x^3}{3} - 15x^2 + 9x + C$

i) $\int (x(3-x)^2)\,dx = \int (9x - 6x^2 + x^3)\,dx$

$$= 9\left(\frac{x^2}{2}\right) - 6\left(\frac{x^3}{3}\right) + \frac{x^4}{4} + C$$

$$= \frac{9x^2}{2} - 2x^3 + \frac{x^4}{4} + C$$

j) $\int ((x+1)(x^2-2))\,dx = \int (x^3 - 2x + x^2 - 2)\,dx$

$$= \frac{x^4}{4} - 2\left(\frac{x^2}{2}\right) + \frac{x^3}{3} - 2\left(\frac{x^1}{1}\right) + C$$

$$= \frac{x^4}{4} - x^2 + \frac{x^3}{3} - 2x + C$$

Q3 $y = \int \frac{dy}{dx}\,dx = \int (1.5x^2 - 4x)\,dx$

$$= 1.5\left(\frac{x^3}{3}\right) - 4\left(\frac{x^2}{2}\right) + C$$

$$= \frac{x^3}{2} - 2x^2 + C$$

Q4 $f(x) = \int f'(x)\,dx = \int (4x^3 + 5x^2)\,dx$

$$= 4\left(\frac{x^4}{4}\right) + 5\left(\frac{x^3}{3}\right) + C$$

$$= x^4 + \frac{5x^3}{3} + C$$

Q5 $\int \left(x\left(\frac{3x^3}{2} - x^2 + 1\right)\right)\,dx = \int \left(\frac{3x^4}{2} - x^3 + x\right)\,dx$

$$= \frac{3}{2}\left(\frac{x^5}{5}\right) - \frac{x^4}{4} + \frac{x^2}{2} + C$$

$$= \frac{3x^5}{10} - \frac{x^4}{4} + \frac{x^2}{2} + C$$

Q6 a) $\int \left(\frac{(x^2+x)(x+1)}{x}\right)\,dx = \int \left(\frac{x^3 + 2x^2 + x}{x}\right)\,dx$

$$= \int (x^2 + 2x + 1)\,dx$$

$$= \frac{x^3}{3} + 2\left(\frac{x^2}{2}\right) + \left(\frac{x^1}{1}\right) + C$$

$$= \frac{x^3}{3} + x^2 + x + C$$

b) $\int \left(x\left(x - \frac{x}{2}\right)^2\right)\,dx = \int \left(x\left(\frac{x^2}{4}\right)\right)\,dx$

$$= \int \frac{x^3}{4}\,dx$$

$$= \frac{x^4}{16} + C$$

Exercise 1.3 — Integrating to find equations of curves

Q1 a) $f(x) = \int f'(x)\,dx = \int 4x^3\,dx$

$$= 4\left(\frac{x^4}{4}\right) + C = x^4 + C$$

At the point (0, 5), $x = 0$ and $f(x) = y = 5$, so
$5 = 0^4 + C$. So $C = 5$ and $f(x) = x^4 + 5$.

b) $f(x) = \int f'(x)\,dx = \int (3x^2 - 4x + 3)\,dx$

$$= 3\left(\frac{x^3}{3}\right) - 4\left(\frac{x^2}{2}\right) + 3\left(\frac{x^1}{1}\right) + C$$

$$= x^3 - 2x^2 + 3x + C$$

At the point (1, –3), $x = 1$ and $f(x) = y = -3$, so
$-3 = 1^3 - 2(1)^2 + 3(1) + C = 2 + C$. So $C = -5$ and
$f(x) = x^3 - 2x^2 + 3x - 5$.

c) $f(x) = \int f'(x)\,dx = \int 6x(x+2)\,dx$

$$= \int (6x^2 + 12x)\,dx$$

$$= 6\left(\frac{x^3}{3}\right) + 12\left(\frac{x^2}{2}\right) + C$$

$$= 2x^3 + 6x^2 + C$$

At the point (–1, 1), $x = -1$ and $f(x) = y = 1$, so
$1 = 2(-1)^3 + 6(-1)^2 + C = 4 + C$. So $C = -3$ and
$f(x) = 2x^3 + 6x^2 - 3$.

d) $f(x) = \int f'(x)\,dx = \int (5x^2 + 2x)\,dx$

$$= 5\left(\frac{x^3}{3}\right) + 2\left(\frac{x^2}{2}\right) + C$$

$$= \frac{5}{3}x^3 + x^2 + C$$

At the point (2, 5), $x = 2$ and $f(x) = y = 5$, so
$5 = \frac{5}{3}(2)^3 + 2^2 + C = \frac{52}{3} + C$. So $C = -\frac{37}{3}$ and
$f(x) = \frac{5}{3}x^3 + x^2 - \frac{37}{3}$.

e) $f(x) = \int f'(x)\,dx = \int 3x^2(x-4)\,dx$

$$= \int (3x^3 - 12x^2)\,dx$$

$$= 3\left(\frac{x^4}{4}\right) - 12\left(\frac{x^3}{3}\right) + C$$

$$= \frac{3}{4}x^4 - 4x^3 + C$$

At the point (2, –10), $x = 2$ and $f(x) = y = -10$, so
$-10 = \frac{3}{4}(2)^4 - 4(2)^3 + C = -20 + C$.

So $C = 10$ and $f(x) = \frac{3}{4}x^4 - 4x^3 + 10$.

f) $f(x) = \int f'(x)\,dx = \int (3x+1)(x-1)\,dx$

$$= \int (3x^2 - 2x - 1)\,dx$$

$$= 3\left(\frac{x^3}{3}\right) - 2\left(\frac{x^2}{2}\right) - \left(\frac{x^1}{1}\right) + C$$

$$= x^3 - x^2 - x + C$$

At the point (3, –3), $x = 3$ and $f(x) = y = -3$, so
$-3 = 3^3 - 3^2 - 3 + C = 15 + C$.

So $C = -18$ and $f(x) = x^3 - x^2 - x - 18$.

g) $f(x) = \int f'(x)\,dx = \int x(x + 3x^2)\,dx$

$$= \int (x^2 + 3x^3)\,dx$$

$$= \frac{x^3}{3} + 3\left(\frac{x^4}{4}\right) + C = \frac{x^3}{3} + \frac{3}{4}x^4 + C$$

At the point (–1, 0), $x = -1$ and $f(x) = y = 0$, so
$0 = \frac{(-1)^3}{3} + \frac{3}{4}(-1)^4 + C = \frac{5}{12} + C$.

So $C = -\frac{5}{12}$ and $f(x) = \frac{x^3}{3} + \frac{3}{4}x^4 - \frac{5}{12}$.

h) $f(x) = \int f'(x)\,dx = \int \frac{9x^3 + 2x^2}{x}\,dx$

$$= \int (9x^2 + 2x)\,dx$$

$$= 9\left(\frac{x^3}{3}\right) + 2\left(\frac{x^2}{2}\right) + C$$

$$= 3x^3 + x^2 + C$$

At the point (–1, 2), $x = -1$ and $f(x) = y = 2$, so
$2 = 3(-1)^3 + (-1)^2 + C = -2 + C$.

So $C = 4$ and $f(x) = 3x^3 + x^2 + 4$.

Q2 $y = \int \dfrac{dy}{dx}\,dx = \int (x-2)(3x-4)\,dx$

$= \int (3x^2 - 10x + 8)\,dx$

$= 3\left(\dfrac{x^3}{3}\right) - 10\left(\dfrac{x^2}{2}\right) + 8\left(\dfrac{x^1}{1}\right) + C$

$= x^3 - 5x^2 + 8x + C$

At the point (2, –3), $x = 2$ and $y = -3$, so
$-3 = 2^3 - 5(2)^2 + 8(2) + C = 4 + C$.

So $C = -7$ and $y = x^3 - 5x^2 + 8x - 7$.

Q3 $y = f(x) = \int f'(x)\,dx = \int (3x^2 + 2x)\,dx$

$= 3\left(\dfrac{x^3}{3}\right) + 2\left(\dfrac{x^2}{2}\right) + C$

$= x^3 + x^2 + C$

At the point (4, 9), $x = 4$ and $y = 9$, so
$9 = 4^3 + 4^2 + C = 80 + C$.

So $C = -71$ and $y = x^3 + x^2 - 71$.

Q4 $y = \int \dfrac{dy}{dx}\,dx = \int (3x + x^2)\,dx$

$= 3\left(\dfrac{x^2}{2}\right) + \left(\dfrac{x^3}{3}\right) + C$

$= \dfrac{3}{2}x^2 + \dfrac{x^3}{3} + C$

At the point (1, 7), $x = 1$ and $y = 7$, so
$7 = \dfrac{3}{2}(1)^2 + \dfrac{(1)^2}{3} + C = \dfrac{11}{6} + C$.

So $C = \dfrac{31}{6}$ and $y = \dfrac{3}{2}x^2 + \dfrac{1}{3}x^3 + \dfrac{31}{6}$.

Q5 $y = \int \dfrac{dy}{dt}\,dt = \int (t-3)^2\,dt = \int (t^2 - 6t + 9)\,dt$

$= \dfrac{t^3}{3} - 6\left(\dfrac{t^2}{2}\right) + 9\left(\dfrac{t^1}{1}\right) + C$

$= \dfrac{t^3}{3} - 3t^2 + 9t + C$

When $t = 4$, $y = 9$, so:
$9 = \dfrac{4^3}{3} - 3(4)^2 + 9(4) + C = \dfrac{28}{3} + C$.

So $C = -\dfrac{1}{3}$ and $y = \dfrac{t^3}{3} - 3t^2 + 9t - \dfrac{1}{3}$.

Q6 $f(x) = \int f'(x)\,dx = \int (x(5x - 1))\,dx$

$= \int (5x^2 - x)\,dx$

$= 5\left(\dfrac{x^3}{3}\right) - \dfrac{x^2}{2} + C$

$= \dfrac{5}{3}x^3 - \dfrac{1}{2}x^2 + C$

When $x = 1$, $f(x) = y = \dfrac{1}{3}$, so:
$\dfrac{1}{3} = \dfrac{5}{3} - \dfrac{1}{2} + C = \dfrac{7}{6} + C$.

So $C = -\dfrac{5}{6}$ and $f(x) = \dfrac{5}{3}x^3 - \dfrac{1}{2}x^2 - \dfrac{5}{6}$.

Q7 $y = f(x) = \int f'(x)\,dx = \int \left(x^2 + \dfrac{x}{2} + 3\right)dx$

$= \dfrac{x^3}{3} + \dfrac{1}{2}\left(\dfrac{x^2}{2}\right) + 3\left(\dfrac{x^1}{1}\right) + C = \dfrac{x^3}{3} + \dfrac{x^2}{4} + 3x + C$

When $x = 1$, $y = -1$, so:

$-1 = \dfrac{(1)^3}{3} + \dfrac{(1)^2}{4} + 3(1) + C = \dfrac{43}{12} + C$.

So $C = -\dfrac{55}{12}$ and $y = \dfrac{x^3}{3} + \dfrac{x^2}{4} + 3x - \dfrac{55}{12}$.

Q8 $y = \int \dfrac{dy}{dx}\,dx = \int \left(\dfrac{x^2 - 6x}{x} + 2\right)dx$

$= \int (x - 6 + 2)\,dx$

$= \int (x - 4)\,dx$

$= \dfrac{x^2}{2} - 4\left(\dfrac{x^1}{1}\right) + C$

$= \dfrac{1}{2}x^2 - 4x + C$

When $x = 3$, $y = -1$, so:

$-1 = \dfrac{1}{2}(3)^2 - 4(3) + C = -\dfrac{15}{2} + C$.

So $C = \dfrac{13}{2}$ and $y = \dfrac{1}{2}x^2 - 4x + \dfrac{13}{2}$.

2. Definite Integration

Exercise 2.1 — Definite integrals

Q1   a) $\displaystyle\int_1^3 3x^2\,dx = [x^3]_1^3 = (3^3) - (1^3) = 27 - 1 = 26$

b) $\displaystyle\int_{-2}^0 (4x^3 + 2x)\,dx = [x^4 + x^2]_{-2}^0$

$= (0^4 + 0^2) - ((-2)^4 + (-2)^2)$

$= -(16 + 4) = -20$

c) $\displaystyle\int_0^2 (x^3 + x)\,dx = \left[\dfrac{x^4}{4} + \dfrac{x^2}{2}\right]_0^2$

$= \left(\dfrac{2^4}{4} + \dfrac{2^2}{2}\right) - \left(\dfrac{0^4}{4} + \dfrac{0^2}{2}\right)$

$= \dfrac{16}{4} + \dfrac{4}{2} - 0 = 6$

d) $\displaystyle\int_{-5}^{-2} (x+1)^2\,dx = \int_{-5}^{-2} (x^2 + 2x + 1)\,dx$

$= \left[\dfrac{x^3}{3} + x^2 + x\right]_{-5}^{-2}$

$= \left(\dfrac{(-2)^3}{3} + (-2)^2 + (-2)\right)$

$\quad - \left(\dfrac{(-5)^3}{3} + (-5)^2 + (-5)\right)$

$= \left(\dfrac{-8}{3} + 4 - 2\right) - \left(\dfrac{-125}{3} + 25 - 5\right)$

$= 21$

Remember you need to do these questions without a calculator, so make sure you're well practised in adding, subtracting and multiplying fractions.

Q2 $\displaystyle\int_0^a x^3\,dx = \left[\dfrac{x^4}{4}\right]_0^a = \left(\dfrac{a^4}{4}\right) - \left(\dfrac{0^4}{4}\right) = \dfrac{a^4}{4}$

So $\dfrac{a^4}{4} = 4$

$\Rightarrow a^4 = 4 \times 4 = 16$

$\Rightarrow a = 2$

a can't be −2 since the question tells you that a > 0. You could have taken ¼ outside the square brackets if you found it easier.

Q3 a) The area is all above the x-axis so just integrate:

$$\int_1^3 (x^3 + 2x)\, dx = \left[\frac{x^4}{4} + x^2\right]_1^3$$

$$= \left(\frac{3^4}{4} + 3^2\right) - \left(\frac{1^4}{4} + 1^2\right)$$

$$= \left(\frac{81}{4} + 9\right) - \left(\frac{1}{4} + 1\right)$$

$$= 28$$

So the area is 28.

b) The limits aren't shown on the graph, but they are just the roots of the equation, so solve it using methods from Chapter 2.

Set $y = 0$:

$4 - x^2 = 0 \Rightarrow x^2 = 4 \Rightarrow x = 2$ or -2.

So the limits of integration are -2 and 2:

$$\int_{-2}^2 (4 - x^2)\, dx = \left[4x - \frac{x^3}{3}\right]_{-2}^2$$

$$= \left(4(2) - \frac{2^3}{3}\right) - \left(4(-2) - \frac{(-2)^3}{3}\right)$$

$$= \left(8 - \frac{8}{3}\right) - \left(-8 - \frac{-8}{3}\right)$$

$$= 8 - \frac{8}{3} + 8 - \frac{8}{3}$$

$$= \frac{32}{3}, \text{ so the area is } \frac{32}{3}.$$

Q4 Work out the area between $x = -2$ and $x = 1$:

$$\int_{-2}^1 (x - 1)(3x + 9)\, dx = \int_{-2}^1 (3x^2 + 6x - 9)\, dx$$

$$= [x^3 + 3x^2 - 9x]_{-2}^1$$

$$= ((1)^3 + 3(1)^2 - 9(1)) - ((-2)^3 + 3(-2)^2 - 9(-2))$$

$$= -5 - 22 = -27$$

So the area is 27.

Q5 If x is positive then $y = x^2 + x$ is also positive so y is positive between 1 and 3 and so you can just integrate normally between the limits.

$$\int_1^3 (x^2 + x)\, dx = \left[\frac{x^3}{3} + \frac{x^2}{2}\right]_1^3$$

$$= \left(\frac{3^3}{3} + \frac{3^2}{2}\right) - \left(\frac{1^3}{3} + \frac{1^2}{2}\right) = \left(\frac{27}{3} + \frac{9}{2}\right) - \left(\frac{1}{3} + \frac{1}{2}\right)$$

$$= 9 + \frac{9}{2} - \frac{1}{2} - \frac{1}{3} = 9 + 4 - \frac{1}{3} = \frac{38}{3}$$

Q6 $y = 5x^3$ is negative for all negative values of x, and so it lies under the x-axis between $x = -2$ and $x = -1$.

So just integrate to find the 'negative' area and make it positive:

$$\int_{-2}^{-1} 5x^3\, dx = \left[\frac{5x^4}{4}\right]_{-2}^{-1} = \left(\frac{5(-1)^4}{4}\right) - \left(\frac{5(-2)^4}{4}\right)$$

$$= \frac{5}{4} - \frac{80}{4} = -\frac{75}{4}$$

So the area is $\frac{75}{4}$.

You could have taken $\frac{5}{4}$ outside the square bracket to make the numbers easier to work with.

Exercise 2.2 — Finding the area between curves and lines

Q1 a) Start by finding the points where the curve and the line intersect. Solve $3x^2 + 4 = 16$:

$\Rightarrow 3x^2 = 12 \Rightarrow x^2 = 4 \Rightarrow x = -2$ or 2.

So the curves intersect at $x = -2$ and $x = 2$.

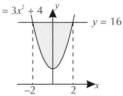

So the required area is the area under the line between $x = -2$ and $x = 2$ minus the area under the curve between $x = -2$ and $x = 2$.

The area under the line is just a rectangle which is 16 by 4 so the area is $16 \times 4 = 64$.

The area under the curve is given by:

$$\int_{-2}^2 (3x^2 + 4)\, dx = [x^3 + 4x]_{-2}^2$$

$$= (2^3 + 4(2)) - ((-2)^3 + 4(-2))$$

$$= (8 + 8) - (-8 - 8)$$

$$= 16 + 16 = 32$$

So the shaded area is $64 - 32 = 32$.

b) This might not look like a line and a curve at first, but if $x = 2$, $y = x^3 + 4 = 2^3 + 4 = 12$, so it's actually this area that you're after:

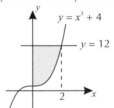

So the required area is the area under the line between $x = 0$ and $x = 2$ minus the area under the curve between $x = 0$ and $x = 2$.

The area under the line is just a rectangle which is 12 by 2 so the area is $12 \times 2 = 24$.
The area under the curve is given by:

$$\int_0^2 (x^3 + 4)\, dx = \left[\frac{x^4}{4} + 4x\right]_0^2$$

$$= \left(\frac{2^4}{4} + 4(2)\right) - \left(\frac{0^4}{4} + 4(0)\right)$$

$$= (4 + 8) - 0 = 12$$

So the shaded area is $24 - 12 = 12$.

c) Solve $-1 - (x - 3)^2 = -5$:

$4 = (x - 3)^2 \Rightarrow x - 3 = -2$ or $2 \Rightarrow x = 1$ or $x = 5$.

Be careful — this area is below the x-axis so the integrals will give negative areas.

So the required area is the positive area between the line and the x-axis between $x = 1$ and $x = 5$ minus the positive area between the curve and the x-axis between $x = 1$ and $x = 5$.

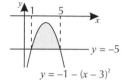

The first area is just a rectangle which is 5 by 4 so the area is $5 \times 4 = 20$.

So the area between the line and the x-axis between $x = 0$ and $x = 5$ is 20. The area between the curve and the x-axis is given by:

$$\int_1^5 (-1 - (x - 3)^2)\, dx$$
$$= \int_1^5 (-1 - (x^2 - 6x + 9))\, dx$$
$$= \int_1^5 (6x - x^2 - 10)\, dx$$
$$= \left[\frac{6x^2}{2} - \frac{x^3}{3} - 10x\right]_1^5 = \left[3x^2 - \frac{x^3}{3} - 10x\right]_1^5$$
$$= \left(3(5)^2 - \frac{5^3}{3} - 10(5)\right) - \left(3(1)^2 - \frac{1^3}{3} - 10(1)\right)$$
$$= \left(75 - \frac{125}{3} - 50\right) - \left(3 - \frac{1}{3} - 10\right)$$
$$= 32 - \frac{124}{3} = \frac{96}{3} - \frac{124}{3} = -\frac{28}{3}$$

So the area between the curve and the x-axis between $x = 1$ and $x = 5$ is $\frac{28}{3}$.

So the shaded area is $20 - \frac{28}{3} = \frac{32}{3}$.

d) Solve $x^2 = 2x$:

$x^2 - 2x = 0 \Rightarrow x(x - 2) = 0 \Rightarrow x = 0$ or $x = 2$.

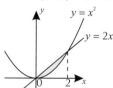

So the required area is the area under the line between $x = 0$ and $x = 2$, minus the area under the curve between $x = 0$ and $x = 2$.

$$\int_0^2 2x\, dx = [x^2]_0^2 = (2^2) - (0^2) = 4$$
$$\int_0^2 x^2\, dx = \left[\frac{x^3}{3}\right]_0^2 = \left(\frac{2^3}{3}\right) - \left(\frac{0^3}{3}\right) = \frac{8}{3}$$

So the shaded area is $4 - \frac{8}{3} = \frac{4}{3}$.

You could also find the area under the line by using the formula for the area of a triangle.

Q2 Solve $x^2 + 4 = x + 4$:

$x^2 - x = 0 \Rightarrow x(x - 1) = 0 \Rightarrow x = 0$ or $x = 1$.

Draw a diagram:

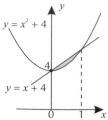

So the required area is the area under the line between $x = 0$ and $x = 1$ minus the area under the curve between $x = 0$ and $x = 1$.

$$\int_0^1 (x + 4)\, dx = \left[\frac{x^2}{2} + 4x\right]_0^1$$
$$= \left(\frac{1^2}{2} + 4(1)\right) - \left(\frac{0^2}{2} + 4(0)\right)$$
$$= \frac{1}{2} + 4 = \frac{9}{2}$$
$$\int_0^1 (x^2 + 4)\, dx = \left[\frac{x^3}{3} + 4x\right]_0^1$$
$$= \left(\frac{1^3}{3} + 4(1)\right) - \left(\frac{0^3}{3} + 4(0)\right)$$
$$= \frac{1}{3} + 4 = \frac{13}{3}$$

So the required area is $\frac{9}{2} - \frac{13}{3} = \frac{1}{6}$.

Q3 Solving $x^2 = ax$:

$x^2 - ax = 0 \Rightarrow x(x - a) = 0 \Rightarrow x = 0$ or $x = a$

Draw a diagram:

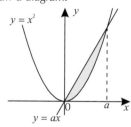

The area is given by the area under the line $y = ax$ between $x = 0$ and $x = a$, minus the area under the curve $y = x^2$ between 0 and a.

$$\int_0^a ax\, dx = \left[\frac{ax^2}{2}\right]_0^a = \left(\frac{a^3}{2}\right) - 0 = \frac{a^3}{2}$$
$$\int_0^a x^2\, dx = \left[\frac{x^3}{3}\right]_0^a = \left(\frac{a^3}{3}\right) - 0 = \frac{a^3}{3}$$

So the area is $\frac{a^3}{2} - \frac{a^3}{3} = \frac{a^3}{6}$.

The area is 36, so $\frac{a^3}{6} = 36 \Rightarrow a^3 = 216 \Rightarrow a = 6$.

Q4 Solving $x^2 = 2 - x^4$:

$x^4 + x^2 - 2 = 0 \Rightarrow (x^2 - 1)(x^2 + 2) = 0 \Rightarrow x^2 = 1$ or $x^2 = -2$. $x^2 = -2$ has no real solutions, so the graphs cross at $x = \pm 1$.

Draw a diagram:

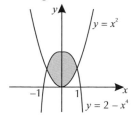

So the area you want is the area underneath $y = 2 - x^4$ between $x = -1$ and $x = 1$ minus the area underneath $y = x^2$ between $x = -1$ and $x = 1$.
The area underneath $y = 2 - x^4$ is:
$$\int_{-1}^{1}(2 - x^4)\,dx = \left[2x - \frac{x^5}{5}\right]_{-1}^{1}$$
$$= \left(2(1) - \frac{1^5}{5}\right) - \left(2(-1) - \frac{(-1)^5}{5}\right) = \frac{18}{5}$$

And the area underneath $y = x^2$ is:
$$\int_{-1}^{1}x^2\,dx = \left[\frac{x^3}{3}\right]_{-1}^{1} = \frac{(1)^3}{3} - \frac{(-1)^3}{3} = \frac{2}{3}$$

So the area between the curves is $\frac{18}{5} - \frac{2}{3} = \frac{44}{15}$.

Q5 Solving $4 - x^2 = 4 - x$:
$x^2 - x = 0 \Rightarrow x(x - 1) = 0 \Rightarrow x = 0$ or $x = 1$,
so the graphs cross at $x = 0$ and $x = 1$.

Draw a diagram:

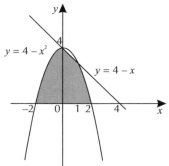

So the area you want is in 3 sections:
The area underneath $y = 4 - x^2$ for $-2 \leq x \leq 0$,
and the area underneath $y = 4 - x$ for $0 \leq x \leq 1$,
and the area underneath $y = 4 - x^2$ for $1 \leq x \leq 2$.
The area underneath $y = 4 - x^2$ for $-2 \leq x \leq 0$ is:
$$\int_{-2}^{0}(4 - x^2)\,dx = \left[4x - \frac{x^3}{3}\right]_{-2}^{0}$$
$$= \left(4(0) - \frac{0^3}{3}\right) - \left(4(-2) - \frac{(-2)^3}{3}\right)$$
$$= \left[0 + \frac{16}{3}\right] = \frac{16}{3}$$
The area underneath $y = 4 - x$ for $0 \leq x \leq 1$ is:
$$\int_{0}^{1}(4 - x)\,dx = \left[4x - \frac{x^2}{2}\right]_{0}^{1}$$
$$= \left[\left(4(1) - \frac{(1)^2}{2}\right) - \left(4(0) - \frac{(0)^2}{2}\right)\right] - \frac{7}{2}$$

The area underneath $y = 4 - x^2$ for $1 \leq x \leq 2$ is:
$$\int_{1}^{2}(4 - x^2)\,dx = \left[4x - \frac{x^3}{3}\right]_{1}^{2}$$
$$= \left[\left(4(2) - \frac{2^3}{3}\right) - \left(4(1) - \frac{(1)^3}{3}\right)\right]$$
$$= \left[\frac{16}{3} - \frac{11}{3}\right] = \frac{5}{3}$$
So the total area is $\frac{16}{3} + \frac{5}{3} + \frac{7}{2} = \frac{21}{2}$.

Q6 Solving $x^2 + x + 1 = 4 - x$:
$x^2 + 2x - 3 = 0 \Rightarrow (x + 3)(x - 1) = 0 \Rightarrow x = -3$ or $x = 1$,
so the graphs cross at $x = -3$ and $x = 1$, but $x \geq 0$
so you can ignore $x = -3$. Draw a diagram:

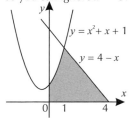

So the area you want is the area underneath
$y = x^2 + x + 1$ between $x = 0$ and $x = 1$ added to the
area underneath $y = 4 - x$ between $x = 1$ and $x = 4$.

The area underneath $y = x^2 + x + 1$ is:
$$\int_{0}^{1}(x^2 + x + 1)\,dx = \left[\frac{x^3}{3} + \frac{x^2}{2} + x\right]_{0}^{1}$$
$$= \left[\left(\frac{(1)^3}{3} + \frac{(1)^2}{2} + 1\right) - \left(\frac{(0)^3}{3} + \frac{(0)^2}{2} + 0\right)\right]$$
$$= \frac{11}{6}$$
The area underneath $y = 4 - x$ is the area of a triangle
with base 3 (from $x = 1$ to $x = 4$) and height 3
(at $x = 1$, $y = 4 - 1 = 3$). So the area is $\frac{1}{2} \times 3 \times 3 = \frac{9}{2}$
So the total area is $\frac{11}{6} + \frac{9}{2} = \frac{19}{3}$.

Review Exercise — Chapter 8

Q1 To find y in terms of x, just integrate $\frac{dy}{dx}$
with respect to x.
$$y = \int \frac{dy}{dx}\,dx = \int \left(\frac{5}{7}x^4 + \frac{2}{3}x + \frac{1}{4}\right)dx$$
$$= \frac{5x^5}{7 \times 5} + \frac{2x^2}{3 \times 2} + \frac{x}{4} + C$$
$$= \frac{x^5}{7} + \frac{x^2}{3} + \frac{x}{4} + C$$

Q2 Integrating gives $y = 3x^2 - 7x + C$; then substitute
$x = 1$ and $y = 0$ to find that $C = 4$. So the equation of
the curve is $y = 3x^2 - 7x + 4$.

Q3 a) $y = \int \frac{dy}{dx}\,dx = \int 2(3x - 6.5)\,dx = \int (6x - 13)\,dx$
$$= 6\left(\frac{x^2}{2}\right) - 13\left(\frac{x^1}{1}\right) + C$$
$$= 3x^2 - 13x + C$$

When $x = 1$, $y = 2$.
So $2 = 3(1)^2 - 13(1) + C = -10 + C$ and
$C = 12$. So the equation is $y = 3x^2 - 13x + 12$.

b) $y = 3x^2 - 13x + 12 = (3x - 4)(x - 3)$.

So $y = 0$ when $x = 3$ or $3x = 4$ so $x = \frac{4}{3}$.

At $x = 0$, $y = 12$.

The x^2 coefficient is positive so the curve looks like this:

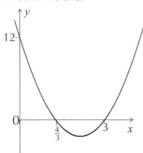

Q4 a) $y = \int \frac{dy}{dx} \, dx = \int (6x^2 + 6x - 5) \, dx$

$= 6\left(\frac{x^3}{3}\right) + 6\left(\frac{x^2}{2}\right) - 5\left(\frac{x^1}{1}\right) + C$

$= 2x^3 + 3x^2 - 5x + C$

When $x = 0$, $y = 0$.

So $0 = 2(0)^3 + 3(0)^2 - 5(0) + C = C$ and $C = 0$. So the equation is $y = 2x^3 + 3x^2 - 5x$.

b) $y = 2x^3 + 3x^2 - 5x = x(2x^2 + 3x - 5)$
$= x(x - 1)(2x + 5)$

This is a cubic graph with a positive x^3 coefficient so the curve will go from bottom–left to top–right. If $y = 0$, $x(x - 1)(2x + 5) = 0$ so $x = 0$, $x = 1$ and $x = -\frac{5}{2}$ are x-intercepts. If $x = 0$, $y = 0$ so the only y-intercept is the origin. The graph looks like this:

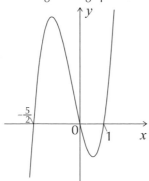

Q5 $f(x) = \int f'(x) \, dx = \int (6x^2 - 12 + 2x) \, dx$
$= 2x^3 - 12x + x^2 + C$

When $x = -2$, $y = 5$ and $y = f(x) = 5$.
So $5 = 2(-2)^3 - 12(-2) + (-2)^2 + C$ and $C = -7$.
So the equation is $y = 2x^3 - 12x + x^2 - 7$.

Q6 a) $\int_0^1 (4x^3 + 3x^2 + 2x + 1) \, dx$

$= \left[4\frac{x^4}{4} + 3\frac{x^3}{3} + 2\frac{x^2}{2} + x\right]_0^1$

$= (1^4 + 1^3 + 1^2 + 1) - (0^4 + 0^3 + 0^2 + 0) = 4$

b) $\int_1^2 (12x^5 + 10x^4) \, dx = [2x^6 + 2x^5]_1^2$

$= [(128 + 64) - (2 + 2)] = 188$

c) $\int_0^1 (4x^7 - 3) \, dx = \left[\frac{x^8}{2} - 3x\right]_0^1$

$= \left[\left(\frac{1}{2} - 3\right) - 0\right] = -\frac{5}{2}$

Q7 a) $\int_{-3}^3 (9 - x^2) \, dx = \left[9x - \frac{x^3}{3}\right]_{-3}^3$

$= \left[9(3) - \frac{(3)^3}{3}\right] - \left[9(-3) - \frac{(-3)^3}{3}\right]$

$= 18 - (-18) = 36$

b)

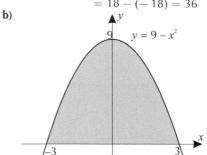

Q8 a) You need to find where the curve crosses the x-axis so set $x^2 + 4x + 3 = 0 \Rightarrow (x + 3)(x + 1) = 0$, so the graph crosses the axis at $x = -3$ and $x = -1$.

So the area is given by the integral of the curve between $x = -3$ and $x = -1$.

$\int_{-3}^{-1} (x^2 + 4x + 3) \, dx = \left[\frac{x^3}{3} + 2x^2 + 3x\right]_{-3}^{-1}$

$= \left(\frac{(-1)^3}{3} + 2(-1)^2 + 3(-1)\right)$

$- \left(\frac{(-3)^3}{3} + 2(-3)^2 + 3(-3)\right)$

$= \left(-\frac{1}{3} + 2 - 3\right) - (-9 + 18 - 9)$

$= -\frac{4}{3}$

So the shaded area A is $\frac{4}{3}$.

b) Again, find where the curve crosses the x-axis.
Let $x^2 + x - 6 = 0 \Rightarrow (x + 3)(x - 2) = 0$
$\Rightarrow x = 2$ or $x = -3$.

So the area is given by the integral of the curve between $x = -3$ and $x = 2$.

$\int_{-3}^2 (x^2 + x - 6) \, dx = \left[\frac{x^3}{3} + \frac{x^2}{2} - 6x\right]_{-3}^2$

$= \left(\frac{2^3}{3} + \frac{2^2}{2} - 6(2)\right) - \left(\frac{(-3)^3}{3} + \frac{(-3)^2}{2} - 6(-3)\right)$

$= \left(\frac{8}{3} + 2 - 12\right) - \left(-9 + \frac{9}{2} + 18\right)$

$= \left(-\frac{22}{3}\right) - \left(\frac{27}{2}\right) = -\frac{125}{6}$

So the shaded area A is $\frac{125}{6}$.

Q9 a) $A = \int_0^2 (x^3 - 5x^2 + 6x)\,dx$

$$= \left[\frac{x^4}{4} - \frac{5}{3}x^3 + 3x^2\right]_0^2 = \frac{8}{3}$$

b) $A = \int_0^2 2x^2\,dx + \int_2^6 (12 - 2x)\,dx$

$$= \left[\frac{2}{3}x^3\right]_0^2 + \left[12x - x^2\right]_2^6$$

$$= \frac{16}{3} + 16 = \frac{64}{3}$$

c) $A = \int_1^4 (x + 3)\,dx - \int_1^4 (x^2 - 4x + 7)\,dx$

$$= \left[\frac{x^2}{2} + 3x\right]_1^4 - \left[\frac{x^3}{3} - 2x^2 + 7x\right]_1^4$$

$$= \frac{33}{2} - 12 = \frac{9}{2}$$

Q10 You want the area under the curve $y = 3 - 2x - x^2$ between $x = -3$ and $x = 1$ minus the area under the curve $y = x^3 - 4x$ between $x = -2$ and $x = 0$.
The area under the curve $y = 3 - 2x - x^2$ is:

$$\int_{-3}^{1} (3 - 2x - x^2)\,dx = \left[3x - x^2 - \frac{x^3}{3}\right]_{-3}^{1}$$

$$= \left[\left(3 - 1 - \frac{1}{3}\right) - (-9 - 9 + 9)\right]$$

$$= \frac{32}{3}$$

The area under the curve $y = x^3 - 4x$ is:

$$\int_{-2}^{0} (x^3 - 4x)\,dx = \left[\frac{x^4}{4} - 2x^2\right]_{-2}^{0}$$

$$= [0 - (-4)] = 4$$

So the shaded area is $\frac{32}{3} - 4 = \frac{20}{3}$.

Exam-Style Questions — Chapter 8

Q1 a) Multiply out the brackets and simplify the terms:
$(5 + 2\sqrt{x})(5 - 2\sqrt{x})$
$= 25 - 10\sqrt{x} + 10\sqrt{x} - 4x$
$= 25 - 4x$
So $a = 25$ and $b = 4$
[2 marks — 1 for each constant]

b) Integrate your answer from a):

$$\int (25 - 4x)\,dx = 25x - 4\left(\frac{x^2}{2}\right) + C$$

$$= 25x - 2x^2 + C$$

[3 marks available — 1 for each term.]

Q2 $\int_1^2 (2x - 6x^2 + x^3)\,dx = \left[x^2 - 2x^3 + \frac{x^4}{4}\right]_1^2$

[3 marks available — 1 mark for each correct term]

$$= \left[(4 - 16 + 4) - \left(1 - 2 + \frac{1}{4}\right)\right] \quad \textbf{\textit{[1 mark]}}$$

$$= -\frac{29}{4} \quad \textbf{\textit{[1 mark]}}$$

Q3 The limits are the x-values when $y = 0$, so first solve
$(x - 2)^2(x + 1) = 0$: *[1 mark]*
$x = 2$ *[1 mark]* and $x = -1$ *[1 mark]*
Hence, to find the area, calculate:

$$\int_{-1}^{2} (x - 2)^2(x + 1)\,dx$$

$$= \int_{-1}^{2} (x^3 - 3x^2 + 4)\,dx \quad \textbf{\textit{[1 mark]}}$$

$$= \left[\frac{x^4}{4} - x^3 + 4x\right]_{-1}^{2} \quad \textbf{\textit{[1 mark]}}$$

$$= \left(\frac{2^4}{4} - 2^3 + 4(2)\right)$$

$$\quad - \left(\frac{(-1)^4}{4} - (-1)^3 + 4(-1)\right) \textbf{\textit{[1 mark]}}$$

$$= 4 - -\frac{11}{4} \quad \textbf{\textit{[1 mark]}}$$

$$= \frac{27}{4} \quad \textbf{\textit{[1 mark]}}$$

Q4 a) The tangent at $(1, 2)$ has the same gradient as the curve at that point, so use $f'(x)$ to calculate the gradient:
$f'(1) = 1 - 2 = -1$ *[1 mark]*
Put this into the straight-line equation
$y - y_1 = m(x - x_1)$:
$y - 2 = -1(x - 1)$ *[1 mark]*
$y = -x + 1 + 2$
$y = -x + 3$ *[1 mark]*

b) $f(x) = \int (x^3 - 2x^2)\,dx$

$$= \frac{x^4}{4} - \frac{2x^3}{3} + C \quad \textbf{\textit{[1 mark]}}$$

Now use the coordinates $(1, 2)$ to find the value of C:

$$2 = \frac{1}{4} - \frac{2}{3} + C \quad \textbf{\textit{[1 mark]}}$$

$$C = \frac{29}{12} \quad \textbf{\textit{[1 mark]}}$$

So $f(x) = \frac{x^4}{4} - \frac{2x^3}{3} + \frac{29}{12}$ *[1 mark]*

Q5 a) Multiply out the brackets in $f'(x)$
$(x - 1)(3x - 1) = 3x^2 - x - 3x + 1$
$= 3x^2 - 4x + 1$ *[1 mark]*
Now $f(x) = \int (3x^2 - 4x + 1)\,dx$

$$= \frac{3x^3}{3} - \frac{4x^2}{2} + \frac{x^1}{1} + C \quad \textbf{\textit{[1 mark]}}$$

$$= x^3 - 2x^2 + x + C \quad \textbf{\textit{[1 mark]}}$$

Input the x and y coordinates to find C:
$10 = 3^3 - 2(3)^2 + 3 + C$ *[1 mark]*
$10 - 27 + 18 - 3 = C$
$C = -2$ *[1 mark]*
So $f(x) = x^3 - 2x^2 + x - 2$ *[1 mark]*

b) First calculate the gradient of f(x) when $x = 3$:

$f'(3) = 3(3)^2 - 4(3) + 1$

$= 27 - 12 + 1$

$= 16$ *[1 mark]*

Use the fact that the tangent gradient multiplied by the normal gradient must equal −1 to find the gradient of the normal (*n*):

$16 \times n = -1$ therefore $n = -\frac{1}{16}$ *[1 mark]*.

Put *n* and *P*(3, 10) into the formula for the equation of a line and rearrange until it's in the form $y = \frac{a-x}{b}$:

$y - 10 = -\frac{1}{16}(x - 3)$ *[1 mark]*

$16y - 160 = -x + 3$

$y = \frac{163 - x}{16}$

So $a = 163$ and $b = 16$. *[1 mark]*

Q6 a) $f(x) = \int \left(2x - 6x^2 + \frac{x^3}{2}\right) dx$

$= x^2 - 2x^3 + \frac{x^4}{8} + C$

[3 marks available — 1 mark for each correct x-term. Lose 1 mark if C is missing.]

Input the *x*- and *y*-coordinates to find C:

$1 = 4^2 - 2(4)^3 + \frac{4^4}{8} + C$ *[1 mark]*

$1 = 16 - 128 + 32 + C$

$C = 81$ *[1 mark]*

So $f(x) = x^2 - 2x^3 + \frac{x^4}{8} + 81$ *[1 mark]*

b) The tangent at (4, 1) has the same gradient as the curve at that point, so use f'(*x*) to calculate the gradient:

$f'(4) = 2(4) - 6(4)^2 + \frac{4^3}{2}$ *[1 mark]*

$= -56$ *[1 mark]*

Put this into the straight-line equation $y - y_1 = m(x - x_1)$:

$y - 1 = -56(x - 4)$ *[1 mark]*

$y = -56x + 224 + 1$

$y = 225 - 56x$ *[1 mark]*

Q7 a) $m = \frac{y_2 - y_1}{x_2 - x_1} = \frac{0 - -5}{-1 - 4} = -1$ *[1 mark]*

$y - y_1 = m(x - x_1)$

$y - -5 = -1(x - 4)$ so $y + 5 = 4 - x$

$y = -x - 1$ *[1 mark]*

b) Multiply out the brackets and then integrate:

$(x + 1)(x - 5) = x^2 - 4x - 5$ *[1 mark]*

$\int_{-1}^{4} (x^2 - 4x - 5) \, dx = \left[\frac{x^3}{3} - 2x^2 - 5x\right]_{-1}^{4}$ *[1 mark]*

$= \left(\frac{4^3}{3} - 2(4)^2 - 5(4)\right)$

$- \left(\frac{(-1)^3}{3} - 2(-1)^2 - 5(-1)\right)$ *[1 mark]*

$= -\frac{92}{3} - \frac{8}{3}$ *[1 mark]* $= -\frac{100}{3}$ *[1 mark]*

c) Subtract the area between the line and the *x*-axis from the area between the curve and the *x*-axis to leave the area in between the line and the curve. The area above the line is a triangle (where $b = 5$ and $h = 5$), so use the formula for the area of a triangle to calculate it:

$\frac{1}{2}bh = \frac{1}{2} \times 5 \times 5$ *[1 mark]* $= \frac{25}{2}$ *[1 mark]*

Shaded area $= \frac{100}{3} - \frac{25}{2}$ *[1 mark]*

$= \frac{125}{6}$ *[1 mark]*

You could also have integrated the line y = −x − 1 from x = −1 to x = 4 to find the area between the line and the x-axis — you'd have got the same answer.

Glossary

A

Algebraic division
Dividing one **algebraic expression** by another.

Algebraic expression
An **expression** which contains **constants** and / or **variables**.

C

Chord
A line joining two points which lie on the circumference of a circle.

Coefficient
The **constant** multiplying the **variable(s)** in an algebraic **term**.

Common denominator
A denominator (i.e. bottom of a fraction) which is shared by all fractions in an **expression**.

Common factor
A factor which is shared by all the **terms** in an **expression**.

Completing the square
Rewriting a quadratic function as: $p(x + q)^2 + r$. Useful for solving equations or sketching curves.

Constant
A fixed numerical value in an **expression**.

Constant of integration
A **constant** term in an **integral** representing any number.

Cubic equation
An **equation** that can be written $ax^3 + bx^2 + cx + d = 0$ (where $a \neq 0$).

D

Decreasing function
A **function** for which the **gradient** is always less than zero.

Definite integral
An **integral** which is evaluated over an interval given by two **limits**.

Degree
The highest power of x in a **polynomial**.

Derivative
The result you get when you **differentiate** something.
$\frac{dy}{dx}$ is 'derivative of y with respect to x'.

Differentiation
An algebraic process for finding the **gradient function** of a **function**.

Discriminant
The discriminant of a **quadratic equation** $ax^2 + bx + c = 0$ is the value of $b^2 - 4ac$.

Divisor
The number or **expression** you're dividing by in a division.

E

Elimination
Method for solving linear **simultaneous equations**, by matching **coefficients** and then **eliminating** a **variable**.

Equation
A mathematical statement containing an '=' sign and at least one **variable** or **constant**.

Expression
Any combination of numbers, **variables**, **functions** and operations (+, −, ×, ÷ etc.) Unlike an **equation**, it doesn't have an equals sign.

F

Factor
A factor of a **term** or **expression** is something which divides into it.

Factor Theorem
An extension of the **Remainder Theorem** that helps you find the **roots** of a **polynomial**. If $f(a) = 0$ then $(x − a)$ is a **factor** of $f(x)$.

Factorising
The opposite of multiplying out brackets. Brackets are put in to write an **expression** as a product of its **factors**.

Formula
A standard **equation** used to calculate a quantity or measure, e.g. volume.

Function
A function gives 'outputs' for different 'inputs'. They are usually defined by an **algebraic expression** — plugging in different input values for the **variable** gives different output values.

Function notation f(x)
Standard way of referring to **functions**. E.g. function f defined by $f(x) = x^2 + 5$.

f'(x)
The **derivative** of f(x) with respect to x.

f''(x)
The **second order derivative** of f(x) with respect to x.

G

Gradient
A number representing the steepness of a straight line or of a curve at a given point.

Gradient function
A **function** that can be used to find the **gradient** at any point on a curve.

I

Identity
An **equation** that is true for all values of the **variable**, usually denoted by the '≡' sign.

Increasing function
A **function** for which the **gradient** is always greater than zero.

Indefinite integral
An **integral** which includes a **constant of integration** that comes from **integrating** without **limits**.

Inequality
An **expression** which contains one of the following symbols: >, <, ≥, ≤. Like an **equation**, but produces a range of solutions.

Integer
A positive or negative whole number (including 0).

Integral
The result you get when you **integrate** something.

Integration
Process for finding the **equation** of a **function**, given its **gradient function** — the opposite of **differentiation**.

Intercept
The coordinates at which the graph of a **function** crosses one of the axes.

Irrational number
A number that can't be expressed as the **quotient** (division) of two **integers**. Examples include **surds** and π.

Limits (integration)
The numbers between which you **integrate** to find a **definite integral**.

Linear inequality
An **inequality** that can be written as $ax + b > cx + d$.

Maximum
The highest point on a graph, or on a section of a graph (this is a local maximum).

Minimum
The lowest point on a graph, or on a section of a graph (this is a local minimum).

Normal
A straight line passing through a curve that is perpendicular (at right angles) to the curve at the point it crosses it.

Point of inflection
A point on a graph where the curve briefly flattens out without changing direction. A type of **stationary point**.

Polynomial
An **algebraic expression** made up of the sum of **constant terms** and **variables** raised to positive **integer** powers.

Quadratic equation
An **equation** that can be written $ax^2 + bx + c = 0$ where $a \neq 0$.

Quadratic formula
A **formula** for solving a **quadratic equation** $ax^2 + bx + c = 0$,
given by $x = \dfrac{-b \pm \sqrt{b^2 - 4ac}}{2a}$.

Quadratic inequality
An **inequality** that can be written as $ax^2 + bx + c \geq 0$, where $a \neq 0$. It can be solved by looking at the shape of the quadratic graph.

Quotient
The result of a division.

Rational number
A number that can be written as the **quotient** (division) of two **integers**, where the denominator is non-zero.

Rationalising the denominator
The process of removing **surds** from the denominator of a fraction.

Remainder
The **expression** left over following an **algebraic division** that has a **degree** lower than the **divisor**.

Remainder Theorem
A method used to work out the **remainder** from an **algebraic division**, but without actually have to do the division. The remainder when f(x) is divided by ($x - a$) is f(a).

Root
The roots of a **function** f(x) are the values of x where f(x) = 0.

Second order derivative
The result of **differentiating** a **function** twice — it tells you the rate of change of the **gradient** of a graph of a function. $\dfrac{\mathrm{d}^2 y}{\mathrm{d}x^2}$ means 'second order derivative of y with respect to x'.

Simultaneous equations
A set of **equations** containing two or more unknown quantities, often x and y, for which the same set of values satisfy each equation.

Solution
The value or values (usually of a **variable**) that satisfy a problem, e.g. an **equation** or **inequality**.

Stationary point
A point on a curve where the **gradient** is zero.

Substitution
Method for solving **simultaneous equations**, where you replace each occurrence of one unknown with an **expression** in terms of the other unknown.

Surd
A number that can only be expressed precisely by using a square root sign.

Tangent
A straight line which just touches a curve at a point. Its **gradient** is the same as the curve's gradient at that point.

Term
A collection of numbers and **variables** all multiplied together.

Turning point
A **stationary point** that is a (local) **maximum** or **minimum** point of a curve.

Variable
A letter in an **expression** representing an unknown which, unlike a **constant**, can take on different values.

Vertex
Turning point of a graph — the **maximum** or **minimum** point for a quadratic graph.

Index

C1 Formula Sheet

The formulas below will be included in the formula book for your exams
— make sure you know exactly **when you need them** and **how to use them**.

Measurement

Surface area of a sphere = $4\pi r^2$

Area of the curved surface of a cone = $\pi r \times$ (slant height)

As you can see, they don't give you many formulas for the C1 exam
— you really do have to learn all the others off by heart, I'm afraid.
They are a little more generous in later modules if that's any consolation...

Finally, don't forget that C1 is a non-calculator exam. So make sure
you're completely happy doing basic arithmetic without your calculator
— you really don't want to throw away marks in the exam because
you're a bit rusty on long division...

All the questions in this book can be done without a calculator
(well, except for a handful of questions which are clearly highlighted),
so put away your calculator and use this book to get plenty of practice.